Out of China

A true story based on the journal of
K. M. Pate

Richard L. Smith

Xulon
PRESS

For Darryl, a lifelong friend and good buddy.

"None who have always been free can understand the terrible fascinating power of the hope of freedom to those who are not free."

Pearl S. Buck

Acknowledgements:

My thanks to Dr. Ron Richter, Ruth Richter and Laurie Holmes for their help in editing this manuscript

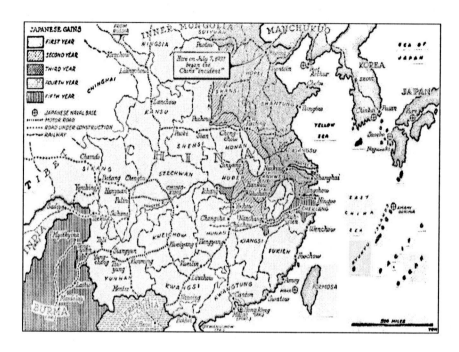

Map of China 1937-1943

Table of Contents

Preface

In July of 1937, the second Sino-Japanese War often referred to as the "China Incident" exploded. By September 1939 the Japanese occupied most of northern China as well as parts of the eastern coast including the cities of Shanghai, Hong Kong, Canton to the south, and eventually Ichang (Yichang) to the west. Nevertheless, throughout World War II Japan was never able to defeat China or gain control of the vast Chinese interior. Under the leadership of Generalissimo Chiang Kai-shek, the Guoimndang, or the Nationalists, based in Chungking and the Communists under Mao Zedong in North China continued to govern a good portion of the country and waged an effective guerrilla warfare in parts of China until the defeat of Japan by the Americans in 1945.

Foreign businessmen who remained in Shanghai after the Japanese occupation in 1937 struggled for a normal daily life and found themselves in a bit of a "sticky wicket" after the Pearl Harbor attack on December 7, 1941. Eighteen months after the Allies declared war on Japan, the Japanese occupational forces in Shanghai rounded up all citizens of "enemy nations", men, women and children, and sent them to various prison camps located near Shanghai and its suburbs. French, Italian, Spanish, Russian, Swedish and Swiss citizens were exempted.

Karoly (Kay) M. Pate was a thirty-seven-year-old British citizen who managed a steamship and salvage company operated by the Ministry of Transport in Shanghai, China. Saturday, April 10, 1943,

Kay and his American wife Lillian and four year old son Darryl were interred in Lunghwa Concentration Camp located on the outskirts of Shanghai. Lillian and Darryl were repatriated (exchanged in Goa, India for Japanese prisoners) in September of 1943 and returned by ship to the U.S. Because he was a British subject, Kay was forced to say goodbye to his family and remain at Lunghwa Prison, presumably for the duration of the war. Determined to escape and rejoin his family, Kay and two friends cut the barbed wire of Lunghwa Camp on August 19, 1944 and with God's guidance and the aid of the Chinese populace, traveled across China to freedom and eventually joined his wife and son in the USA.

Out of China is based on Kay Pate's journal relating his own story of imprisonment, escape, and the long trek to freedom. This journey took Kay and two friends across China, by airplane over Burma to India and by ship to Australia and eventually reunion with his family in America on January 12, 1945. This translates into a journey of 23,000 miles in one hundred and forty-six days by foot, sampan, junk, rail, jeep, airplane, and ship. It is not only a story of escape from the Japanese, but also a story of a man's transformation from unbeliever to believer. A journey of personal conversion from agnostic to "born again" Christian in a world immersed in evil.

While some portions of this novel are dramatized, it is entirely based on a true story recorded in K. M. Pate's unpublished manuscript written in 1945. Kay's story is as he wrote it, unaltered as to the historical facts or descriptions related therein. Some of the narrative may be considered graphic and "politically incorrect." Nevertheless, in order for the reader to appreciate that evil can thrive and yet never destroy the human spirit or its propensity for good, Kay's biases, quaint British Empire attitude and his sentiments toward the Japanese have been preserved. They are an important part of his ordeal, as is his respect for the Chinese and their culture.

Cartographic name changes from Wade-Giles to Pinyin translations (intended to facilitate proper English pronunciation) may cause some confusion as the reader attempts to trace Kay's trek across China. For instance, on old maps, Beijing was spelled Peking, and Nanjing was spelled Nanking, Chongqing was Chungking, and

Sichuan Province was Szechwan Province. I have retained the Wade-Giles place name spellings as they appear in Mr. Pate's journal.

Richard L. Smith
Garden Valley, Idaho
November, 2004

CHAPTER ONE

Internment

❖⫘⫘❖

December 8, 1941, Shanghai

The double ring of Karoly Pate's telephone woke him from a sound sleep. Kay looked at his luminous wristwatch. It was 5 a.m. Monday morning. Kay threw his covers aside, stumbled across the room and picked up the receiver.

"Are you there Old Bean?" Kay recognized the voice on the line belonged to Mr. Vickers, the wharf manager.

"Bloody right I'm here, what else could you expect at 5 a.m. in the morning?" Kay grumpily answered.

"War has been declared by the Americans on Japan!" Mr. Vickers exclaimed. "The Japs bombed Pearl Harbor and now they are shooting at all the British and American gunboats moored here in the harbor."

Kay could hear the muffled "toong-toong-toong-toong" interspersed with deeper booms in the background.

"Sit tight Vickers, keep your head down, and I'll be down to the office as soon as I can get dressed," Kay answered.

Despite the Japanese occupation of Shanghai since 1937, the British steamship and salvage business Kay managed for the Ministry of Transportation was allowed to continue operations. Nevertheless, the relationship between Japan and the British, Belgian, Dutch and American governments continued to deteriorate throughout 1940 and 1941. It was apparent to the foreign community of Shanghai that war between the Allies and Japan was inevitable. They all sensed that they would end up caught in the middle of a war; nevertheless, there was nothing at all that they could do about it.

"Keep a stiff upper lip," the Brits would say.

With war declared on Japan, everything was about to change for Kay and his family. Kay was a British citizen, but Lillian his wife and his four-year-old son Darryl were American citizens. Travel by Enemy Nationals was restricted to the city limits of Shanghai. In 1942 it was not pleasant to be a foreign national in Shanghai, unless you were German, Russian, Vichy French or Italian. The Japanese considered these countries to be their partners. Swedish, Spanish, Portuguese and Swiss citizens were regarded as "neutrals" and although they were subjected to some of the same travel restrictions, they did not suffer the other insults imposed on Allied citizens.

January 10, 1942

After Pearl Harbor, Kay, Lillian, and Darryl were classified as Enemy Nationals and forced to register and carry identification passes. The registration process itself was designed by the Japanese government to demoralize so-called Enemy Nationals. Kay received notice that he and his family were required to be at the Gendarmerie H.Q. at 10 a.m. to register. Kay, Lil, and Darryl arrived at the Gendarmerie at 9 a.m. where they were confronted by a line that extended out the door and down the street. Hundreds of families were given the same date and time to register. Kay took his place in line and within minutes, it extended behind him and around the block.

Ten o'clock came and went yet the line did not move forward until well after noon. It was a windy and cold day in Shanghai and it wasn't long before Darryl began to cry. Lil took him into a restaurant across the street while Kay held their place in line. A Jap soldier saw Lil and Darryl leave the line. When they returned he would not allow them to rejoin Kay, but forced them to go to the end of the line that by now extended several hundred yards behind the place where they formerly stood. With a smirk, the soldier announced that anyone who left the line would have to go to the end. Kay gave up his spot and went to stand with Lil and Darryl.

As the day progressed, the line moved forward at a snail's pace. Toward mid-afternoon, some in line fainted, children cried, and the line behind Kay grew even longer. There was no place for anyone to relieve himself or herself and it was especially hard on the children. It took until 9 p.m. that evening before Kay was able to register. They had stood in line for twelve hours. After registration, everyone was forced to wear armbands marked with a big "B" for British, "A" for American, "N" for Dutch, and "X" for Belgian nationals.

Throughout 1942, Japanese Military proclamations directed toward Enemy Nationals grew increasingly restrictive. After the humiliation of being forced to register in person at the Gendarmerie H.Q., other regulations, and restrictions came in quick succession. First firearms, then radios, motor cars, boats, and some household goods were either confiscated or declared property of the Japanese government. All stocks, bonds and cash holdings had to be listed, along with all personal items such as furniture, carpets, curtains, kitchen utensils, etc. Everything of value was marked as property of the Japanese Army and Enemy Nationals were forbidden to remove any items under the threat of being "dealt with according to military law." While the foreign community didn't know exactly what penalties the threat involved, no one wanted to test it, so compliance was the rule of the day.

Eventually, additional proclamations forbade them from attending any movie theaters, nightclubs, or bars. Even their country clubs were taken over and only Japanese were permitted. The Methodist Church Lil attended every week was closed and boarded up, as were all other churches throughout the city. All the priests and ministers disappeared from town and rumor had it that they had either been imprisoned or deported.

The closing of churches and banishment of ministers was especially difficult for Lillian. She missed her Sunday services, yet for Kay this was no loss. He had always resisted Lil's efforts to get him to attend church services with her. Kay considered Sunday a day best-spent hunting or playing golf or cricket with his friends. As far as he was concerned, if there was a God, He certainly didn't give a damn about Kay and the feeling was mutual.

After the churches were closed, Lil and her friends organized a Sunday Bible Study in individual homes. Such meetings were strictly forbidden by the Japanese, and if caught, they could find themselves in jail or worse. Kay refused to attend these services even when the Japanese banned hunting trips to the country, took over his favorite golf links, and prohibited cricket matches. Kay spent his free time on long walks, fishing near the harbor with Darryl, or playing softball with the neighborhood kids.

April 10, 1943, Shanghai

Kay knew that it would only be a matter of time before he and his family was assigned to one of the internment camps being prepared for Enemy Nationals. That day came with a loud pounding on their door at 2 a.m. on April 10, 1943. Kay opened the door to six armed Japanese soldiers who ordered him and his family into the back of a waiting truck. Kay had been prepared for this roundup, and packed essentials into two duffel bags. Lil wrapped Darryl in a blanket as Kay threw their duffel bags into the back of the truck and helped Lil and a sleepy Darryl into the truck bed. Along with a truck full of other foreign nationals, they were driven to Lunghwa Camp in the Shanghai countryside. Kay's elderly mother was also interned at Lunghwa a few days later.

Lunghwa Concentration Camp, a former Chinese college and middle school occupied forty-four acres four miles west of the Shanghai City limits. The front entrance was off a branch of Minghong Road that led from Shanghai. All the college buildings sustained considerable damage in 1937 and several buildings were reduced to piles of brick and mortar when the Chinese Army unsuccessfully defended the property during the Japanese invasion. In the preceding five years, Lunghwa had been used as a Japanese army post. The damaged buildings were repaired to meet the army's needs, but for the most part the camp was a stinking shanty town of poorly repaired and unheated dormitories, inadequately served by putrid toilet facilities and cold water showers located on the north side of camp. Each family was assigned a twelve by twelve-foot room and given thin flea-infested bedding. For reasons only known to the Japanese bureaucrats, Kay's mother was assigned to the women's barracks and not allowed to share Kay's family room designed for four persons. Since the Japanese insisted on four to a room, they assigned the fifteen-year-old son of another family to share the Pate family quarters.

Three long wooden barracks designated "A," "B," and "C," were arranged in rows beside the large parade grounds. The inside plaster walls of the huts were pockmarked with shrapnel holes and most of the windows were either missing or broken. Inmates attempted to fill the glassless windows with plywood scraps or newspaper, but both were inadequate to prevent the wind and rain of a cold, wet winter from penetrating into the barracks. At one end of the recreation ground stood the Assembly Hall and across from it were the brick "D" "F" and "E" barracks. The only hot water available to prisoners was in the laundry building next to the "F" barracks. The southeast corner contained a large vegetable garden, and there was a second vegetable garden next to the commandant's building and guard barracks located on the eastside of the grounds. The hospital was also located near the commandant's building. A drainage ditch fed by a two acre holding pond paralleled the west side of the compound, and another drainage ditch blocked the east side. The access road ran alongside the entire south side of camp, and beyond the north side was a fifty-yard wide "no man's land" bounded by a thick forest.

Meals were served in two dining halls designated "East" and "West," yet together they were too small to accommodate all eighteen hundred prisoners. The once-a-day meal was served each evening in rotating shifts of three hundred persons, and each group had to get its food and eat quickly as the next shift was herded in every fifteen minutes. No one was allowed to take food or utensils outside, and any uneaten food was disposed of in a garbage can by the door. The meals were "coolie food" as Kay put it, consisting of a fist sized ball of sticky rice, a bowl of watery cabbage soup, a slice of dark insect infested bread, and a cup of green tea.

Darryl and the other children regularly raided the garbage cans outside of the officer's quarters. From the goodies that Darryl and others stole from those garbage cans, it appeared that the Japanese officers ate well, very well indeed. The camp commandant was

Major Hirro Sato, considered by the inmates as a thoroughly despicable and sadistic chap. He was suspected of using his camp food budget to purchase cheap "coolie food" and pocket the resulting excess cash.

Major Sato was bald, about five feet three, stocky and walked with a slight limp. Kay only met him once when Sato addressed the newcomers. The feature that made the most lasting impression on Kay was Sato's eyes; narrow slits that bracketed a bulbous nose dominating a rotund pockmarked face. His eyes were the blackest, meanest eyes that Kay had ever seen, and they darted from prisoner to prisoner as Sato inspected each new arrival, never spending more than a fraction of a second on each inmate.

A long scar marked the right side of his face, and his disposition seemed equally scarred. The camp prisoners thoroughly despised him and even the Japanese guards held Major Sato in low regard. By fattening his own pocket and shortchanging the camp food budget, Sato added malnutrition to the list of camp atrocities for which he was personally responsible. Were it not for the monthly Red Cross packages, most inmates would have been nothing but skin and bones after several months in Lunghwa.

Diseases were rampant throughout camp. Dysentery, malaria, and yellow fever were the worst of the maladies. Several very competent doctors who were interned at Lunghwa tried to make the best of inadequate hospital facilities stocked with few medicines or supplies. Quinine and Sulfa were in high demand and short supply, although these drugs were often included in the Red Cross parcels. Unfortunately, such valuable medicines seldom escaped theft by the guards who inspected the parcels for contraband. Cigarettes and foodstuffs that the Japs didn't want were the only items that made it to the prisoners. One guard, Sgt. Kitamura, with considerable personal risk, brought confiscated medications to the doctors. This and other similar acts proved that a few of the guards were humanitarians. Many lives were subsequently saved by such kindness.

Once a month the much-anticipated Red Cross parcels arrived, but there were never enough for distribution to each prisoner as intended. Most months less than eight hundred of the eighteen hundred parcels shipped by the Red Cross survived Jap confiscation.

Each barrack had an inmate "ichibahn" or "number one person" assigned by the Japanese to enforce military rules, keep order and see to it that the contents of the remaining parcels were fairly distributed. The parcels contained cans of food (sardines, spam, corned beef and the like), soap, medications (the few that the guards overlooked) unsweetened chocolate and cigarettes. The ichibahn was also expected to report military infractions to the guards, but few ever did. Nevertheless, not all of these ichibahn were on the up and up. Many readily took bribes so that distribution in the barracks they were in charge of was far from fair or even. Kay noted the names of lowlifes in his journal, and promised that, if given the opportunity, he would personally deal with them after the war.

Rain or shine each morning at 6 a.m. all prisoners had to quickly dress and line up outside in straight rows for roll call. The head of each family was required to answer for his entire family and respond to the called family name for example with a "present, count of three." The Japanese guards taking role had a terrible time pronouncing the various western names, especially names such as Worrington and Lainey. If a prisoner didn't recognize his mispronounced name and immediately answer roll call, the officer would come down the aisle and stop in front of the offending person and scream, "Wooington" or "Whiny", then whack that person on the head with his baton for not answering promptly. Fortunately for Kay, the guards could pronounce "Pate" just fine.

There was one fellow, Dansk Von Derhoofen, whom the Jap guards disliked intensely and continually treated him with contempt. Perhaps it was because he had been an officer in the Dutch Army Corps in New Guinea, or maybe it was that he was effeminate, frail, and soft-spoken. Whatever the reason, the Jap guards incessantly abused him. One "gunso" (Sergeant), Hirro Ito, was a sadistic son-of-a-bitch with a bad temper and breath to match. When he took roll call, he would pause in front of Dansk and shout "Fonhoof," and if he did not get a satisfactory response, he would hit the poor fellow with his baton.

One morning Dansk was ill and did not answer roll call on time. When he joined ranks, Sgt. Ito marched over to him and punched him in the face. Von Derhoofen collapsed onto the ground with a broken nose and Ito stood over him, kicking him in the stomach. The poor Dutchman groaned and attempted to get back on his feet, but Ito kept hitting him with his baton and kicking him until Dansk fainted. Kay was standing in the row immediately behind Dansk and broke ranks, grabbed the baton from Ito's hand and tried to revive Von Derhoofen. Sgt. Ito went ballistic. He screamed and hit Kay repeatedly until two guards rushed over and dragged Kay and Dansk away and threw them into "sweatboxes."

The sweatbox was a windowless doghouse capped with a tin roof and designed to produce maximum discomfort for offending prisoners. Four of these doghouses were strategically placed in the middle of the parade grounds where all prisoners could view them. There was only enough headroom to sit up or lie down, which required the prisoner to assume a fetal position when sleeping. Even in the coolness of the winter, the sun beat down on the tin roof and heated the interior to unbearable temperatures. At night, it was cold enough to freeze urine in the tin can urinals. In the summer, no prisoner could survive more than two or three days in the sweatboxes.

Kay was left in the sweatbox for three days without food or water. When he was finally released, he was extremely dehydrated and couldn't walk or even stand. For a week after his release, Lil nursed Kay back to health. Dansk was not so fortunate. When they opened his sweatbox, he was covered in his own excrement and quite dead.

In the summer of 1943, rumors of repatriation for Americans circulated throughout camp. Lillian and Darryl were listed as "Americans" on the camp register. Kay had registered them separately as an American mother and son, rather than including them on his own British registration. As such, they were high on the repatriation list. Had he registered them as the wife and child of a British Citizen, they would have been at the bottom of any possible repatriation list.

On September 15, the Japanese announced that a repatriation ship, the *Toia Maru*, had docked in Shanghai. Lillian and Darryl applied for passage on that ship, and were fortunate to be included with the twenty-three Lunghwa Americans selected for a prisoner exchange in Goa, India. They were only given an hour to pack and board the bus for Shanghai harbor. They were to be exchanged in Goa for captured Japanese soldiers and after the exchange they boarded the SS *Gripsholm*, bound for South America and ultimately ended their journey in New York City.

September 16, 1943, Lunghwa Camp

Kay hugged Lillian and Darryl for what could be the last time. As the bus left camp, Kay jumped on the back bumper and pressed his face against the window to say his last goodbye, only to be knocked off the bumper with the butt of a Jap rifle. He stood up, with tears marking his dusty face and watched as the red bus passed through the camp gate, and disappeared down the dusty road toward Shanghai. Although relieved to see his wife and son repatriated, Kay knew that it would be a long "sit out" for him. He had no idea how long it would be before they were a family again. Would he ever see his son and wife again? Would they be all right in America without friends, money, or a job? Separation from his family was indescribably painful.

Nevertheless, Kay realized that repatriation was "jolly well better" for Lil and Darryl than sitting the war out in a disease ridden Japanese prison camp. At first, Lil refused to leave without her husband, but Kay convinced her that it was best for their son. As a very capable and independent woman, Kay was certain that Lillian could make it alone. At the same time, he couldn't bear the thought of sitting in this hellhole prison without Lillian and Darryl.

This camp was lousy enough, but without his family, it was all the more unbearable. From the moment the red bus drove through the camp gate and disappeared down the road to Shanghai, Kay's mind hinged on one idea: escape.

CHAPTER TWO

Escape.

⊶⟴⟸⊷

Kay returned to his family room to pack his things. He knew that since his family was gone, he would be required to transfer to the bachelor barracks. He was thoroughly overwhelmed by sorrow. Kay packed his few possessions, and moved into the "E" block barracks, the male prisoners' dormitory. The Japanese kept assuring the remaining U.S. and British prisoners that repatriation was just around the corner, and a ship would arrive "any day now" to take them to India or Australia. Kay suspected that this was an empty promise designed to discourage any escape attempts. No repatriation ship for U.S. or British prisoners ever came. The resolve to escape intensified for Kay day by day. He began to formulate specific escape plans all that summer and into the fall.

Days became months as winter blasted Lunghwa Camp. There was no heat in any of the barracks, and night after night, the temperature was below freezing. If a prisoner placed a glass of water on the table in the center of the room in the evening it soon had a film of ice on it, and by morning, the glass was a solid chunk of ice. The only way to stay warm that winter was to dress in layers of clothing, then work, and sleep in those clothes. Kay wore his blue wool sweater day and night.

The men's barracks had a shower room, as did most barracks, yet no heated water was available for prisoners except at the camp shower room that was at the opposite end of camp. The Japanese guards and officer quarters had hot water showers, but the Japanese considered hot water to be an extravagance for prisoners. Kay showered early in the morning then shivering uncontrollably quickly dressed and returned to bed to warm up before the 6:00 a.m. roll call. He was careful to conserve his only bar of soap that had to last until the next Red Cross packages arrived. Every Tuesday and Thursday hot water was available to prisoners to wash clothes in the camp laundry, but the Japanese did not provide soap.

One of the prisoners, Sam, was an amateur radio operator, and as such knew how to construct a radio. Over the course of a few weeks, he managed to put together a working crystal radio from components that friends on the outside smuggled into camp for him. In the men's barracks downstairs bathroom, someone had attached an old leather suitcase to the wall to use as a cabinet for various bathroom items. They removed a couple of bricks from the wall behind the suitcase to make a niche for the radio. A little antenna wire strung inside the bathroom and they were in business. Each evening, after lights out, Sam would retrieve the radio from its hiding place, don the earphones, and tune into the BBC broadcast from New Delhi. Sam carefully wrote down salient news and then passed it on the next day. The news spread throughout camp like wildfire, and gave prisoners much hope for an end to the war. The BBC news reported Allied victories in the Pacific Theatre and in Malaysia and Burma, whereas the Japanese-English news daily broadcasts by Tokyo Rose and blasted over the camp loudspeakers only reported news of the glorious Japanese victories over Allied forces. Prisoners grew to hate the very sound of this traitorous woman's syrupy voice as she spewed her lies and misinformation at full volume all over camp.

Tokyo Rose, her real name was Ikuko Toguri, was a twenty-eight-year-old Japanese-American born and schooled in California. After Pearl Harbor, she immigrated to Japan where she got a job as a typist for Radio Tokyo. In November 1943, Toguri began her career as a broadcaster for Radio Tokyo, a job that was to bring her notoriety and eventually result in her conviction for treason and finally imprisonment in the United States. Her program, known as the Zero Hour, became part of Japanese psychological warfare designed to lower the morale of the United States Armed Forces. Zero Hour was broadcast daily, except Sunday. Toguri was introduced on the program, which usually began with band music, as "Orphan Annie," or "Your favorite playmate and enemy, Ann." Typical broadcasts made by Toguri in 1944 went:

> *"Hello, boneheads. This is your favorite enemy, Ann. How are all you orphans of the Pacific? Are you enjoying yourselves while your wives and sweethearts are running around with the 4-F's in the States? How do you feel now when all your ships have been sunk by the Japanese Navy? How will you get home? You are going to die! Here's another record to remind you of home."*

Toguri's average time on each program was about twenty minutes, and most of her comments were similar to the above example. Between her diatribes, she played popular records of the day such as *"Speak to Me of Love," "In a Little Gypsy Tea Room,"* and *"Love's Old Sweet Song."*

The camp underground radio-news contradicted the lies spewed by Tokyo Rose, bolstered internee spirits and created hope for the eventual defeat of the Japanese military. Many prisoners worried that when liberation day came, the Japanese guards might just shoot all prisoners to obliterate any witnesses to Japanese atrocities. They were correct to harbor such concerns, for toward the end of the war this is exactly what the Japanese did in many POW camps. However, thankfully this never happened to the camps surrounding Shanghai, partly because the Japanese left in a big hurry when the camps were threatened by the Chinese guerrilla troops.

Health conditions for the prisoners of Lunghwa Camp were appalling. Every day somebody died in Lunghwa, whether it was from dysentery, scurvy, or the many other diseases that raged throughout camp. Illness, encouraged by malnutrition and poor sanitary conditions and exacerbated by overly cramped quarters, took a heavy toll on the young, old and weak inmates. Some prisoners simply starved to death.

The hospital was located in the northwest corner of camp.

Several imprisoned doctors did their best to treat prisoners with inadequate equipment and few medications. Every day bodies were collected from the hospital and prepared for burial in the cemetery outside of camp. The burial detail included four prisoners selected at random by Sgt. Ito. He preferred to select those prisoners that he held a grudge against and he especially disliked Brits. After recovering from his own experience in the "sweatbox," Kay was selected by Ito several times for burial detail. It was common to throw the dead bodies into a ditch and cover them in lime to accelerate decomposition. The unmarked common graves were just outside the camp perimeter fence, and Kay considered the burial detail as an opportunity for escape. He planned how he would distract the guards and then make a break for the woods.

However, an incident changed his mind about the wisdom of such plans. One day Kay was one of four prisoners assigned to the burial detail. Unknown to Kay, the other three prisoners had formulated an escape plan for one of them. Kay was digging in the bottom of the burial trench when two of the prisoners above started a fight. As Sgt. Ito ran over to stop the fight with the butt of his rifle, the third prisoner dropped his shovel and ran toward the forest twenty yards away. A soldier in the guard tower saw what was going on and fired a burst from his machine gun in the direction of the escaping prisoner. The unfortunate man dropped to the ground, mortally wounded, ten yards short of the trees. Sgt. Ito forced the two prisoners to pick up their wounded comrade and throw him into the trench. Then Sgt. Ito kicked the two prisoners into the trench and with a burst from his tommy gun, killed all three. Kay stood frozen in the trench until the guard motioned him to climb out and shovel lime and dirt over the bodies.

That spring Kay was assigned a job as bricklayer and boilermaker. Kay was proficient at both assignments, and his skills with machinery soon earned him a key to the camp machine shop. One day the hot water tank in the Japanese officers quarters developed a leak and Kay was assigned to repair it. Kay was fluent in English, French and Chinese, as well as conversational Japanese. As he repaired the hot water tank, one of the Japanese officers discovered that Kay spoke French, and struck up a conversation in that language.

This officer, whose name was Lieutenant Kato Sugura, had been schooled in Paris, and spent some time in Ottawa, Canada, where Kay had also attended college. Kato was well educated and articulate, and enjoyed speaking French with Kay. He was not like most of the other Japanese officers in Lunghwa, for he was kind, generous, and ashamed of the despicable behavior of his fellow officers. Over the next few weeks, Kay became very friendly with Lieutenant Sugura, and was invited several times to the officers' recreation room to play Mahjongg, an Asian game played with tiles and relished by the Lunghwa Japanese officers. Although Kay was very good at Mahjongg, he was careful to win only occasionally to avoid angering the Japanese guards. Most of them were ungracious losers, especially when beaten by a lowly Brit.

After Lil and Darryl were repatriated, Kay's mind never strayed far from his desire to escape. When he first saw the large map of China pinned to the wall of the Japanese Officer's recreation room, his breakout plans began to take formal shape. The map was conveniently marked with cross-hatching to show the extent of Japanese occupation in China, which in 1943 extended from Manchukuo in the north to Chekiang Province south of Shanghai, and the city of Ichang to the west. The Japanese controlled major cities such as Canton, Hong Kong, Amoy, Hangchow, and Nanchang. All other occupied cities were underlined on the map in red pencil. Kay always seated himself at the Mahjongg table so that he could study the map as he played. He later drew a copy of the map from memory, adding details from his own knowledge of the surrounding Shanghai countryside.

With free access to the machine shop, Kay began to assemble or steal items he would need for his escape. This included a pair of wire cutters, a flashlight with extra batteries, a lightweight green shower curtain that would make a fine tarp, a rucksack, a Dunlop air mattress (called a li-lo), a cigarette lighter, a canteen and tin cup, a first aid kit, a bottle of chloride tablets, a Boy Scout pocket knife, several candles, a magnifying glass, boxes of matches, a flint and striker, and a wool blanket.

A compass carelessly left on a table in the recreation room soon found its way into Kay's pocket. He also hoarded several tins of tuna, salmon, spam, chipped beef, condensed milk, sardines, and several packages of cigarettes from his Red Cross packages.

The spring weather at Lunghwa had been very wet. It rained daily, and even into late April, it remained unseasonably cold. The thought of escape was never far from Kay's mind, but he was a patient man and disciplined enough to bide his time and wait for warmer weather and a suitable opportunity. He studied the nightly patrol patterns of the guards and planned the safest place to cut the wire and scamper into the woods without detection. Wide water-filled drainage ditches blocked both the east and west sides of camp. The access road into camp paralleled the south side. Two hundred yards from the guards' barracks, Kay determined that the north side behind the hospital was the safest place to attempt an escape.

On May 23, word got around that six men from another British barracks, Uhlich, Murray-Kidd, Scott, Levy, Huxley and Condor had escaped the previous evening. They had cut the wire near the gymnasium on the southeast side of camp opposite where Kay planned to make his escape. Their escape caused quite a commotion among the prison guards, and the scuttlebutt was that a few of the guards had been reprimanded for not noticing the escape for a full day. Consequently, prisoners were forced to "fall out" for role call at random times of the day and night. One of the most dreaded sounds to hear was that of the guards crashing into the barracks, often in the dead of the night, and shouting, "Woll Caul, out...out!" In addition, guard patrols along the fence perimeters were increased to prevent further breakouts; nevertheless, Kay would not let increased surveillance or roll calls deter his escape plans.

Kay wished the runaways luck, yet even if he had been aware of their plans, he would not have asked to join them. Kay planned to "go it alone," and did not even let his mother know his intentions. To do so would have placed her in danger, for it was standard procedure to punish the relatives of fugitives. Although it was uncertain if the Japanese knew that Mrs. Pate was Kay's mother, the less she knew the better for her. Kay figured that if he took on escape partners, it would require sharing his intentions with others, and the more persons who knew his plans, the less chance he would have of success.

Some prisoners, only concerned with their own survival, were informants and no one knew who could be trusted and who could not. He hoped that the Murray-Kidd group would make it, but held out little hope for their success. What chance would six Brits, none of whom spoke Chinese, have to make it seven hundred miles overland to Guoimndang (Nationalist China)?

Days later, more rumors circulated that the fugitives had been caught and executed. Kay didn't buy it! If the Murray-Kidd party had been caught, the Japs would have brought their bodies back and hung them in the recreation grounds as an example to all prisoners. Furthermore, the Japs were always starting rumors designed to discourage any escape attempts. Although the odds were against successful escapes, desperate prisoners occasionally gave it a go. Success depended on the cooperation of the local Chinese farmers, the help of Nationalist Chinese guerrillas, and a whole lot of luck. Chungking, the capital of Nationalist (Free) China, was over twelve hundred hostile miles away and the Japanese Army patrolled the entire area between Shanghai and Szechwan Province. Since none of the Murray-Kidd escapees could speak Chinese, it would be difficult for them to solicit the help of local farmers and guerrillas.

On the other hand, Kay spoke fluent Kyangsher dialect Chinese and had a rudimentary understanding of several other dialects such as Cantonese. He felt that this skill would be essential for a successful trek across China. Kay knew that even if he made a successful escape from Lunghwa, should he be caught by either a Japanese patrol or the Chinese Wang Ching-wei puppet soldiers (Chinese soldiers in the pay of the Japanese), a bullet through the back of the head was the best he could expect. The worst was to be thrown into one of the Chinese prison camps, a veritable hellhole. Kay prayed that the fugitives would be safe.

Pray? Kay was surprised that he was entertaining such an unfamiliar thought as prayer. Kay was a lifelong Atheist, or perhaps Agnostic would be a more apt description. As far as he was concerned, if there was a God, He didn't know Kay and Kay didn't know Him, and that was just the way it was. An Almighty God certainly couldn't be all that interested in folks like Kay, or the machinations of humans for that matter. Kay always had better things to do with his time than pray, and had a special disdain for Bible-thumping folk and churchgoers in particular.

Church attendance on Sundays? That was for women and children. Sunday was a day better spent playing golf or hunting pheasant in the Chinese countryside. If there was a God, He could be found in the beauty of the mountains and fields, not in a dark brick building lit by candles and bits of colored glass. Church was a waste of good time as far as Kay was concerned, and throughout his short life, he was totally unconcerned about the possible existence or non-existence of a Divine Being. No, Kay would leave prayer up to people like his wife Lil, who seemed to find solace in her Bible and church attendance.

Lil was careful not to try to convert him. At best, it would have been wasted effort on her part, and at worst, Kay would probably go on an anti-religious tirade. Through their years of marriage, she knew better than to try to bring up the subject of religion. Weird what incarceration could do to a person! Perhaps his clumsy attempt at prayer was due to the lack of proper food. Kay had dwindled from his pre-war robust one hundred and seventy pounds on his five-foot-eight inch frame, down to about one hundred and thirty pounds. He was nothing but skin and bones. He assumed that prison had not only affected his body, but likely his mind as well. Only months before he could not have imagined himself praying, of all things.

Moreover, if he was going to pray, he thought, to whom should he direct his prayers. The Hindu gods, the Buddhist god, or Jewish God were all good choices. Perhaps the Christian God would be the best choice, after all that was Lil's preference. Yet, how could any of these deities be expected to take an interest in Kay's problems? What did the Christian God care about humankind? If He did care as some insisted, why then did He allow all this evil and suffering? How could a loving God allow the Japanese and Germans to do such evil to good people like these poor Chinese coolies or Jews? Perhaps the Buddhist god was a better listener. After all, were they not the same god, so what did it matter? Such strange thoughts! Alien…even silly! He concluded that such ideas were a figment of his imagination caused by this hellhole prison, or perhaps a delusion brought on by starvation. And yet…

Without Lil or Darryl around to give him solace, his brain was drifting. He felt he was the loneliest man on earth. Only the thought of escape and seeing his family again gave him focus and hope. He missed Lil and Darryl so much and so longed to be reunited with them that he had a hard time concentrating on such abstractions as religion. Yet, he kept asking God questions. Were Lil and Darryl all right? Had they made it safely to New York? For the first time in his life, he felt a genuine need to pray. He prayed for the safety of Lil and Darryl. He prayed for the Murray-Kidd escapees. He prayed for a successful end of the war, and victory for the Allies. He prayed that God would favor his escape and keep him safe.

Nonsense! All this was utter nonsense…and yet…was it possible that prayer might actually work? Well, he determined, only if he did it right. Then Kay realized that he didn't have the slightest idea of how to pray, or where he should pray. Well, at church of course! He asked around and discovered that a Dutch priest, one of the original Lunghwa inmates, had permission to conduct Sunday services in the Assembly Hall next to the Recreation Ground.

With such turmoil eating away at him, one Sunday morning Kay attended these services. He sat on a bench along with several dozen other worshipers and listened to a priest mumble something in a language that he did not recognize and conduct a ritual that he did not understand. Was this what prayer was all about? He didn't know, yet in a sense the service was completely understandable. He recognized that these worshipers were giving homage to their God and receiving solace from doing so. He joined with them as they knelt, sat and stood and read words from a prayer book and sang with them as the ritual progressed.

The priest gave his homily partly in English, Chinese, and French to accommodate his cosmopolitan congregation. Kay was fluent in all three languages, and did not miss out on a word. The sermon concerned some Biblical fellow named Job. Job was a faithful servant of God; nevertheless, God allowed Job to suffer terribly. All sorts of dreadful luck befell Job, yet he stoically accepted all the pestilence that God allowed and remained true to his faith. Kay envied those who had the gift of faith, for he had none. Yet after the service, Kay felt strangely calm and satisfied.

He thought, "this praying stuff has strange powers over humans. It gives them hope and strength, even under such circumstances. Could it be that there actually is someone up there who listens to human requests, and perhaps, just perhaps, He really cares about us and will answer such prayers?"

Strange thoughts! Two days later, Kay sat down at supper next to the priest, Father Germain, and shared his troubled feelings. He said that he could not bring himself to believe in a loving God, and yet... The priest told Kay that he was the recipient of a powerful gift from God, the gift of inquiry, and the gift of faith was sure to follow. Moreover, yes, God did care about him and would listen to his prayers, and grant any sincere and well-intentioned request. Prayer and faith would give him strength and fortitude to endure Lunghwa or any other test God should ask of him. God would do for Kay just as He did for Job.

Kay returned to his bunk and from under it dragged out the duffel bag that contained the few possessions he and Lil had brought from their home in Shanghai. Inside he found a pocket size black-leather covered Bible trimmed in gold leaf and embossed with the title:

"The King James Version of the Holy Bible."

Actually, this was Lil's Bible, and in her hasty departure, she had left it behind. Lillian attended church regularly and Kay often saw her reading from this book. She seemed to find succor in these pages, and for the first time Kay sat on the edge of his bed, opened the book and read on the inside page,

"PROPERTY OF THE UNION CHURCH of SHANGHAI."

He found the Book of Job that the priest had mentioned, read it and was amazed how profound and applicable the story was to his situation. Afterwards he casually open the book to Chapter Two of the Song of Solomon. The passage read:

*My beloved spake, and said to me, "rise up, my love,
my fair one, and come away.
For lo, the winter is past, the rain is over and gone.
Until the day break, and the shadows flee away, I
will get me to the Mountains of myrrh, and to the hill
of frankincense."*

For Kay, this passage from the book of Solomon was a clear answer to his prayers. The message was to *come away* when the winter and rain was over, then "at dawn go to the mountains."

Only those who have lived under tyranny can fully appreciate the magnetic power of freedom. Those deprived of freedom will endure all the dangers, hardships, privations, and pain necessary to grasp it. It was this very craving for freedom and a new found trust in God that motivated Kay to get on with it and plan his escape. It was a plan born of desperation and a painful longing to be with Lil and Darryl. It was a dangerous plan that would result in a perilous trek across China through Japanese-infested territory. Most prisoners preferred to sit out the war in prison rather than take risks that were apt to end badly for them.

Kay had personally witnessed what he could expect from the Japanese if he was caught escaping. Only two months earlier a man and his young wife attempted to flee by scaling the Lunghwa fence at a spot where the barbed wire was only six feet high. Their plan was ill conceived and botched when they attempted an escape at twilight. Detected by one of the guards as they climbed over the top of the fence, and without even giving them a chance to climb back down, the guard sprayed them with bullets from his tommy gun. Their lifeless bodies, abused by crows, were left hanging from the barbed wire fence until the next evening, an example of what could be expected for those who dared to attempt an escape.

Two of Kay's bunkmates in the men's barracks were Scottish chaps named Tommy Crosthwaite and Bill Henry. Kay, Tommy, and Bill became lifelong friends while at Lunghwa. All three men worked together as bricklayers repairing two of the destroyed buildings on the northwest perimeter of camp. Their friendship survived the war and they remained friends for the rest of their lives. They would meet yearly to hoist a few beers, celebrate their escape, and relive old times.

Thomas "Tommy" Crosthwaite, 55, was a prominent Shanghai stockbroker before the war and found himself in Manila on business when, on December 7, 1941, he was stranded and unable to return home. Initially detained by the Japanese, he was declared a foreign national and sent to Santo Tomas Concentration Camp. After eight months, he was herded below deck on a filthy tramp steamer, transported to Shanghai's Pootung Prison, and eventually transferred to Lunghwa.

About five-foot-six in stature with a generous crop of salt-and-pepper hair, a thin mustache, and a square jaw. Tommy was on the surface serious, and determined, a no-nonsense hyperactive fellow always on the go. Although he seldom smiled, once Kay got to know him, he found him affable with a dry sense of humor. While in camp, Kay and Tommy became the closest of friends.

Tommy's wife, who he had just married in August 1941, was safely in Los Angeles visiting her parents at the start of the war. Tommy could not bear the thought of sitting out the war in China without her. He confided to Kay that he would risk life and limb to join his wife back in the States.

William C. "Bill" Henry was the Works Manager for the Shanghai Natural Gas Company. An inch or two taller than Tommy, his triangular face was graced with a prominent forehead and topped with a thinning stock of short black hair. A good conversationalist, Bill had a quick and sharp wit and an engaging laugh to match. He enjoyed a good story or joke and would spin a yarn whenever the opportunity arose. His wife of twenty years was Swedish, and therefore classified as a "neutral." She was employed by the Swedish Consulate in Shanghai and as a neutral, the Japanese had not imprisoned her. Bill felt that as a loyal British subject and a member of the British Army it was his duty to escape. Bill had signed up as a second lieutenant just before his internment and was awaiting his commission, when the Japanese threw him into jail. It was better for him that the Japs thought him a civilian, for as a British officer his treatment would have been much worse. In fact, some of his fellow officers had been sent to Burma to build a bridge on the river Kwai. He could do more for his country on the outside than he could by sitting out the war in a concentration camp or building some damned bridge in Burma.

The Japanese guards for some unknown perverse reason intensely disliked Bill. For no apparent reason, on several occasions the guards beat him senseless with their wooden Samurai sword scabbards. Tommy and Kay hated the Japanese, but based on such sadistic treatment Bill had developed an especially deep loathing, and this hatred would explode during their trek to free China.

One day Kay, Bill, and Tommy were walking across the parade ground toward their barracks after a hard day digging a drainage ditch just outside the front gate, when three Japanese guards approached them. One of three guards they had nicknamed "Puke" (because they said this is what his pockmarked face made them want to do) marched over to the three prisoners, scabbard in hand and began to hit Bill while the other guards held Tommy and Kay. He landed blow after blow until Bill lay in the dirt of the parade grounds. As Puke ground his face into the dirt with his boot, Bill hissed that he would "kill the bloody Jap son-of-a-bitch." Fortunately for Bill, Puke did not understand a word of English and with a final kick to Bill's side, turned, and walked off. Bill was so badly beaten that he could not make it back to the barracks and Kay and Tommy had to carry him back to his bunk. However, Bill's vow remained deep within his heart and if ever given the chance, he would have his revenge.

After lights-out each evening, the three friends whispered about escape. Tommy's bunk was to Kay's right and Bill bunked to his left. Kay initially planned to go it alone, even leaving his mother behind. Bill and Tommy said that they all had a duty to escape, and eventually convinced Kay that three would have a better chance than one. A lone person in the middle of Japanese-held China had little chance of success, but three could make it, especially if one of them could speak the local language.

It was a tremendous advantage for all three that Kay could speak Kyangsher Chinese. Neither Bill nor Tommy spoke a word of Chinese and would be unable to solicit the help of locals without knowing the language. They were all very aware that by escaping they risked a bullet in the back of the head or a slow death in a Chinese prison. Danger aside, they agreed to chance it and planned a joint escape.

Although fugitives were always concerned about Japanese retaliation to relatives left behind, there was no danger for Bill's "neutral" wife. Kay also did not think that the Japanese would retaliate against his mother, because through a typical Japanese bureaucratic snafu, they had never connected Kay with his mother. This was the reason she was assigned to a different barrack at Lunghwa. Lillian also had relatives incarcerated in other Japanese prison camps in China. Her mother, sister, and niece were in Yangchow prison, while her brother-in-law was at the Haiphong Road prison. None of Lillian's relatives could be connected with Kay.

Kay had been given keys to the machine shop, and at the end of their bricklaying day and before supper the three friends would bolt the machine shop door and study Kay's hand-drawn maps. The maps included details of Anhwei, Chekiang, Hunan, Hupeh, and Kiangsi Provinces. Fortunately, due to Kay's many hunting trips, he knew the countryside immediately surrounding Shanghai by heart. That countryside was the Yangtze River delta district crisscrossed with thousands of creeks, rivers, and canals and dotted with rice paddies. They would have to avoid the few roads through the area and stick to paths or go crosscountry. The plan was to stay west of Hangchow Bay and follow the Shanghai-Hangchow-Ningpo railway toward Kashing, where they hoped to meet up with the Chinese guerrillas reported to be in the area. It would be rough going, but it was the shortest route to Guoimndang and if they could make contact with the Chinese guerrilla forces in the nearby provinces, these soldiers were sure to aid them in their escape.

Bill argued that they should make their way to Chungking in Szechwan Province by following the Yangtze River. Chungking was the provisional capital of Nationalist China and headquarters for Generalissimo Chiang Kai-shek and the British and American China operations. Located eight hundred miles up the Yangtze Kiang through Japanese infested territory; Chungking might as well have been located on the moon.

"We could get passage with friendly Chinese on the Yangtze

and by sticking to small villages and towns we would avoid all the Jap-held cities marked on Kay's map," Bill contended.

Kay knew that Bill's plan was inherently flawed. The Japanese patrolled the entire route up the Yangtze River, and they were in control of every large city between Shanghai and Ichang in Hupeh Province. Ichang, five hundred miles distant, was at the entrance to the Three Rivers Gorges on the Yangtze, and the only way through that area was to travel on the well-patrolled river. Kay convinced Bill that even if they secured river passage with friendly locals, such a plan was certain to end up in their recapture.

After much discussion, they agreed to Kay's plan to make their way to Kashing, then to the city of Yu-shan through Changshan, about two hundred and fifty miles southwest of Shanghai. Changshan was in Guoimndang, and the Chekiang-Kiangsi railroad passed through Yu-shan on its way to Kunming. Tommy said that it was rumored the railway had been bombed and was not operating all the way to Kunming. Kay hoped they could meet up with the Nationalist guerrillas rumored to be operating in the Kashing area. With the help of those folks, they could then make their way to Kanchow, where the Japanese map marked an Allied airfield. Bill heard that there was a joint U.S. and British operation at this airbase. The Americans could take them by air to Kunming and India.

Along the journey to Guoimndang, they would have to avoid large cities, trains, or main roads that would be controlled by the Japanese. The main obstacle would be the Chekiang Mountains southwest of Shanghai. If, with the aid of guerrillas, they could make it over the mountains into Kiangsi and Hunan Provinces, they could expect assistance from the Free China Chiang Kai-shek government based in Chungking. The British Embassy was also located in Chungking, with a Consul office in Kunming, and it was rumored that the British Government had set up an operation there to help escapees out of China. Tommy had managed to scrounge two more rucksacks and another two-inch compass as well as a medical kit. The route to Yu-Shan was agreed on and the rucksacks packed. The only remaining decision was when the best time would be to make their escape.

From the calendar on the wall in the Japanese officers' recreation room, Kay noted that a new moon would occur on August 12, which would help hide their dash from the camp fence into the forest. A no-man's land, one hundred yards wide, had been cleared around the entire camp and a full moon could betray them as they scampered across this clearing. On the other hand, since they decided to travel only at night, some moonlight would be essential. A good compromise would be a quarter to full moon that would occur in the second half of August. The Red Cross parcels were due in Lunghwa on August 19, and in retaliation, the Japs might withhold these precious packages from prisoners if they left before then. The camp commandant had done so before, as when Ulrich and party escaped, and this certainly did not endear the inmates to the escapees. Thus, the three friends agreed that their escape would have to be after delivery of those parcels on the night of August 19.

One reason that Kay dared not share his escape plans or expect much sympathy from fellow prisoners was his concern about other Jap retaliation to those folks. Worse than withholding Red Cross parcels, the Japs had threatened physical torture to anyone that knew of escape plans and did not report them. It was likely that others in Kay's barracks would be tortured in an attempt to extract information from them about Kay's escape plans, even if they knew nothing about Kay's plans. Therefore, it was best not to include anyone other than Bill and Tommy. Even under torture, fellow prisoners could not tell what they did not know. Despite tight lips, a rumor began to circulate in camp that Bill was collaborating with Kay and Tommy to plan an escape.

Bill suspected the source of this rumor was a comely young American woman who went by the name of Betty, although Kay doubted that this was her given name. Bill had the task to dye all their white clothes dark blue, and was using the communal wash tubs to do so. Betty happened into the laundry while Bill was busy with this task and began to ask questions. Bill told her that the white clothes were impossible to keep clean, and this was his idea to make them more presentable. Betty was suspicious of his explanation and eventually figured out that Bill and his friends were planning an escape. A very determined young woman, she invited herself along with the escapees and began to gather food and other supplies for her escape attempt. She kept asking Bill when they planned to escape, but he denied that escape was what they had in mind. She didn't believe Bill and threatened to expose them if they didn't allow her to join. Kay was entirely against letting Betty become part of their team. He argued that Betty was not physically or mentally prepared for such a challenge and most likely would bog down and get all four of them caught. Besides, what would their wives say if they traveled cross-country hundreds of miles with a young woman? Nevertheless, they could not afford to have Betty become angry and spill the beans to the Japanese. They decided to string Betty along and make her think she was a member of their team. They fabricated an escape plan that would take them across the Wangpoo River and skirt Hangchow Bay to Hanghsein, where they claimed Kay had friends that would help them to Chungking. As it later turned out, under intense interrogation and torture, Betty spilled this false plan to the Japanese and it sent them looking in the wrong direction.

A camp escape committee led by a British colonel had been organized early in the year, but Kay was distrustful of this committee and refused to solicit help from them. He suspected that someone on that committee was a Jap collaborator. The man and woman who had been shot trying to escape asked the committee to condone their escape plans; nevertheless, the committee refused to do so and ordered them not to try. Then on the evening of the planned escape, the perimeter guard was suspiciously doubled and the couple ended up dead hanging on the fence.

Since the rumors of their escape were circulating, Kay met with the committee and without revealing specifics, verified their intention to escape. Because they were afraid the Japs would punish the entire camp for any escape, a few of the committee members argued against any escape attempts. Kay reminded them that they were compelled by their governments to escape if possible. To prevent such escapes, the Japanese military was forced to commit many soldiers to camps as guards. The more troops the Japanese were forced to use as guards the fewer soldiers would be available for the front lines. Besides, they would leave a note explaining that no one in camp knew their plans, which was the truth, and this note should be given to the camp commandant after they left. Reluctantly, the committee eventually gave its blessing.

August 19, 1944, Lunghwa Prison Camp

On the evening of August 19, the Red Cross parcels arrived as expected. A rainstorm had moved in over the Shanghai coast that day bringing with it driving rain, thunder, and layers of thick clouds. The dark night provided by thick clouds was a mixed blessing. While it would help to cover their escape, they would be wandering about the muddy countryside unable to see more than a few yards in front of them. Becoming lost in the woods was a real concern. Fearing they would be spotted, they dared not use the flashlight until well beyond the Lunghwa fence.

A stroke of luck occurred two days before the planned escape. A storm had shorted out the camp electric lights that were placed every fifty yards along the entire fence perimeter. An electrician was hired to come from Shanghai and make the necessary repairs, but he had been delayed by the same storm. On the night of August 19 the perimeter light standards were inoperative.

Even a driving rain could not dissuade them. In fact, the moonless night and disabled light standards would help hide them, and the driving rain would keep all but the perimeter guards in their barracks. They synchronized their watches and agreed to meet at the rendezvous point behind the hospital at 9:50 p.m. For several days, each took turns watching this portion of fence and timing the guard's rounds. A guard tower loomed over each corner of the fence eight hundred yards apart, with additional towers placed at two hundred-yard intervals. Each tower, about thirty feet high, was equipped with powerful searchlights and floodlights that illuminated a thousand square-foot area around each tower. These lights had not shorted out. The darkest spot between the towers was about twenty yards from the billet where they were to rendezvous, and the absence of working light standards created an expanded dark area.

Two guards patrolled each section of fence between the guard towers, one guard starting at one tower and a second guard at the other. They walked in opposite directions covering the intervening two hundred yards in about five minutes, passing each other at the halfway point. In addition, searchlights scanned the fence at two-minute intervals. At precisely 10 p.m. each evening, there was a changing of the guard in the towers and on the ground. Typically, there was a break of about five minutes before the new shift began its patrol. Sometimes the old and new guards would talk for a few additional minutes, but the escapees dared not count on this extra time. This presented a narrow window of time that gave Kay, Bill and Tommy less than two to five minutes to cut the wire, crawl through, then repair the wire and dash across the one hundred yard no-mans land and into the forest.

At 9:50 p.m., they met behind the hospital on the north perimeter of camp, hid next to a storage shed and waited until the guards passed each other for the last time before going off duty. The steady rainfall picked up in intensity and they could hear thunder and see flashes of lightning in the distance. The air was unusually cold for this time of year, and their breath condensed in the humid air. Kay's heart pounded. At 9:55 p.m., the guards were at least one hundred feet away with their backs to the chosen escape spot. The escapees quickly ran over to the fence and Kay prepared to use his wire cutters to cut the wire. The fence consisted of twelve double strands of taut barbed wire that extended from a few inches off the ground to about eight feet high. Topping the eight-foot fence were several strands of sharp razor wire. Kay carefully cut the bottom two strands of wire, which made a recoiling twang sound. They held their breath for a few seconds to make sure no one heard the noise. The cut wire gave them only about a nine-inch space through which to crawl, but Kay dared not cut additional strands.

They took their rucksacks off and squirmed on their backs under the wire. Bill went first, then Tommy. Kay stretched the topmost strand to give them maximum clearance. As Tommy crawled through, he caught his leg on one of the barbs, which ripped his pants and gave him a nasty scratch on his lower leg. Bill and Tommy ran into the woods about fifty yards from the fence. Kay crawled through, then using a pair of pliers and three strands of extra wire repaired the fence so the guards would not notice the damage.

Suddenly the whole camp was lit up by a tremendous flash of

lightning that struck the ground less than a mile away. A second flash stronger and longer lasting than the first flickered across the sky an instant later. Kay lay exposed and completely visible to anyone who looked his way. Fortunately, the tremendous clap of thunder that followed the first flash captured the attention of the guards and no one looked in his direction.

He got up and ran into the woods just as the searchlights swept past the repaired section of fence. He expected to hear the ack-ack-ack of machine gun fire or sirens shrieking at any minute, but he heard nothing except the sound of his heart pounding, crickets in the forest and the rumble of the camp generator. They lay in the woods as quietly as possible, barely daring to breathe and trusting that the guards would not notice the repaired fence. As soon as the two guards passed each other at the escape point and were well on their way toward the next guard tower, Kay stood up and ran deeper into the forest. Tommy and Bill followed closely on his heels.

It was inky dark in the forest and the trees collected the sheets of rain and poured it nosily onto the leaf-covered ground. Trees and hanging branches slowed their escape. In their headlong rush away from the camp, they tripped over invisible brush and ran into low hanging branches that scratched them as they attempted to duck under them. Only the occasional flashes of lightning kept them from colliding head-on with several large trees. Tommy made enough noise to rouse the entire camp as he stumbled deeper into the woods, so much so that Bill eventually slowed and warned him to stop making such a clatter. After several hundred yards, Kay stopped to catch his breath and collect his thoughts. Bill and Tommy soon caught up with him.

"We're FREE, actually free!" Bill exclaimed. "On the other side of the wire at last!"

"On the lam, so to speak," Tommy added.

"There are no sounds from camp," Kay said breathlessly.

"Thank God! The Nips must not have detected our escape; otherwise, we would be hearing sirens by now," Bill added.

"They won't miss us until rollcall tomorrow morning," Tommy surmised, "and by then we will be miles away."

So they hoped. Yet what a glorious moment for them. Free at

last, and on the other side of the wire. As far as they could tell, their escape hadn't been detected. Phase one of the escape plan had been successfully executed. Now they had to focus on phase two: to get as far away from Lunghwa as possible by morning.

Kay said a quick prayer of thanks as they ran deeper into the forest.

CHAPTER THREE

The Yangtze River Delta

After a few more minutes crashing blindly through the forest, Kay assumed that they were deep enough into the woods to chance using his torch (flashlight). The torch was a big help to avoid the trees, low hanging branches, and bushes. After a quarter mile, the woods thinned and then abruptly ended. They found themselves at the edge of a wide canal edged by six-foot levees. Kay blew up the li-lo, placed their rucksacks on it, and then they removed their canvas shoes, pants, and jackets, and entered the water. The water was ice cold for this time of year, and by the time they climbed up the opposite bank they were all shivering uncontrollably. A brisk march down the towpath adjacent to the canal quickly warmed them. They had until dawn to put as much distance between themselves and Lunghwa as they could, and they intended to make every minute count. Kay knew that they would be missed at the 6 a.m. rollcall, and soon afterwards, the guards and dogs would come looking for them.

The rain continued to fall, and they were soaked to the skin by their swim across the canal and the incessant rain. As long as they kept moving, they remained warm, but when they stopped to take a rest and have a smoke, they began to shiver. Lighting cigarettes in the rain was not only difficult but also dangerous, as a match or even a lit cigarette could be seen for hundreds of yards. Nevertheless, the smoke calmed them and if they lit the match close to the ground and cupped the cigarette in their hands while they smoked, detection seemed unlikely.

A path led west from the levee and since this was their chosen direction, they tried to follow it in the dark. Nevertheless, they soon lost the path and found themselves ankle deep in a muddy rice paddy. They trudged through the paddy until it felt as if they had ten pounds of mud clinging to their shoes. They had chosen to wear canvas shoes rather than boots for this journey, but after an hour of sloshing through the rice paddy they were wishing they had worn boots instead. Confronted by another canal, they washed the mud off their feet, inflated the li-lo, and with the knapsacks on the mattress swam across the canal and scrambled up the muddy bank. They walked for several hours down the towpath unable to see much of anything in the darkness. Kay looked at his luminous wristwatch to decide how much time they had until dawn, but his wrist was bare. Somewhere in the night, the buckle came loose and his watch was now probably at the bottom of a rice paddy. It would be a great find for some farmer, but it was a serious loss for them. Bill still had his pocket watch, but it did not have a luminous dial. By the light of a match, they discovered that it was 3:30 a.m.

A few minutes later they came to a wide river that blocked their westward progress. They had to cross this deep and swift river, but were hesitant to do so in the dark, so they walked a mile or so downstream looking for a bridge. Unable to find one, they decided to backtrack and look for a bridge in the opposite direction. It stopped raining and a sliver of moon finally broke through the cloud cover and provided the faintest illumination, yet it was sufficient to find their way along the towpath. After another mile, they spotted a bridge, one of those typical Chinese camelback bridges, but some coolies were sitting on the peak. Kay didn't dare confront them, so they hid in some reeds and waited for the coolies to leave. After a few minutes, they got up and walked down the towpath in the direction from which Kay and his friends just came.

They successfully crossed the bridge; unfortunately, the river and the path that followed it were in a north to south direction. This forced them to slosh through several more rice paddies to keep on a westward track. Narrow footpaths led through the paddies, but they were muddy and only about one foot wide. Everyone kept slipping off and splashing into six inches of water and mud in the rice paddy. At 7 a.m. the sun broke in an orange ball over the rice paddies and despite a night of sloshing through the mud, they had had not made it very far from Lunghwa. By now the Japanese guards would have taken the morning rollcall and would be aware of their escape.

"We need to find cover to hide during daylight," Kay warned. "As soon as they can organize a search party, the Nips will have their dogs out looking for us."

According to Kay's detailed map, they were only about two miles from Lunghwa, hardly the six miles their plan called for. The good news was that since they had sloshed across so many rice paddies, the dogs would be unable to track them. Nonetheless, they were gravely discouraged by their lack of progress, for at this rate, it would take them months to get to Nationalist China.

Notwithstanding, at the moment this was not the main problem. They needed a place to hide, but where? A nearby Chinese cemetery contained a grove of Mulberry trees that could provide cover for the day. Nevertheless, the Mulberry trees had sharp thorns, and they were about to reconsider their selection, when they heard someone approaching. They ducked into the Mulberry thicket and watched as a Chinese farmer led his water buffalo down the path and began to hitch him to a waterwheel only fifty yards from their hiding place. Kay thought the farmer hadn't seen them, but after the fellow finished hitching up his buffalo he looked in their direction and waved to them. He continued to gesture with a downward sweeping motion of his open hand. Kay initially didn't know how to react to this gesture. Was the farmer just being friendly, or did he have something else in mind?

"Fei gei, fei gei," the farmer yelled.

"There's an airplane coming! He's warning us to get down!" Kay whispered, and they hit the dirt.

The farmer returned to his job of encouraging the buffalo to continue trudging around the waterwheel as a single engine airplane cleared the adjacent rice paddy and buzzed the cemetery, no more than one hundred feet overhead. They hugged the ground and ignored the sharp Mulberry thorns as the airplane passed overhead, then made a second pass over the paddy and cemetery. The farmer paid no attention to the airplane and continued lightly whipping his buffalo. After a third pass, the airplane moved on to the next rice paddy and buzzed it in the same manner. It then moved off and disappeared over the horizon. The Nips were surely looking for them, and if they came down the path with their dogs, the fugitives would surely be discovered. The cemetery provided little cover, so they gathered their rucksacks, fieldstripped their cigarette butts, and walked down the levee past the farmer. As they passed him, he gestured and said something in Chinese. Kay answered him.

"What did he say?" Bill asked.

"He invited us to stay in his farmhouse today," Kay replied.

"Can we trust him?" Tommy asked.

"I think so," Kay said. "He seems like a good enough chap. We really don't have any choice. If he is friendly with the Japs, he will betray us whether we are in his house or on the run. It would be best to trust him."

They followed the farmer down the levee and after a mile or so arrived at a thatched-roof farmhouse. Pigs, geese, and chickens mingled in the front yard, and another water buffalo was in a corral next to the house. The geese made a terrible ruckus as they approached the yard. They entered the dirt-floor farmhouse and the farmer gestured for them to sit at a round wooden table. A young Chinese woman appeared with three bowls of rice topped with generous pieces of chicken. She set a pot of green tea along with three cups on the table, then gave a slight bow and left the room as silently as she had entered.

After breakfast, Kay talked with the farmer for some time, and when he finished, sat down with Bill and Tommy and gave them the scoop. The farmer hated the Japanese, and like most Chinese, was eager to help them in any way he could. He never asked who they were or where they came from, but said that he would walk into the nearby village to see if there were any rumors of their escape. They were to stay inside and rest until nightfall. The farmer warned them that if they heard the geese honk again they must hide in the house as best they could.

Kay had always known that the rural Chinese were a wonderful bunch, and this farmer confirmed his beliefs. The farmers were exceptionally hospitable, friendly, and generous, even when giving aid to foreigners would mean placing themselves at personal risk. Although dirt poor, they freely offered their meager supply of food and possessions to complete strangers, even if that meant depriving themselves and their families of necessities. Soon after the farmer left to walk to the village meeting house, the young woman reappeared with a basin of warm water and a wash cloth for each. They took a sponge bath of sorts; while the woman took their mud-caked clothes, washed each of them, and hung them to dry inside on racks so their prison clothes could not be spotted by a Japanese patrol.

A couple of hours later, the farmer returned. The news was not good. He said that a convoy of Japs visited the village while he was there and questioned everyone about the missing prisoners. Of course no one, including their farmer host, knew anything about missing prisoners and hadn't seen foreigners for weeks. The soldiers overturned a few tables and threw a chair or two out closed windows before they left; just to remind the villagers who was boss around these parts. The farmer warned Kay that he and his friends could not stay here for very long, as Japanese soldiers would soon be conducting a house-to-house search, probably by that evening.

At sunset, they prepared to depart. The farmer cautioned them that they should keep to the canal levees and towpaths and stay away from the main road that led from Shanghai to Hangchow as it was busy with Japanese convoys and marching troops, even at night. He also warned them that there were Japanese sentries on duty on all roads leading into or out of large cities such as Hangchou or Shaoxing.

"Keep to small villages and the paths between them," he warned. Before they left, he handed each of them a straw coolie hat.

"So you look like Chinese coolie," the farmer explained.

Kay thanked him, and they put on their packs and hats and headed down the muddy levee. The rain clouds of the previous night had dissipated and the moon helped light the narrow paths crossing the rice paddies. To throw the dogs off their track, they trudged through the mud of several rice paddies. Kay's objective for that night was to cross over the Shanghai-Hangchow Railway line.

This railroad junction with the Minghong Highway, about ten miles west of Lunghwa, was a major milestone on Kay's map. The going was tough, one rice paddy after another, but they dared not take the highway or even stay on the cross-country paths.

They were still exhausted from the rigors of the previous day and soon the weight of the thirty-pound packs dug into their shoulders and backs. It was unbearable, so Tommy suggested sitting down on a grassy knoll to lighten their loads. Kay spread the green shower curtain out and they emptied their rucksacks onto the tarp. In addition to the items they had previously agreed to, Bill and Tommy's packs contained several additional items of questionable value. This included a three-pound sack of sugar, an axe, tins of butter, syrup, honey, a bologna, and a two-pound package of nails. Kay had not included any of these items on his original packing list.

"Where did you get the bologna?" Kay asked Bill.

"From Betty," he answered. "I figured we'd keep it. If we took her bologna it would certainly not add much to her anger after she discovered we left without her."

"What do we need with sugar and a package of nails?" Kay asked. "Except for the bologna, all this stuff that was not on the original list has to go, including extra tins of food."

They buried the items in the mud so that the Japanese would not know that they had passed this way.

"How about that book," Tommy said pointing to Kay's Bible. "It must weigh almost a quarter of a pound."

"I'd give up my cans of tuna before discarding the Bible," Kay insisted. "Besides, it's small, and will easily fit into my rucksack. This is all I have of Lil's things."

The Bible remained in Kay's backpack. They kept the bologna and tins of tuna, sardines, clams, corned beef and salmon and survival items such as pocketknives, a compass, matches and flint, flashlights and first aid kits. What remained in the way of food was about one-third pound per day for each, or about thirty pounds total; enough rations for a month, but minimal calories considering what they were burning. Moreover, in their present thin condition brought on by months of scant food, they didn't have much fat stored on their frames. Kay figured that they could make five to ten miles each night and the fifty-two miles to Kashing would take at least a week. The food could be made to last that long, but it was not much to sustain them on such a forced march. It would have to do, and perhaps other generous farmers would give them something to eat along the way. After that, they would have to depend on the guerrillas rumored to be around Kashing for sustenance.

After rearranging the rucksacks and throwing out unnecessary items, each sack was ten pounds lighter and considerably easier on the back and shoulders. They started out again and after the usual slogging through paddy after paddy, they finally they came to the Minghong Highway at a point barely one hundred yards from a Japanese pillbox (fortified shelter). Fortunately, the pillbox was deserted this time of night. They waited in the bushes beside the highway until they were certain that there was no traffic, then dashed across to the safety of the koliang (sorghum) fields on the opposite side. They hiked a well-used path westward through the sorghum fields that Kay assumed led toward the main rail line from Shanghai to Hangchow. The railroad was a sort of milepost on their planned path to Kashing.

The path went through several villages that they skirted because of their reluctance to enter any towns. Kay decided to chance passing through some of the smaller villages, as it would take forever to skirt every little hamlet they came across. The village streets were deserted at this time of night (about midnight). Most of the inhabitants were in bed at such a late hour. They walked through several of these villages without seeing a soul.

About 2 a.m., they came to a dirt motor road that headed west and decided to follow it toward the railway tracks. Where the road crossed the raised rail bed, they could see several Japanese soldiers on duty patrolling up and down the tracks at the crossing. They hastily retreated down the road about a half-mile, cut across a bean field for a few hundred yards, and then headed back toward the rail line. They eventually spied the railway roadbed raised six feet above the surrounding fields. Since the sky showed the signs of false dawn, they thought it too risky to cross the rail line in the increasing light. They would have to find daytime cover and wait for darkness before they could chance a crossing. Unfortunately, there was not much around that one could consider good cover. As dawn broke, the only concealment they could find was a reed patch alongside one of the canals and right next to the path. They crawled into the reeds intending to spend the day sitting in ankle deep water and mud.

It was not long before a farmer came down the path leading two water buffaloes secured to a two-wheel wagon filled with hay. Water buffalo are splendid beasts of burden with usually placid temperaments, but can become two thousand pounds of deadly flesh if angered. They will often charge in an instant if they catch the sent of foreigners. As the farmer and his animals passed the reed patch only a few yards from the escapees, the buffalo caught just such a whiff and began to act up. They snorted and raised their heads into the wind and tried to escape the yoke that held them in place. The farmer struggled to get his animals back under control. The fugitives stood up ready to run if the Buffalo escaped and headed toward the reed patch, but the farmer was able to get his animals headed back down the path. He glanced at Kay and friends as he passed by and with a shrug continued down the path. Although it seemed unlikely that this fellow would warn the Japanese, the escapees had been spotted. If the farmer detected them, so could the Japanese. By now there was certain to be a reward on their heads and any poor and desperate farmer might be tempted by the promise of cash. They would just have to trust that he was not that desperate.

All day long, Chinese farmers walked up and down the towpath that followed the canal, passing only yards from their hiding spot in the reeds. One time Kay was certain that a small boy had spied them. The boy ran over to the adults walking ahead of him and said something that Kay could not quite hear. Their hearts pounded for fear of being discovered, but the farmers continued to walk along the towpath and didn't look in their direction. Not ten minutes later however, a patrol of Japanese soldiers marched down the path from the direction that the boy and adults had disappeared. They held their breath, certain that the farmers had alerted the soldiers to their presence and they were about to be captured. Distracted by a group of children further down the path, the soldiers marched right past them without even looking at the reed patch.

Although he did not know the entire prayer, Kay did his best to whisper the Lord's prayer and thank God for protecting them. Tommy looked at Kay as though he had gone bonkers. Kay was actually praying and had refused to discard a Bible. Odd behavior for a man his Shanghai friends had nicknamed "Kay the Agnostic." Not that Kay didn't believe there was a God, he just saw no evidence that if such a being existed He showed any interest at all in humankind. Bill was also puzzled by Kay's newfound interest in religion. He knew Kay as a man who often made denigrating remarks about religion and prayer, and ridiculed those who spent time worshiping a Deity. He pondered that perhaps the hot sun or lack of sleep and proper food was affecting Kay's mind. In any case, neither Bill nor Tommy questioned Kay about his unusual behavior and tried to ignore it.

They needed rest, but to rest while squatting in the mud was impossible. The hot and humid day seemed interminable and they longed for sunset. When it the sun finally slipped below the fields and darkness descended, they climbed back onto the towpath and cautiously made off toward the rail line.

Kay thought it peculiar that he had heard no trains pass during their long stay in the reeds, neither a whistle, nor the rumble of a passing train from a rail line that was only a quarter mile away. The Shanghai-Hangchow-Ningpo Railroad was a very busy line and if this was the main line into Sungkiang, they should have heard several trains pass during the day. In the gathering darkness, Kay crawled to the top of the railbed, looked up and down, and listened for Japanese soldiers. There apparently were none, but it was evident why they heard no trains pass by that day. There were no rails, no railroad ties, just an empty railbed stretching far into the distance. This could not be the main line, but must have been a spur line. The Japanese had evidently pulled up these tracks for some other need. It seemed strange that soldiers would guard a rail crossing on an abandoned rail line. Perhaps the Japs had another reason for being there. Kay motioned for his companions and all three crossed over the railbed and followed muddy paths that led west through endless rice paddies. They stopped occasionally to rest and have a smoke, again cupping the cigarettes in their hands so they would not be detected.

The moon hid behind scattered clouds which drizzled intermittently throughout the night. The containment levees and paths across the rice paddies were built so they could be easily breached to allow water to flow from field to field. Without the moon to light their way, it was difficult to stay on the narrow muddy paths that crossed through the rice paddies. Occasionally Kay chanced using his flashlight; nonetheless, several times they lost the path altogether and ended up slogging through the slimy mud of a rice paddy. The thick mud stuck to their canvas shoes until it felt like they were wearing lead boots. When this became too burdensome, they had to stop and scrape the clay-like mud from their shoes with a stick.

By 5:30 a.m. they were too tired to go any further and took cover in a bean field. The bean plants, suspended from wires strung across eight-foot stakes, were not yet ready for harvest, yet several times during the day farmers came into the field to inspect their crop. Each time the farmers showed up, the fugitives flattened themselves against the damp ground and remained as quiet as possible. Several times, they were only yards from being detected, but again providence intervened and the Chinese farmers did not see them, or pretended not to see them. Considering how well the farmer treated them the first night, Tommy wondered if perhaps it wouldn't be so bad if the farmers did spot them. He argued that a warm meal and dry place to sleep would be worth some risk. Kay felt that they could not take that chance, especially so close to Lunghwa. The farmer last night said that Japanese patrols were searching for them and had placed a generous reward on their heads.

Nevertheless, they knew that the Chinese farmers were "with them" so to speak. These folks hated the Japanese just as much as Kay, Bill, and Tommy did, and as the first farmer had told them, they considered all escapees to be heroes and worthy of their help. Yet, people were people, and one could never be certain how some folks might react in the face of personal danger. The reward would be quite a temptation for a starving farmer and should anyone betray them, it would probably result in capture and death. No trial or mercy could be expected, only summary judgment and on the spot execution.

The Japanese military officers had a well-deserved reputation for their ruthless treatment of captives. Captives were troublesome. They had to be marched, guarded, watered, and fed. The Japanese soldiers could not be bothered with such annoying baggage. It was better to put a bullet in the head of prisoners and be done with it. No, Kay argued, with such ruthless attitudes, it was better to be safe than sorry and avoid all contact with people.

August 21, 1944, Shanghai countryside

By the end of the third night, they had expected to be at least thirty miles away from Lunghwa but had achieved only six miles. They were tired, footsore, and discouraged. Kay suggested a change in plans. He knew of a friend who was a Chinese farmer in Hungjao, about eight or nine miles north of their present position. The farmer had allowed Kay and his Shanghai friends to hunt his fields for pheasants, and Kay was certain that he could be trusted. Hungjao was out of their way, but Kay was certain that his friend would put them up for a day or two. They badly needed rest and warm food if they were to continue.

Since the plan was acceptable to all, they hid out in a Chinese cemetery and at nightfall hiked toward Hungjao, following the towpath alongside a canal for a while, and then crossing open fields to keep on compass point. It was necessary to cross numerous creeks and canals, and by midnight, they were chilled to the bone. Close to dawn, Kay climbed a hillock to get the lay of the land and discovered that they had gone too far during the night. They were now on the outskirts of Shanghai, a very dangerous place for them. They backtracked three miles and decided to chance taking the Hungjao road, as it appeared quite deserted this time of the morning. They soon came to a small village on the outskirts of Hungjao, and were forced to hide in another bean field as the sun rose.

August 22, 1944, Hungjao

The evening was warm and by 10 p.m. they were on the move again. Bill was anxious to find Kay's friend in Hungjao and suggested that they take a chance and go through a small town along the way, reasoning that most farmers would have retired by this hour. His thinking was flawed. The warm and sultry evening had kept most folks on their doorsteps rather than in their beds. They hurried down the main street past a group of men and ignored their shouts to stop. Several men started after them shouting as they ran. The fugitives ran all the faster, past the last house in the town and into the bean fields beside the road. Their pursuers chased after them hollering as they ran. Kay and friends soon ducked between rows of beans and running a zigzagged path finally gave them the slip in the dark. The townsfolk eventually gave up the chase and cursed as they went back to the road. Tommy wanted to stop and catch his breath, but Kay insisted they continue without taking a rest. Kay suspected that the folks who chased after them were probably friendly and just wanted to find out who they were. Nonetheless, they could not take any chances. They had been warned that some townsfolk were Jap collaborators and would most likely turn them in. And then there was that damned reward offered by the Japanese...

Eventually they came to the banks of Siccawei Creek, blew up the li-lo, stripped, and swam across. They hurriedly dressed and put on their coolie hats. As they walked down the path, a farmer with a small boy came down the towpath from the opposite direction. Kay shined his torch in the man's face and asked brusquely in Chinese, "What are you doing out so late?"

The man seemed flustered but answered that he had been visiting friends and was returning home. Then he gathered his wits and asked, "What are YOU doing out here?"

The moon was hidden behind clouds, so Kay knew that in the dark and blinded by the flashlight the farmer could not clearly see their faces. He bluffed and answered that they were Wang Ching-wei soldiers on patrol and that the fellow had best mind his business and hurry along. The ruse seemed to work and the man and boy broke into a trot and hurried past them down the path.

Most of the fields in this area contained dry crops such as beans, carrots, cabbages, and melons. This made hiking across the fields much faster and easier than sloshing through rice paddies, although they had to skirt several impenetrable sugarcane fields that covered much of the countryside. They stopped in a melon field to rest and Tommy cut into a nearly ripe melon. They all enjoyed a piece of melon and the sweet juice was refreshing. After two hours of cross-country walking, they came again to the Hungjao road, and the silhouette of the town against the pre-dawn sky was less than a mile away. Kay knew that the Japanese patrolled this road, so they had to be very careful as they walked along. A couple of times a car came down the road from town, so they jumped into the ditch beside the road and hid in the reeds until it passed. As they drew closer to town, the ditch was clear and there was nowhere to hide. They donned their coolie hats and kept their heads down as they walked along the path beside the road. Several cars passed by, but none paid any attention to them.

They entered the main part of town, ducked down a small alley, and soon were knocking at the door of Kay's friend, Jiong Xu Jing. Jiong met the three at the door and pointed a Luger pistol in their faces. As soon as he recognized Kay, he lowered the pistol.

"Pate hsien-sheng (Mister Pate), what you do here?" Jiong asked wide-eyed, and immediately invited then inside and led them into the kitchen.

He was perplexed to see Kay and his friends. After explanations and introductions, Jiong's wife and daughter came into the kitchen, made a pot of green tea, and fed them leftovers from that evening's dinner. The hot tea and food warmed their bodies and spirits. Kay asked Jiong if he knew how to contact the Chinese guerrillas rumored to be operating in Chekiang Province.

"Guerrillas everywhere, even in Shanghai, yet I not know how to contact them. Better you go see Captain Waxmouth tomorrow night and ask if he can help. Waxmouth know these things."

Captain Waxmouth was a mutual friend of Kay and Jiong, a British national who worked in the Swiss consulate, therefore had been given a Swiss passport, and had not been sent to prison. In years past, he hunted pheasants with Kay in Jiong's fields just outside of town.

After Kay told Jiong that the men in the neighboring village chased them, Jiong said that they were probably just trying to help. Perhaps Jiong was right and these farmers just wanted to offer help. Nonetheless, Jiong warned that while most of the town folk were friendly and hated the Japanese, there were Chinese soldiers employed by the Japanese Army also operating in the area, and these fellows would be certain to turn them in.

"How are we to know friend from foe?" Kay asked.

"When strangers approach, look see if they carry weapons," Jiong cautioned. "If they have weapons, they are soldiers. Chinese farmers no carry weapons."

"How about the guerrillas," Kay asked, "won't they carry weapons? How will we know them from the puppet soldiers?"

"No guerrillas in Hungjao," Jiong answered, "maybe closer to Kashing. But not to worry, you not find them, they find you."

Jiong brought out two thin futon pads, three pillows and some blankets. He apologized that this was all he had to offer them, but Kay said that it was a damn sight better than sitting in the mud. They made their beds in the kitchen. Kay blew up the li-lo and was about to offer it to Tommy, but he was already asleep, and so was Bill. Kay climbed on the air mattress and fell asleep as soon as his head hit the pillow. They remained in Jiong's house all day Friday, washed and dried their filthy clothes, bathed, and repacked their rucksacks.

August 23, 1944 Hungjao

That evening they donned their coolie hats and some Chinese pajamas that Jiong gave them and went searching for Captain Waxmouth's house. Before they left Jiong's house, he smiled and pressed the Luger and a box of bullets into Kay's hand.

"You take," he said emphatically. "Put bullet in Jap head!"

Kay didn't want to take the gun, but Jiong said that if the soldiers found it in his house, they would shoot him. Weapons in Chinese households were forbidden.

"Gun too dangerous to have," Jiong claimed.

Kay, Bill, and Tommy thanked Jiong and walked into the night.

They soon found Waxmouth's house up a narrow alley off Hungjao road. Waxmouth answered Kay's knock and was surprised and overjoyed to see Kay.

"Capital, Old Bean, great to see you!" Waxmouth exclaimed as he gave Kay a bear hug. "I thought you were a guest of the Nips. What in the bloody hell are you doing in Hungjao?

"Well, for damn sure we're not here to hunt pheasants," Kay laughed

Introductions and explanations aside, Kay asked if Waxmouth could put them in touch with the Chinese guerrillas in Kashing or Shanghai. Kay wanted to get word to the guerrillas to look out for them when they arrived in the Kashing countryside. Waxmouth said that he was sorry, but didn't think he could be of much help in this regard.

"You know old friend, I have to keep a rather low profile nowadays. My friends at the Consulate gave me a fake Swiss passport, so the bloody Nips think I am Swiss. They have yet to come calling on me and I don't want to alert them to my British citizenship."

He suggested they visit a mutual friend, Captain Navrotsky, a former Consular for the Russians. The Ruskies were Japanese allies in 1943, and it was only in the concluding days of the conflict that Russia declared war on Japan. The next day Waxmouth took them to Navrotsky's house on the outskirts of Hungjao. Navrotsky was home with his son Nikita. He immediately invited them inside and served them a bowl of steaming rice and a pot of green tea as they discussed contacting the Chinese guerrillas in Shanghai.

"This is a very dangerous thing to do," Navrotsky said. "Some Chinese in Shanghai cannot be trusted, but I know some good people. I will get word to them. My suggestion is that you continue toward Yushan as you have planned and try to connect with the guerrillas near Kashing. Avoid making contact with anyone else. The Chungking government has control of most of Szechwan and Hunan Provinces, but the Japs are throughout Kiangsu, Chekiang, Anhwei, and Hupeh Provinces. Don't worry about finding the guerrillas along the way, they will find you."

"That is what everyone tells us, but how will we know if anyone is friend or foe?" Bill asked.

"You will know they are guerrillas if they do not try to shoot you," Navrotsky said.

"That's little comfort," Bill muttered.

Young Nikita said it would be safer for them to travel cross-country rather than follow the Hungjao Road, which was well patrolled and extremely dangerous for escapees, so Nikita went off on his bicycle to scout the countryside and determine the safest route for the escapees. He returned about an hour later and spread a detailed map of Hungjao on the kitchen table. Nikita said that they should walk past a boarded up church and sanitarium and proceed across the golf links, but detour around the clubhouse because it was presently occupied by the Japanese army. Then they should cut across the rough surrounding the golf club grounds and find a dirt road that skirted a large pond and led to a bridge that crossed over a wide creek. Nikita said to cross the creek on the bridge but take care that there were no Japanese patrols on the road.

"On the side opposite the creek there is a single telegraph pole guyed by two wires. It is the only one like that around. So that we will know you were successful, please tie a bit of cloth to one of the guy wires," Navrotsky asked as they said goodbye.

August 24, 1944, Hungjao

The moon was in its gibbous phase and shone brightly in a cloudless sky providing good visibility all across the Hungjao countryside. They shouldered their packs and as directed by Nikita proceeded down Hungjao Road past the church and sanitarium toward the golf club. After making sure the road leading into the golf club was clear, they sneaked across the golf links and skirted a brightly lit clubhouse filled with the singing and laughter of partying Japanese. They found the dirt road and the bridge, crossed over and looked for the telegraph pole. A few feet up the road in full view of the bridge, they found the guyed telegraph pole and Bill tied a piece of cloth to one of the guy wires. As they were about to leave, someone shouted, "Stop" in Chinese. They froze in their tracks, and turned around. Although it was dark, the moonlight coming from behind Kay allowed him to make out two armed Japanese soldiers standing on the opposite side of the bridge.

"Who are you and what is your business here?" the shorter of the two soldiers demanded in poorly articulated Kyangsher dialect.

Since the moon was behind Kay, he knew that the soldiers would be unable to see them clearly. Dressed as they were with dark coolie pajamas and coolie hats, it would be easy to pretend that they were Chinese. Kay answered in Chinese that they were farmers returning to their homes in the village down the road.

The two soldiers talked to each other for a few seconds. Then the one who told them to stop crossed over the bridge while the second soldier remained on the opposite side with his rifle ready. Kay took the Luger from his belt and hid it behind his back as he released the safety. His heart was pounding when the Japanese army officer walked up to them and shone a flashlight first in Bill's face, then Tommy's, and finally in Kay's face.

"You not Chinese!" the officer whispered in English. "You Brits!" "What you do here?"

Kay fingered the trigger on the Luger and thought, we are about to be captured, yet why is this Jap whispering to us in English? Impulsively, he decided to be honest with this fellow. Something about the way he said "you Brits" put Kay at ease.

"We escaped from Lunghwa and are trying to make it to Changshan," Kay whispered in English.

"You Brits git outa here, quick like the devil!" the soldier whispered, and gestured with his flashlight toward the road leading away from the bridge.

They didn't argue but immediately turned around and trotted down the road half expecting to feel a bullet in the back at any moment. They ran on for twenty minutes, then stopped beside the road to catch their breath.

"What in the world was that all about?" Tommy asked. "The damned Nip bloody well knew we weren't Chinese."

"Why did he let us go?" Bill asked.

"Damned if I know," Kay answered, "he surely had us dead to rights. Perhaps he just did not want to shoot us. I guess it goes to prove that not all Japanese soldiers are rotten bastards."

"All the ones I ever met certainly were!" Bill quipped.

"Did you see the ring he wore?" Tommy observed. "It was a class ring, like the ones most college graduates wear. I'll bet he went to a university somewhere in the U.S."

"Were you really going to shoot him?" Bill asked as Kay put the gun back into his belt.

"I bloody well would have," Kay answered, "and without any regrets. If it came down to either him or us, I would have put a bullet between his eyes.

"Why in the hell did you tell him we escaped from Lunghwa?" Tommy asked.

"Something about his attitude made me hesitate shooting him, and when he spoke to us in English, I figured he was okay. I took a chance that if I told him the truth, he would be more likely to let us go." Kay explained.

"Yeah, and there was that other Nip across the bridge pointing a rifle at us," Tommy moaned.

"Kay, you could have been wrong!" Bill said exacerbated.

"I could have been, but I wasn't now...was I!" Kay responded somewhat smugly.

"Enough of this, let's go!" Tommy finally said. Tommy was always saying, "let's go." He did this so often that Bill nicknamed him "Let's Go Tommy."

They hadn't gone very far when they saw a light coming toward them along the road. They ducked into a field of bush beans and laid flat on the ground as a Japanese patrol of about ten soldiers heading toward the golf club rushed past. Kay and friends were only ten feet off the road and not very well hidden by the low-lying bushes. Had the soldiers shone the light in their direction, they would have certainly seen the escapees. Nevertheless, distracted by their talking and laughing and apparently in a hurry to join the other partygoers at the clubhouse, they walked on past keeping the flash beam on the road ahead.

"That was too close for comfort," Tommy whispered after the patrol had passed.

They remained quiet for the next ten minutes to make sure that the soldiers had really gone.

"Let's go!" Tommy finally said, and they resumed their hike down the road. Tommy took a new compass reading and they abandoned the road and followed a narrow path that crossed over open fields

They were making good progress, when after a couple of hours, they came across another of the many rivers that crisscrossed the countryside. The river was too wide and swift to cross, so they searched for a bridge, and after a mile found one. However, there was something constructed in the middle of the bridge. Since the moon had set, it was quite dark, and Kay could not make out what the structure on the bridge was, so he removed his pack and crawled up closer for a look. The object turned out to be a brick wall constructed to prevent anyone from crossing over the bridge. They walked on a bit further and came to another bridge that was blocked in the same manner. They continued down the path until they came to a wire and bamboo fence that wound through the fields up to the river. Kay realized that this was the fence built fifteen miles from Shanghai intended to prevent the Chinese from bringing any produce into the city without first paying a tax to the Japanese.

Kay took out his wire cutters and cut a hole in the fence large enough for them to slip through, then repaired the fence. Once inside the fence, they found another bridge that was not walled off as the others were. Unfortunately, there was a Japanese sentry post and a gate guarding it. Kay sneaked up for a closer look, and discovered that the sentry post was deserted. They crossed over the bridge and followed the path westward as it crossed several more fields. The path also went through several small villages, and as before, they chanced walking through rather than around them. This time no one stirred as the escapees walked through the villages.

August 25, 1944, 20 miles outside of Shanghai

About 5 a.m. there was a faint hint of light in the sky, so the fugitives began to look for cover. Again, they could not find anything better than a bean field in which to hide for the day. As soon as the sun was fully up, it became quite hot. After a night of constant walking, the warm day made them sleepy, so they hid in some bulrushes and stretched out in the wet mud to snatch a few hours of sleep while taking turns to keep watch. As Kay took his turn on watch, he noticed a large snake crawl through the bulrushes. He had no idea if this snake was poisonous or not, but he certainly did not want to find out. The snake was about five feet long and looked very much like a snake the Chinese called the "one hundred pace" snake, because after a bite from this creature, that is about as far as a person could go before he dropped dead. Kay remained frozen as the snake crawled within several feet of his sleeping

69

friends and then slithered off into the bulrushes. This was the first of many snakes they encountered while hiding in the reeds or bulrushes, but never did the snakes threaten them. Tommy was deathly afraid of snakes, and whenever he saw one he would insist that they leave immediately, but this was not always practical. One time they were hiding in a patch of bulrushes only a few feet from the banks of a busy canal. Even late at night, this canal had a lot of sampan traffic, and as luck would have it just as a sampan passed by, a snake crawled out of the reeds and headed toward Tommy's feet. Tommy suddenly jumped to his feet and yelled "Snake!" at the top of his lungs. His sudden appearance and scream startled the coolies in the sampan, so much so that they rowed away as if possessed, and probably told the other farmers there was a devil hiding alongside the banks of the canal. Many of the farmers believed in such things as spirits and devils, and often their celebrations involved firecrackers and loud noises to drive such creatures away. The frequent yet uneventful encounters with various snakes finally convinced the escapees that if they remained motionless, the snakes would not harm them. By the time they got out of the lake country, Tommy had learned to tolerate these animals.

To find a comfortable yet well-hidden place to rest during the day was almost impossible. Ever tried to rest stretched out on cold mud? Needless to say, you soon become one big ache and feel like you must get up and stretch. Bill felt this urge, and stood up to stretch in the muddy bean field where they had remained hidden for hours. Some children spotted him and cried out, "Ngahkohning (foreigners) are hiding in our bean field!" They debated if someone should go into the field and investigate or run off to the village to tell their elders. Eventually they ran off toward the village, leaving one of the larger boys to guard the foreigner's location. The escapees knew they had been discovered and they were about to make a run for it when several farmers came into the field armed with hoes and pitchforks. Directed by the boy, the farmers began to search for them. Kay expected that they would soon be discovered, so he decided to stand up and show himself. As he did so, he explained in Chinese that they were foreigners who were running away from concentration camp. Were there Japanese soldiers in these parts? The farmers said there were not, and much to Kay's surprise asked if they could help. Everywhere the escapees went in China the Chinese country folk were wonderful to them.

It was an intensely hot day, yet after lying in the cold mud for eight hours the fugitives were chilled to the bone and asked if they could have something warm to drink. Shortly, a man came with several pots of hot tea and they sat beside the bean field and enjoyed a spot of tea with their newfound friends. The Chinese told them that the Japanese soldiers had committed many atrocities in their village. It was little wonder that the Japs were so hated. Daughters and wives had been raped, men shot for no reason whatsoever, and homes looted and torched, sometimes with people locked inside the houses.

After tea, two men offered to lead them across the countryside that night so that they could get a good start to their trek. They led them along winding paths and across several bridges that they would never have found on their own in the dark. They traveled with the Chinese at a good clip until about 9 p.m., when their guides said they had to return home. They handed Kay a scrap of paper with a scrawled map that showed the best way to get around the farmlands and across the many canals and rivers that criss-crossed the countryside. Bridges and Japanese sentry posts were well marked. This was another example of the generosity and hospitality one could expect from the Chinese. Such courage and generosity always impressed them. The escapees thanked their benefactors and followed the map westward.

Later that night, they could see the lights of a large city looming in the distance. Kay consulted the map, and the Chinese character identified this town as Szeking, a walled city that straddled a wide canal. About two miles from the city, they arrived at the banks of the canal and considered inflating the li-lo to swim across in the dark. Nevertheless, they thought better of it since Bill was not a very good swimmer and the canal was swift and at least one hundred and fifty yards wide. They searched for a bridge, but in the dim moonlight, the only bridge visible was inside the arched gateway leading into the city proper.

Since no one was around, Kay decided to give this bridge a go, and, despite the obvious danger, he sprinted toward the archway. It was inky dark and he ran headlong into a wire fence, which threw him back onto the ground as the wire made a loud twang. The noise roused several dogs and their incessant barking brought several guards to life. Kay and his buddies turned and ran down the towpath for two or three miles and eventually hid behind a buffalo water-wheel shed. It didn't appear that they had been followed, so they moved off the towpath as the sun rose and hid in a bunch of black-berry bushes. Kay spread his green shower curtain and the li-lo out on the ground and they remained in the bushes until dusk.

August 25, 1944, Szeking

As Kay repacked his knapsack that evening, he held Lil's leather-covered Bible in his hand for a few moments. The Bible was the only thing he had of hers, and every time he touched it, Lil seemed closer to him. Rather than put the book back into his knap-sack, he opened it at random and in the diminishing light read the following passage from Psalm 91:

> *"No evil shall befall you, nor shall affliction come near your tent, for to His Angels God has given command about you, that they guard you in all your ways. Upon their hands they will bear you up, lest you dash your foot against a stone."*

This passage was so appropriate, and that Kay should have opened to that exact Psalm was extraordinary. It was exactly the words of comfort and hope that he needed at that moment. He carefully placed the Bible back into his knapsack and prepared to move on.

They decided that it would be foolhardy to go near Szeking again, since it was obviously occupied by Japanese. They walked all that night to get away from Szeking and search for a bridge where they could cross over the wide canal. With dawn approaching and unable to find a bridge, they decided to swim across the canal with the help of the li-lo. Bill blew up the air mattress but it leaked badly. Evidently, it had been punctured when they hid in the blackberry bushes. Dawn was breaking, and the canal was too swift and wide to cross safely without the mattress, so Bill hailed a passing yulohing (sampan). The sampan boatmen rowed off down the canal as fast as their oars would take them. Kay hailed a second yulohing in Chinese, and it immediately came over. The two women who were rowing the boat graciously helped them on board and then rowed them to the opposite bank. The women never asked what they were doing or who they were; in fact, they didn't say a word to them. Kay profusely thanked the women, and as the sun began to peak over the fields, the three scurried off to find a hiding place for the day.

August 26, 1944, Szeking countryside

The farmland in this area was planted with more dry crops including beans, barley, and melons. Unlike the blackberry bushes and sugarcane fields of the day before, none of these fields could provide adequate cover to hide for the day. They followed a path marked on the map that led them about a mile inland from the canal to the only farmhouse in the area. By now, they had grown to trust the Chinese locals who always had shown them hospitality and a willingness to help. Tommy knocked on the door and an elderly man with a long stringy beard answered. Kay asked him if they could come in and rest for the day, but he seemed very frightened. Although he did not refuse them, Kay thought it best not to impose on the obviously reluctant farmer, so they left.

They were forced to continue walking in broad daylight across open croplands covered by newly sprouting plants. Every few hundred yards there were small clumps of trees, but nothing else could provide cover. While hiding in the blackberry bushes the day before, they heard several airplanes buzz the area, an indication that the Japanese were still looking for them. With no cover, they would have to take their chances and cross these fields as quickly as possible. They walked several more miles cross-country until mid-morning when they spied a road leading past a Chinese cemetery. The cemetery did not provide much cover; nevertheless, they hid in the tall weeds between the grassy knolls that marked individual graves. That day many Chinese walked down the road that led past the cemetery, but no one noticed them. The afternoon was hellishly hot, so they stripped and took a swim in the creek next to the cemetery.

It wasn't long before they were discovered by a passing group of farmers. Kay told them that they had escaped from a Jap prison camp and were traveling to Sungkiang, the next large city. The farmers were very friendly and kind, and soon brought them bowls of rice and pots of green tea. Tommy opened two cans of smoked oysters, and they enjoyed a great dinner on the grassy burial mounds. Kay offered to share the oysters with the farmers; however, apparently these farmers had never before tasted oysters. At Kay's insistence, one fellow tried to eat one and made an awful face then spit the oyster onto the ground, commenting to his neighbors that the foreigners ate rotten fish filled with sand. After that, none of the Chinese wanted to taste one. One chap had a festering sore on his leg, so Tommy took out their medicine kit and dressed and bandaged the open abscess. The man was most grateful, and asked if they would come to his village and treat others who were sick. They agreed and followed the farmer back to his village.

Tommy had studied first aid in Shanghai and treated several women and children in Lunghwa who were suffering from boils, dysentery and infected sores. Their medical kit was not extensive, yet they never hesitated to use most of the salves and bandages on these villagers. One young girl, perhaps about ten, was suffering with a raging fever. The young girl's illness looked like malaria to Tommy, an illness he had caught in the Philippines and with which he had some first-hand experience. Her mother was distraught and said she feared that her daughter would die. Tommy treated her with sulfonamide tablets and gave her a couple of aspirin. Then he gave one of the two remaining sulfonamide bottles to her mother and instructed her to give the child two tablets morning and night until they were gone. The mother smiled and bowed deeply to Tommy.

No one ever asked them any questions. The Chinese were discreet to the nth degree! The farmer looked at the map the last farmer gave to Kay and shook his head. He asked for a pencil and drew another map showing the safest and shortest route to Sungkiang. The sun had set when Kay said their good-byes and hurried down the path, determined to make the outskirts of Sungkiang by morning.

It was at this point that Tommy discovered that he had left his baseball cap at the cemetery the day before when they took their swim. They could only hope that the Japs would not discover the cap embroidered with the logo of the Shanghai cricket team to which Tommy belonged. This would be a telltale sign that the escapees were in the area.

They stopped every hour for a ten-minute break and a smoke. On one of these breaks, a Chinese farmer carrying a load of sugar-cane stopped to chat with them. Again, consistent with other Chinese who had helped, he never questioned them about their business. When he left, he gave each of them a piece of cane. The cane was a great treat and they sucked on it as they walked.

When they stopped again for a break, Bill discovered that he had lost his wristwatch, probably when he took if off at the last rest stop. This was another grave loss. With the loss of Kay's watch, the only timepiece they now had was Kay's pocketwatch, which indicated that it was 10 p.m. Besides the loss of critical equipment, they were leaving a careless trail of their belongings for the Japanese to follow, just like Hansel and Gretel breadcrumbs!

They came to a wide canal and hiked along the towpath looking for a bridge to cross over. They soon came to a camelback bridge where several Chinese were sitting on the steps at the crest chatting in the cool evening breezes. Kay boldly walked up to the bridge and asked them to make way. They did so without saying a word, and Kay, Bill, and Tommy crossed over the canal unopposed. Just past the bridge was a small village and they walked down the main road that passed through it and right past a police station. Remarkably, although several Chinese police were lounging on the steps of the station, no one confronted them. The strategy of trying to look like Chinese going about their daily business was paying off.

On the other side of the village, they passed through a long grove of trees that branched over the path to create a narrow, covered corridor. A Chinese Christian church stood at the end of the tunnel-like pathway. It was nearly midnight, and the church was dark and empty. Behind the church and partially hidden by it, there was a brightly-lit building. Kay heard voices coming from within the building and immediately recognized that the residents were speaking Japanese. He read the large sign in Kanji that hung over the front door. It identified the building as a Japanese army post.

Although not fifty yards from the post and in full view of the brightly-lit building, they were partially hidden in the shadows cast by the church. They froze in their tracks wondering what to do next.

A soldier came out of the building and stood on the porch, lit a cigarette and started to read from a paper in his hand. Kay whispered for everyone to stay still and hoped that the soldier would not notice them in the dim light. Once his eyes adjusted to the dark, he would surely see them if he looked up. However, he seemed intent on reading the paper and smoking his cigarette and never did look in their direction. After two long minutes, he finished his cigarette, flicked it onto the road leading past the post, and went back inside. They quickly turned and backtracked through the corridor using the church to block any possible view of them from the post, then cut across a barley field. Another close call!

They finally reached the main road, and anxious to put some distance between them and the army post, disregarded the obvious risk and walked along the road. The road followed the main canal for quite a distance until it came to another small village. As they came close to the village, a car came down the road toward them. Caught in the glare of the headlights, all they could do was to break into a trot and to look like Chinese coolies hurrying home toward the village. The car had small rising sun flags on each fender indicating that it belonged to some Japanese official. The vehicle accelerated as it passed by and disappeared into the night.

Guarding the road leading into the village was a Japanese pillbox. The escapees climbed down into the ditch beside the road and carefully crept up to the pillbox. It was deserted. Nonetheless, deserted or not the pillbox and car indicated that the Japanese were bivouacked in the village. They got off the main road and bypassed the village, keeping to the grass path alongside the main canal. They remained poised to duck into a ditch if anyone came along.

Kay was familiar with this area from his many hunting trips. He remembered that there was only one bridge crossing over the canal between Sungkiang and Szeking. It was a famous camelback bridge, the longest and highest in Chekiang Province. As the moon set over the fields they found the main canal and walked down the towpath searching for the famous bridge. They walked for hours without any sign of the bridge, then began to wonder if in the darkness they passed it.

They decided to wear canvas shoes when they escaped, and up to now walking on dirt paths had been relatively easy, but the stone chips that covered this towpath were very hard on their feet. Kay soon developed a painful blister that was to give him hell for weeks to come. Several times during the night farmers with oxcarts drove down the path, forcing Kay and his friends to hide in the ditches. The towpath was taking them further and further south. They had to cross over the canal to follow their compass point westward, and it was imperative that they find the bridge before daybreak. They stopped for a short rest and a smoke, and after another hour of walking Tommy discovered that he had left his water bottle at the last rest stop. This was a serious loss for they rarely came across potable water, but whenever they did so, they filled their water bottles to save the chloride tablets necessary to disinfect ditch water. Equally serious was the telltale trail of litter they were leaving behind for the Japs to follow. First Kay's wristwatch, then Tommy's baseball cap and Bill's watch, and now the water bottle. They had to be more careful.

Kay was certain that they were near the bridge, and sure enough, in the gloom of false dawn he spied the large Buddhist temple that he remembered sat next to the bridge. What a relief! Kay had his hunting trips to thank for knowledge of this area. Additionally, in another stroke of luck, the bridge was not guarded this time of the morning. They hurried across the bridge and into the fields alongside the road. A tributary canal flowed into the main canal from the west, so they decided to follow the towpath beside it. Dawn was breaking and they were completely exhausted from the long night's march. They took refuge in a shrub-encircled graveyard that was the best cover in sight, although it was right next to a buffalo-powered waterwheel.

August 27, 1944, Sungkiang countryside.

As expected, about 8 a.m. a farmer came along and hitched his water buffalo to the waterwheel. Soon thereafter, they heard the clack-clack-clack of the wooden paddles as the buckets scooped up canal water to irrigate the farmer's rice paddy fields. The farmer spied them hiding in the shrubs, and although Kay called out that they just wanted to talk with him, he took off for Sungkiang like a scared rabbit. Sungkiang was only about a mile away, and the Chinese farmers had warned them that there was a large contingent of Japanese soldiers encamped in that city. By now, it was full daylight and they had to find a safer place to hide. They could not risk that this fellow would not come back accompanied by a contingent of Japanese soldiers. They kept a good distance between themselves and the walls of Sungkiang, and although the city was only two miles wide, it seemed to go on forever. The two tall pagodas that stood in the center of town appeared to stand still and mock them as they trudged on for another four hours. They were careful to keep out of sight and avoided the small villages that encircled the city. At last they came to another shrub-covered cemetery, and crawled under some bushes for a well-deserved rest. It was then that Kay discovered that he had left Tommy's silver matchbox sitting on the waterwheel. Another breadcrumb left for the Japs!

The Japanese had certainly not given up searching for them, for that very afternoon they saw the first of many airplanes flying low over the paddies and fields. Japanese airplanes continued to fly low over the fields all that afternoon. Although it was likely that these aircraft were searching for them, the cemetery provided adequate cover. As it grew later in the afternoon and there had been no further sign of airplanes for over an hour, Kay thought it safe to pack up and cover another few miles before sunset. He was wrong! As they crossed through a field of low-lying young bean plants, Bill heard the unmistakable drone of an approaching airplane. They were out in the open in broad daylight with nowhere close by to hide. They were certain to be spotted as the airplane was on a direct path to pass over them.

Kay reached into his knapsack and took out the green shower curtain they had used for a ground cover. They lay flat among the young bean plants and covered themselves with the shower curtain, which fortunately was the same color as the bean plants. The airplane passed directly overhead not more than one hundred feet above and continued into the distance.

Again, their luck had held, although Kay gave the credit to God and said a prayer of thanks out loud. As before, Tommy and Bill were a bit surprised by Kay's newfound religious fervor. Kay looked at them and said that there were no atheists in foxholes, and he felt that God had been looking after them from the start. It sure appeared that way! Bill said that it was just dumb luck.

They continued to walk until darkness fell. Kay reached into his backpack for the flashlight, but it was not there. Evidently, he lost it when he took out the shower curtain in the bean field. The trail of breadcrumbs continued to grow, and the loss of the flashlight was especially disturbing. They debated going back to retrieve it, but it was miles back and their chances of finding it in the dark were remote. They would sorely miss the flashlight, but would have to go on without it. Tommy reached into his backpack and threw the extra batteries onto the ground.

"Tommy!" Bill shouted. "What are you trying to do, lead the Japs right to us? Bury those bloody batteries!" Tommy looked a bit sheepish as he dug a hole and buried the batteries in a ditch beside the path.

The path led through a large village and past farmers sitting on their door stoops. Despite their Chinese garb and coolie hats, Kay and his friends must have looked obviously out of place to these folks, yet no one challenged them or even stared at them. Quite the contrary as they approached the Chinese would most often glance away and deliberately take no notice of the escapees. Again, typical Chinese discretion.

Bill was very footsore, and Kay's blisters made his every step painful. As they passed the open door of a large house, inside they could see eight men, women, and children sitting at a low round table. Kay stepped inside and asked one of the men if they could have some rice. Without saying a word, everyone shifted position at the table to make room for the three strangers. The man motioned for them to sit, and one of the women placed three bowls of rice with large chunks of fish in front of them, along with pots of hot tea, pickled radish, salt cabbage and peanuts. They were treated as honored guests and stuffed themselves accordingly. The homeowners were amazed that Kay could speak Chinese so fluently and with proper pronunciation. When Kay affirmed that he was Canadian, one elder wanted to hear all about Canada where Kay went to college. Kay had a long discussion with him about the British role in prewar China. He was intelligent and very well educated, although he never shared where he had been schooled.

As Kay got up to leave, the elder warned him that Japanese were bivouacked in the village and told them where they were stationed and where they could be expected to be on patrol. Kay thanked the man and they made their way out the door and down the street. They detoured down a side street bypassing the building where the man warned the soldiers were stationed. They tried to look as Chinese as possible as they trudged along the side roads and out of the city, yet they never came across any soldiers.

Just beyond the village, they came to another wide canal and motioned to a man in a sampan for a lift. He paddled over to the bank without hesitation and took them across. They were now in the "water country", a region between the Taihu Lake and Hangchow Bay, where rivers and canals bisected the countryside creating thousands of islands. Whenever they had to cross a canal or river, someone in a yulohing would respond to their wave and give them a ride. The boatmen never asked questions and in fact didn't say much to them at all.

August 28, 1944 Chekiang Province

Toward morning, they came to the main Shanghai-Hangchow rail line. A cantilever railway bridge crossed over the wide river that Kay surmised was the Hwangpu Kiang. Dozens of Japanese soldiers guarded the bridge, so they beat a hasty retreat down river and away from the railroad. It began to drizzle and they were soon soaked to the skin. Bone tired, wet and cold they searched for a safe place to hide for the day. As dawn broke, they could only find an old grass-covered waterwheel platform on the outskirts of a large town. They climbed up on the platform and covered themselves with the green shower curtain. It blended well with the platform grass so that Kay felt that they could not be seen from the air. After lying on the wet grass all day, by evening they were stiff as boards. Tommy complained that his spine felt like a corkscrew. They stood up and began to jump up and down and flail their arms to get the circulation going again. Several curious Chinese came over from nearby houses to see what these crazy foreigners were all about, and soon they surrounded the platform. These city men were not as friendly as the country farmers but neither were they hostile. Kay spoke with them and unlike the farmers in Kiangsu Province, they acted apathetic and unhelpful. This was such a contrast to the country folk, yet it apparently never occurred to them to ask Kay if they needed anything.

The escapees climbed down from the platform and walked through the Chinese crowd and past the houses. They swam a small canal to a boat dock, and when they climbed onto the dock and up the steps leading from the canal they found themselves in front of a large farmhouse with an armed Chinese sentry standing guard at a bamboo gate. By the Kanji sign posted over the gate, Kay recognized the house as a Chinese Wang Ching-wei Puppet Troop post. These Chinese soldiers were in the pay of the Japanese army and would certainly turn them over to the Japs. The guard saw them and called out in Chinese that they could not go any further.

"I can see that," Kay yelled back, and whispered to Tommy and Bill to turn around and retreat, fast!

"You cannot go that way either," the sentry shouted as he unshouldered his rifle. "Wait there while I get my captain," he warned, and went through the gate.

This is not what Kay wanted to hear. To be questioned by the puppet Chinese troops who were in the pay and under the direction of the Japanese could not go well for them. They understood now why the men at the river were so cool toward them. This region was under Japanese army control. As Kay was about to turn and run, a second soldier appeared at the gate and held his rifle as if he was ready to shoot. Kay knew that they could not outrun bullets, so he stood his ground. The Chinese Captain, still dressed in his underwear, came out of the farmhouse and gave them a look-see. Holding a toothbrush in one hand and a glass of water in the other, he motioned for them to approach.

"Who are you?" the Captain asked in English. Obviously, their Chinese clothes had fooled no one. Kay had to think fast.

Kay feigned that he did not understand the question. The Captain repeated his question in Chinese, but again Kay shook his head as if to say he did not understand. Kay then asked in broken Chinese if the Captain could speak French. He said he could, so the Captain repeated his question in very poor French.

Kay decided to fabricate a story. "We are three members of the Shanghai French Municipal Police."

"Then what are you doing here?" the Captain inquired.

"Well, it is this way," Kay lied. "As you probably know, many foreigners in Shanghai take the train to Hangchow or Ningpo for summer hiking vacations. While returning home on the train from Hangchow, we decided to get off and purchase a meal from a street vendor. However, we misjudged the length of the stop and the train left without us. We were told that we could get another train to Shanghai from Kashing and got a sampan ride but the boatman let us off at this place. Is this the correct road to Kashing?" Kay mentioned Kashing as their destination because it was occupied by the Japanese, so his French police story would make more sense if they were headed in that direction.

"Yes, the road over there will take you to Kashing, but it is a long walk," the Captain answered. "Please, let me see your passes."

Kay's mind reeled, but he continued his bluff. "Passes? Passes? What passes? You should know that the Vichy French Police do not need passes in Japanese China!"

The captain seemed flustered by Kay's rebuke.

"Let me inspect your packs then," he requested. "You do not have any weapons, do you?"

"Of course I have a weapon," Kay shot back, "Did you not expect the French police to carry a weapon on a hiking trip, especially with all these Chinese guerrillas and bandits about?"

The captain's French was rudimentary, so he did not fully understand Kay's answer. Kay repeated it, only slower this time.

"My French is poor," the Captain admitted. "But my lieutenant speaks fluent French. He also knows members of the F.M.P. (French Military Police). Stay here and I will fetch him." He then instructed one of the guards to find the lieutenant as he kept a careful eye on the escapees. After a couple of awkward minutes, the lieutenant came out of the farmhouse.

"These men say they are members of the F.M.P.," the Captain said in hushed tones to the lieutenant. Kay was able to overhear the gist of the conversation and understood the captain's dialect. "You know some of the F.M.P. folks in Shanghai, so perhaps you should question these foreigners." The lieutenant answered that indeed he knew a Sgt. Versailles who was in charge of the F.M.P. motor pool in Shanghai. The lieutenant offered to question them in French and introduced himself to Kay as Lieutenant Wang.

Kay understood what they had said; including the name and assignment of the F.M.P. Sgt., yet neither the captain nor the lieutenant realized that Kay spoke Chinese in addition to French.

"Do you know a Mr. Versailles at the F.M.P.?" the lieutenant asked Kay in French.

"Oh, do you mean Sgt. Versailles, the man in charge of the F.M.P. Shanghai motor pool?" Kay responded. "Yes, I know him very well."

Lieutenant Wang took a hard look at the three escapees. They looked terrible. They were dirty, their clothes soiled and torn, and their bare arms and legs were covered with scratches and bug bites.

The lieutenant smiled. "You three look like you have been through hell!"

"That we have…that we have," Kay responded, "we got lost on our hike out of Ningpo and had to walk crosscountry, through thorn patches and all, before hitching a ride in the sampan."

The lieutenant nodded then turned to the captain and told him that these men were indeed F.M.P.

The captain looked somewhat embarrassed, but motioned for them to open their packs for inspection. Kay's Luger pistol was the first item to tumble out of the pack. The captain picked it up and carefully looked it over.

"Is it the habit for the French police to carry a German weapon?" he asked.

"It is a good pistol, better than the one I was issued by the French police. I bought it from a Shanghai gunsmith and always keep it handy," Kay shot back.

The captain checked the safety and handed the pistol to Kay as he examined the other items in the backpack. All the items looked like those French tourists might carry on a holiday walking trip into the countryside, except perhaps for the green shower curtain.

"Why do you carry a shower curtain with you?" the Captain asked.

"It has worked well to keep the rain off us as we sleep, " Kay answered.

"How is it that you and your F.M.P. friends do not understand Chinese?" the Captain continued. "I thought all Shanghai F.M.P. were instructed in Chinese."

It is amazing how one can come up with creative answers when under pressure. "You know about French Indochina, do you not?" Kay began. The Captain nodded. "Well then, you also must know that the Japanese Army now occupies that country by Vichy French permission. We were no longer needed there, so my companions and I were transferred to Shanghai only a month ago, and we have not had much time to learn Chinese. We thought this trip to the countryside might help us to learn Chinese faster."

Satisfied with the results of the questioning and anxious to get back to his toilet, he instructed the lieutenant and his guards to help repack the rucksacks.

Kay was emboldened by his success and asked, "You have delayed us here for almost a half hour now, and I wonder if you should not now owe us some help."

The captain nodded.

"It indeed is a long walk to Kashing, across many canals and rivers. Could you possibly arrange a yulohing ride for us?"

The captain smiled and said, "Of course, wait here a minute."

The captain walked down to the dock and called out for a passing sampan to stop, but the boatmen called back that they were in a hurry, and he should stop the next boat. The Captain was furious. A pair of lowly sampan men had slighted him, a Chinese Army captain. This would not do! He grabbed the sentry's rifle, snapped back the bolt, rammed a cartridge home into the breech, and fired. The bullet chipped a piece from the bow of the sampan and whined off into space. The two coolies immediately brought the boat to the dock as ordered. The sentries dragged the poor boatmen off of the sampan and threw them at the feet of the captain, who proceeded to kick them without mercy.

As he kicked them, he screamed, "The next time an Army captain gives you an order, you obey it without question!"

When he finished with the coolies, the soldiers threw them back into their sampan then placed a plank between it and the dock for Kay, Bill, and Tommy to board. Kay thanked the captain for his help, and told the lieutenant that he would give his regards to Lieutenant Versailles back at F.M.P. headquarters. As the sampan rowed off down river, the captain warned them not to get off until they reached the heart of Kashing, as there were many bandits in the area who would rob and kill them if given the chance. Kay nodded and waved goodbye. Of course, they did not intend to go into Kashing with these boatmen and after a few miles upriver, Kay had the boatmen row them to the opposite shore. The poor boatmen were bruised and sore, and Kay told them he was sorry that they had been so mistreated by the captain.

As soon as they made it to the shore, they hurried off, anxious to get as far away from that territory as possible. There was a Christian church in the next village, and as they passed by, Kay took off his Coolie hat and went inside. The sign out front announced the church as St. Ann's, a Jesuit Mission. Inside, the church was dark except for the light of two candles flickering next to the altar. It was empty and smelled of incense and candle wax. Kay knelt and said a prayer of thanksgiving. He was more certain than ever that they were in God's care.

Tommy and Bill were irked at this stopover and initially refused to come inside with Kay. They stood outside the Church and waited for Kay to finish but as the minutes passed, their insistence that all of their good fortune was only due to good luck began to crumble. After a while, they both joined Kay inside and reluctantly knelt beside him. They were even more mystified at Kay's behavior than before, but had to agree that something or someone was surely protecting them. It could not be just dumb luck. Time after time they had barely avoided capture. The captain had been charmed by Kay's story, yet as suspicious as he was it was a wonder that he let them go. Bill really didn't think the captain had been fooled, but simply let them go to save face. Nonetheless, a simple thank you addressed to whomever or whatever was responsible for their safe journey seemed to be the right thing to do. To have come this far was truly miraculous, and if it was the Christian God protecting them, it wouldn't hurt to petition Him for continued help. After all, they had a long and dangerous trek yet ahead of them. Tommy looked over at Bill. He had his eyes closed. "Oh well," Tommy thought, "perhaps after all God was indeed looking after them. In any case, they needed someone." Tommy shut his eyes as well and prayed. Afterwards, all three felt reassured and filled with hope that their escape would be successful.

The sky was clear and the moon bright as they left the church. They trudged along keeping to a westerly compass point. They passed through several more villages until about midnight when their progress was blocked by a very large river. There were no bridges visible either up or down river. Bone tired, they sat down on the grassy bank of the canal to rest. A Chinese junk was moored to a dock about fifty yards from where they were resting, and after a time the "Number One Laodah" (boat captain) and a small boy came over to see who these strangers were. He did not ask any questions but after exchanging some small talk with Kay, he seemed to know instinctively who they were. He asked if they would like some rice and hot tea. Would they ever!

The Laodah sent the small boy back to the junk and two men soon returned with three bowls of steaming rice, a pot of tea and cups. Kay spread one of the cans of salmon over the rice and they enjoyed a hearty meal. The captain was most gracious and as they sipped tea together, finally asked where they were going.

"We are headed to Yushan through Kashing, where we hope to meet up with the Chinese guerrillas," Kay answered.

"This you cannot do," the Laodah warned, " You cannot walk to Kashing, except on the main road, and on that road there are many soldiers. Best you avoid Kashing. The trail to Kashing is thirty more miles of nothing but rice paddies, rivers, canals, and swamps. He said that they were on what the locals called the "no can walk" trail.

"I go near Kashan on my way to Pinghu and you can ride with me," the Laodah offered. They thankfully accepted his kind offer and boarded the boat. The Laodah went into the galley and returned with more rice and a bowl of flower balls in a white sauce. They were still hungry, and gleefully devoured the food. Kay accidentally dropped one of the flower balls on the deck and bent over to retrieve it with his chopsticks.

"No, no!" the Laodah cried, "throw that away! This is a moh-dong boat, and you cannot eat that!" Moh-dong boats transport manure, and in China they use human feces along with cow, buffalo and horse dung to fertilize their fields. As much as Bill disliked throwing food away, he quickly threw the flour ball overboard. Kay was surprised that they hadn't smelled the moh-dong when boarding the boat, but the Chinese are fastidious and the deck had been recently swabbed. Bill and Tommy laughed at Kay's embarrassment and teased him about his Scotch thriftiness. They sat on deck and Kay talked with the deck hands for some time. Eventually, they lay on the deck and caught a few hours of sleep as the junk placidly sailed up the canal.

August 29, 1944 "No-can-walk" trail

By the next morning, the junk had traveled many miles up the canal which had merged with a large river, the Ping-hu Kiang. This river flowed into Hangchow Bay and would take them away from their planned southwestward course so after a few more miles, the Laodah put them off and told Kay to follow the road that went toward the hills away from the river. They were very wary to travel on the road in broad daylight, so Kay decided to head crosscountry on a trail marked on his map. The Laodah was correct. This countryside was truly a "No-Can- Walk" trail. The path crossed creek after creek and since there were few bridges, they were forced to swim several canals before resting in another Chinese cemetery.

While walking alongside another canal, they came upon a man tending a flock of hundreds of ducks and geese. He used a long bamboo pole with a piece of fluttering cloth tied to one end to control his flock. He would call to them if they got too far out into the canal, and upon hearing his call, the ducks returned to him. They certainly knew their master's voice! Kay began a conversation with him. The duck man told them to continue southwest and follow the canal towpath. He said they would find several towpath bridges that crossed the many tributary streams and canals that fed into this main canal.

They took the duck man's advice, and the bridges saved them many hours of wading and swimming. They made good time and by the end of the day had covered several more miles before the canal emptied into a wide river that flowed in the wrong direction. The river was very wide at this point, wide enough that they couldn't clearly make out the opposite bank. Kay decided they would have to cross over the river to continue on a southwestern trek. He hailed another "duck man" herding his flock of ducks along the river from a sampan. Kay asked him for a ride over to the other side, but he said "No!" and waved his arms. They didn't know what to make of his adamant refusal since he was the first person to spurn their request. Bill cursed the fellow and Tommy added a word or two wishing him residence in the hot fires of hell. They inflated the leaky li-lo, and began the swim across the river.

The three found that distances could be quite deceptive in unfamiliar territory. What had appeared to be a river only a few hundred yards wide turned out to be closer to a mile wide. Tommy was not a very strong swimmer, and the current became stronger in the middle of the river. It appeared that Tommy was growing increasingly tired and after a few minutes began to gasp for air and hang on to the li-lo. Kay had to blow up the leaky mattress several times as it lost air even faster with the burden of their backpacks and Tommy's added weight.

Although a stronger swimmer than Tommy, Bill was also beginning to become tired as well. The situation was desperate, and they were still hundreds of feet from shore. The air mattress would not remain afloat with the added burden of both Bill and Tommy. Kay spotted another yulohing heading down river in their direction. He yelled and the boatman rowed over to them, helped all three into his boat, and took them to the nearest shore.

They soon discovered their mistake and realized why the duck man had refused to give them a lift. They were on an island! Now they felt ashamed that they had damned the poor duck man and wished that his ducks would all die. The man was just trying to warn them. Yet, he could have simply told them that this was an island. Perhaps his behavior was just typical Chinese taciturnity, but they would never know.

They found a roofed buffalo waterwheel on which to rest. No sooner had they spread out their belongings out to dry on the platform, when two farmers came along, hooked their buffalo to the wheel and started to pump water into the fields. The men paid no heed to the escapees; in fact, they totally ignored them. Kay and friends hurriedly gathered their belongings and found shelter under another roofed waterwheel further down river. They had rested there for two hours when three small boys wandered up. The boys were very curious about the foreigner's possessions, and began to take things out of their packs and examine everything. The boys soon made pests of themselves, and Tommy finally shooed them off.

It was only a couple of hours until sunset and to make better time they walked along the river levee rather than the muddy riverbank. The river became even wider as it merged with countless canals and tributaries on the opposite side. They were still on the island with little prospect of getting off, when a man and a woman in a large sampan offered them a lift, which they gladly accepted. It took twenty minutes before they arrived on the opposite shore and Kay began to appreciate just how wide this river had become. The sampan man told them that there were many islands in this province, and that it was a "No-Can-Walk" trail. The junk captain was correct; it was indeed a "No-Can-Walk" trail, crisscrossed by "no-can-swim" wide rivers and deep, swift canals.

The boatman poled up a tributary creek and let them off on a small dock. He told them that they would find a walled city, Shedong, about an hour's walk up the path and there were no Japanese around there. He claimed that there were many Christians in this area, and he was a Christian himself. He said that there was a Jesuit mission in Shedong, and it would be worthwhile if they visited the pastor of that church. He might be able to help them. They followed the boatman's advice and after walking for a couple of hours, entered the city at dusk.

They had no trouble locating the small church, for its steeple soared high above the thatched roof houses of Shedong. The church was empty, but a light shone from a window in the small house next door. Bill knocked on the front door, and soon an elderly Chinese woman answered. She motioned them to come in and led them into the kitchen. The priest, dressed in a black cassock, was eating dinner at a small table in the center of the kitchen. As soon as they entered, he stood up and welcomed them in French and introduced himself as Father Leland, then graciously invited them to join him for supper. He was a small man with thinning gray hair, a large hooked nose and deep-set sparkling eyes, and he immediately made them feel at home. The Chinese woman brought extra bowls of rice covered with bits of chicken and water chestnuts with a sweet peanut sauce. Father Leland was a French Jesuit, but spoke fluent English and Chinese. He told them that the Japanese had taken over the town some weeks ago and sent the Christian mayor and town council to a concentration camp. Because he was French, the Japanese permitted him to stay and tend his parishioners. He made a point to Kay that he was French, NOT Vichy. When the Japanese Army finally left, he became the town mayor by proxy. The Japanese abandoned Shedong two months ago and retreated to Kashing for reasons the priest did not know, although he heard rumors that recently there had been considerable guerrilla activity in the Kashing area, and the soldiers were probably needed there.

"Do you know where we might find the Chinese guerrillas?" Kay asked.

"I do not know, but rumor has it that they are operating a few miles outside of Kashing, in the Taihu Lake region. Nevertheless you should take care to avoid the Chinese Puppet troops who patrol the area," Father Leland warned.

Father Leland was very helpful and instructed them where they would find bridges and the best route to reach the outskirts of Kashing without being seen.

"Keep off the main road," he warned, "and do not go into the city proper. It is a nest of Japanese soldiers."

The priest also said that rumors claimed there was a garrison of about four hundred Japanese soldiers stationed in Kashing. Although they seldom ventured far outside the city, Kashing and the surrounding countryside were dangerous places for Kay and his friends to travel. Unfortunately, Kashing was directly on their planned route to Yushan and the area where they might meet up with the guerrillas. While they could skirt Kashing city, they could not entirely avoid the area. They would have to chance traveling there.

After dinner, Father Leland led them into the darkened church and lit up the building with several candles. After a few minutes, Chinese peasants began to filter into the church and silently slide into the pews. Soon the entire little church was packed. Father Leland went into a back room and shortly reappeared dressed in ornate garments. He then led the congregation in several prayers, then went to the pulpit and gave a wonderful sermon about Job.

Kay was enraptured by the priest's homily. He had formed a kind of relationship with this Job fellow, the same person Kay had read about in his Bible back in Lunghwa. According to the priest, Job's stoic acceptance of the pain and suffering that God set upon him proved Job's loyalty. Job did not complain or curse God, but accepted pestilence as a test. The story was very meaningful to Kay. Unfortunately, for Bill and Tommy who did not understand Chinese, the sermon was incomprehensible, but later that night Kay repeated the story for them.

After the sermon, Father Leland conducted a service that none of them fully understood. It involved alternate periods of standing, kneeling, and lots of incense, bell ringing, as well as singing, and prayers in Latin. After the service, they thanked the priest and were about to leave when he invited them to spend the night in his rectory. That night, they enjoyed comfortable beds with clean sheets, warm blankets and a hot shower with soap. While they showered the Chinese woman took their filthy clothes, washed, and mended them. This was the best sleep and the only hot shower they had had since escaping. By morning, they felt clean, rested and renewed.

August 30, 1944 Kashing

After they awoke and dressed in their washed and mended clothes, the fugitives were served a hot breakfast of rice cakes with honey and tea. They thanked the priest and prepared to walk toward Kashing. Before they left, Father Leland gave each of them a special blessing and a St. Christopher medal to pin on their shirts. He also explained the legend of St. Christopher, the patron saint of travelers. Now they had someone else to help look after them.

Kashing was several miles away, and although they walked the entire day, by late afternoon there was still no sign of the city. They found a deserted reed-roof hut, and went inside to lie down for a short rest. About an hour later, they heard voices approaching. Bill peeked outside and spied a group of five or six men inspecting the adjacent rice fields. As they approached the hut, Kay hid his pistol in his back belt, then went outside, and waved to them. They were all dressed in long white gowns, which was typical garb for the leading citizens of large cities. Kay wondered if they were from Kashing and remembered the warning about Chinese Puppet troop sympathizers who might turn them in. The Chinese were surprised to see foreigners, and one of the "white gowns" asked who they were and what they were doing here. Kay told them that they were travelers going to Kashing to catch a train back to Shanghai.

"No more trains from Kashing to Shanghai!" one of the men said rather sternly.

One of the "white gowns" seemed unusually inquisitive for Chinese, and began to ask bold questions. When he asked to see their passes, Kay grew indignant.

"Who are you to ask us for passes?" Kay demanded. "We have passes in our backpacks but do not have to show them to the likes of you!"

Kay then turned to Bill and Tommy and verbally spelled out, "P-A-C-K U-P Q-U-I-C-K!"

The "white gown" then said, "Why quick? Why you say pack up quick?" Kay was very surprised that this fellow understood English spelling. He was beginning to make Kay extremely nervous. Why was he so curious and how was it that he knew English so well. Who was this "white gown?" He could be connected to either the Puppets or the Japs. If this were the case, it would not go too well for Kay and his friends.

"Go to hell, we are none of your concern," Kay protested, as he slowly clicked off the Luger safety, yet still kept the weapon hidden from the "white gown." The Chinese man backed off and gave Kay a menacing look. He again demanded to see their passes. Kay had enough of these fellows. He brandished the pistol and told them to get lost. The "white gown" was not intimidated by Kay's pistol and firmly stood his ground. Kay fired a shot over the man's head. Now he was intimidated! The man backed up, and then he and his friends all turned around and ran down the path toward town.

"Let's get out of here!" Kay bellowed.

They shouldered their backpacks and hurried down the towpath leading away from Kashing and toward the Kashing-Soochow spur rail line. By the time darkness enveloped the countryside they had hiked about eight miles from Kashing. They came upon another Chinese graveyard, and it looked like a good spot to spend the night. They spread out the shower curtain and lay down. The ground was so rocky that no one could get any restful sleep. Each time Kay woke, Bill and Tommy were sitting up smoking a cigarette. They had been on the trail for twelve days and it was unlikely that the Japanese were still looking for them, unless of course those damn "white gowns" had alerted the local soldiers. They had made it down the no-can-walk trail; nevertheless, they were still many miles from Yushan and Free China and almost out of food. It was apparent that if they were to escape, they really needed the help of the local guerrillas.

Tomorrow they would circle west of Kashing. Kay remembered his friends' admonition that they would not find the guerillas, the guerillas would find them. Yet wandering blindly about the countryside was a recipe for disaster. By now, the "white gowns" had surely alerted the Japanese about the three fugitives and the soldiers would be searching for them. Kay's plan was to visit the local farmers and hope the word would get to the right folks that three foreigners were wandering around in the area. He couldn't just ask the locals where the guerrillas were. To ask such a question to the wrong person would alert the Japanese or Puppet troops. He had no idea just how they would make this critical contact with the Nationalist Chinese. Perhaps this was best left in the hands of God.

CHAPTER FOUR

Into the Hands of the Guerrillas

August 31, 1944, Taihu Lake country.

Awake at dawn, Kay sat on a hillock in the cemetery and watched a lovely sunrise that began as a faint greenish tinge in the eastern sky and slowly turned to a fiery red as the sun appeared over the horizon.

Bill woke up and joined Kay. "Red sky in the morning is not a good omen," he commented. Kay woke Tommy and they ate the last of their foodstuffs for breakfast and shouldered their packs.

After walking several miles, they came to a junction of several canals that emptied into a large lake. This was the Taihu Lake area, ten miles outside Kashing. They waited on the shore until a sampan came along and Kay hailed it for a ride. The sampan boatman took them across the lake and deposited them onto the shoreline where there was a dock and a road leading away from the lake. As before, the boatman asked no questions or for that matter even spoke a word to them. Nonetheless, how helpful these yulohing men were, and they never asked a thing in return. What would they have done without them?

About noon, after following the road for several miles, they came to a Chinese farmhouse set in a grove of trees. They walked up the road toward the house and asked a group of Chinese sitting under a huge Banyan tree if they could have some tea. One of the men went into the farmhouse. Soon after another man appeared with a bench for them to sit on, followed by three women carrying several bowls of rice and other bowls of fried pork and chicken, salt cabbage, bean curd and pots of green tea. They sat on the bench in the shade of that Banyan and enjoyed a scrumptious lunch.

The farmers were generous and gracious, and asked no questions, although they were obviously curious about these foreigners. However after the escapees finished eating, a young girl, perhaps ten years old, came up to Kay and shyly asked where they were going. Kay said they were going to Free China. The girl smiled and left them without asking any further questions.

Behind the farmhouse in another grove of trees was a Buddhist temple. Kay asked one of the men if he could light a candle in the "joss" to show their respect and gratitude for the graciousness extended. Kay had only white candles in his pack, whereas the Chinese usually burn red candles in their temples. Nevertheless, the farmers seemed very touched when the foreigners set up their white candles and lit them in the joss house. Kay apologized for his very "un-Chinese" way and explained that they wanted to show respect to the Chinese gods and pray for their continued protection. The farmers seemed very moved by this gesture of appreciation and respect.

They remained at the farmhouse until late afternoon, and then feeling refreshed and rested, thanked their hosts and continued down the road. There was much more traffic on the road this afternoon than there had been in the morning, and Kay became concerned when they had to duck into the bushes to hide from an approaching motorcar. They decided to abandon the road and walk on a narrow crosscountry path. They were beyond all the dry crop fields and were now walking in Mulberry country, where Mulberry groves dominated a landscape interspersed with rice paddies. The Mulberry groves provided excellent cover, but the sharp thorns seemed to reach out and punish them from every side. By evening, their shirts were torn and their arms and legs were covered in scratches. They stopped at a farmhouse and the residents told them that Kashing was about ten miles to the south, and the Kashing Railway spur line was about another six li (two miles) further down the path. It was still twilight, and Kay didn't want to attempt to cross the rail line until dark, so they took their time. They sat in a bean field until it was dark, then headed for the railway.

When they arrived they looked carefully around for Japanese soldiers, but there were none, not even at the railroad bridge that crossed the main canal. Kay thought this was strange, as Jap guards were always positioned at major bridges to guard against possible guerrilla activity. With no soldiers in sight, they scampered up the railroad bed. Rusted rails betrayed that the line was seldom used anymore. What the "white gowns" had told them was evidently true and passenger service had been discontinued on this spur line. Probably now only an occasional freight train used it.

It began to rain very hard, so they looked about for shelter and found another waterwheel shed where they could spend the rest of the night. When they climbed onto the raised platform, dozens of rats scurried out of the shed. Kay had always had an aversion to rats, more than any other animal. The floor of the shed was covered with dirt and rat excrement, and Kay commented that he would rather sleep outside in the mud than lie in such filth. Rattan mats covered the roof of the shed, so they took three of them off to use as cover for the filthy floor. Kay was kept awake all night by the rats as they scurried about the shed and occasionally crawled over him. The rats didn't seem to bother Bill or Tommy, but they kept Kay awake all night. He hated rats.

September 1, 1944, Near Kashing

It was still drizzling the next morning; nevertheless they packed up and started on a westerly compass point following a canal levee. They decided that in order to be found by the guerrillas, they would have to chance it and walk in the daytime. The Mulberry bushes grew right down to the canal edge and blocked their hike along the levee. To avoid more scratches from the Mulberry thickets they hiked cross-country following the narrow paths that crisscrossed countless rice paddies, yet still kept to a westerly compass point. They soon came to a wide north-south canal with a considerable amount of boat traffic traveling up and down. Kay thought that this was the Peking to Hangchow Grand Canal. Apparently they were walking in circles and were now close again to Kashing. They needed to find a bridge, and could see one in the distance to the south, but that route would take them closer to Kashing and the Japanese garrison. They walked the canal towpath away from Kashing and looked for another bridge to continue their westward journey.

About a mile along the way, they met a farmer leading a water buffalo. Kay asked him where they might find a bridge, and the farmer told them that the only one for miles around was six li south. They had avoided this same bridge earlier. They then continued north and hoped to find a willing sampan boatman to give them a lift across the canal.

Their guardian angel was still with them. Only a half-mile further, they spotted a sampan loaded with buckets and other parts of a waterwheel. Kay asked for a lift, and the boatman came over to the shore. There was barely enough room for the three of them among the various buckets and wheel spokes, but they found a spot to sit as the boatman poled toward the opposite shore. The sampan was dangerously overloaded, so they sat very still. Any indiscreet movement could capsize the boat and send them all into the canal. They arrived safely, thanked the boatman, and climbed up the bank to resume their southward journey away from Kashing.

By that afternoon, they had only put another three miles between themselves and Kashing, and yet had not seen any sign of Japanese patrols. It was hot in the summer sun, and they were thirsty and tired of drinking creek water, because the chloride pills they used to make the water safe left a fuzzy sensation and a bad taste in their mouths. The Mulberry thorn scratches on Kay's unprotected legs were festering and the salve he used didn't seem to help much. His legs burned, itched, and showed signs of festering.

They stopped at a farmhouse to ask for some tea but found the place deserted. It was very unusual for the Chinese to leave their houses open, yet there was no one around. They tried the next farmhouse and the next, but they were all as empty as the first one was. Kay worried that perhaps the Japs had raided this part of the country and everyone had either fled or been taken away. Should they hide or chance continuing and perhaps walk right into a Japanese patrol. They walked a bit further and came upon a Buddhist temple filled with chanting worshipers, each participant bowing and waving incense sticks in synchrony. What a relief! Everyone was here, and there were no Japanese about. It must have been a very special day for these dedicated Buddhists.

They were thirsty and out of water and chloride tablets. A beautiful seven-tier pagoda caught Kay's attention. It dominated the top of an isolated hill, was exceptionally ornate, and painted red and gold with a green-copper tile roof. It seemed out of place in the poor rural countryside. They decided to climb up the hill and investigate; perhaps they could find a drink of water there. Outside the pagoda was the remnant of what had once been lovely Chinese garden and enclosed courtyard, but was now overgrown with weeds and vines. A large fountain in the center of the courtyard was filled with undrinkable stagnant water. The pagoda was entirely deserted and looked as though it had been abandoned for some time. The barren floor was upswept and covered with feces. Cobwebs decorated the low ceilings. Several rats the size of a housecats scurried outside as Kay entered the building to look for water, but there was no water inside either, so they left.

Still thirsty, they spied another rather large farmhouse surrounded by a sturdy fence and an arched gateway (moongate) leading into a courtyard. Kay was in the lead, and walked up to the moongate. He suddenly spun around and hissed, "Let's get out of here, quick!" Kay had spied a pair of Zeiss binoculars hanging on a post at the front door of the farmhouse. No Chinese farmer could afford such a luxury as binoculars. They had stumbled onto either a Japanese or Puppet Chinese army post.

As they ran, four Chinese ran through the gate and shouted for them to come back. The fugitives ran all the faster, expecting to hear the crack of a rifle and a bullet in their backs at any moment. The men chased them, continuing to shout, "Come back, come back!" They were not about to come back! Kay took the pistol from his backpack as he ran. If it came down to a fight, he was determined to give them one. Nevertheless, in their weakened state, they were unable to outrun the Chinese for very long, and several hundred yards down the path a fleet footed young man caught up with them and blocked the path. He wore typical Chinese garb with a bullet strap over his left shoulder and carried a sidearm on his hip.

His pistol remained holstered as he held up his hand as if to say "stop" and smiled broadly at them. Kay judged that he was only a teenager and certainly did not look very menacing. Nevertheless, he released the safety on his pistol and held it behind his back ready to use should it become necessary. The other Chinese soon caught up and gathered about the teen. They were each wearing sidearms, yet were not otherwise dressed as soldiers. Kay remembered the warning that farmers did not carry sidearms, and these men could be puppet troops. Kay tightened his grip on the pistol, yet none of the men made any threatening moves and stood grinning at them. One of the men extended his hand. He wanted to shake hands!

With the pistol still in his right hand, Kay did not accept the offer to take the man's hand. After a few painful seconds, the man slowly withdrew his hand, took his sidearm from the holster, and offered the gun to Kay.

"Not to worry, we are friends," he said in Chinese, "you need not run away." Each of the other four men continued smiling from ear to ear. These were certainly not Puppet Chinese soldiers!

Kay stuck his pistol into his back belt and took the man's sidearm. He checked to see if it was loaded, and there was a live round in the chamber. Satisfied, he extended his hand and everyone shook hands in that over exaggerated pumping motion common in China.

"We are Chiang Kai-shek soldiers. We fight the stinking Japs, not help them. Come with us and meet our captain," one of the men said in English.

They were led into the farmhouse and invited to sit at a large round table. Steaming green tea soon appeared on the table along with hard dough biscuits. The captain entered the room and introduced himself as Captain Liu She-tsung of Chiang Kai-shek's Nationalist Army.

"From which prison did you escape?" the Captain asked in excellent English but with a decidedly American accent.

"We escaped from Lunghwa prison about two weeks ago," Bill answered.

"You are safe now here with us. We will help you get to Changshan, just as we did for six other Lunghwa prisoners a few weeks ago," he said.

Six others from Lunghwa? This could only be the Uhlich group.
Kay had stumbled on the exact same escape route that led those
folks to Captain Liu. Miraculous! God was indeed showing them
the way. It was wonderful to know that Uhlich and others had safely
arrived this far. The captain opened a photo album and there was a
picture of all six, with their signatures on the back of the photo,
Uhlich, Murray-Kidd, Scott, Huxley, Condor and Levy. They were
here only weeks ago, and by now might be safely in India.

Captain Liu explained that he had graduated in 1937 from UCLA
and joined Chiang Kai-shek that same year. The Generalissimo
commanded several guerrilla operations in this area. Captain Kai's
job was to harass the Japanese Army and confine it to the cities. This
was why there were no Japanese in the countryside, only in Kashing
and other large towns. The Japanese were afraid to send out patrols,
because every time they did so, Captain Liu and his men would
ambush them and inflict heavy casualties. As it turned out, throughout the fifteen years of war with China, the Japanese Army never
penetrated any further west than Ichang, about two hundred miles
east of Chungking, and no further south than Nanchang in Kaingsi
Province. This was due to activities of the guerrillas like Liu.
Although Kashing was still a long way from Guoimndang, Kay, Bill,
and Tommy could feel safe in the hands of the Chiang Kai-shek guerrillas. The fear that had gripped them day and night for the past two
weeks suddenly drained away.

The words of Captain Liu rang in their heads; "You are safe
now here with us." What awesome words. What marvelous allies
these Chinese were! How grand that God had delivered them into
Captain Liu's hands. Furthermore, it was amazing that all this
should happen to Kay Pate, a non-believer. a man who relied on his
own guile and never gave a thought to God or church. That God
should care for Pate and his friends and deliver them from the
Japanese was unfathomable. Kay now realized that his pain and
suffering had brought him to believe that God really did care for
him. Such a life altering event was, for Kay, as dramatic as it had
been for St. Paul two thousand years ago. In an allegoric fashion,
both men had been knocked from their horse by a bolt of lightning,
and that event was to change each in a fundamental way.

Captain Liu asked them if they were tired and hungry. Were they ever! Liu offered that since they were also hot and dirty, they should first have a swim in the canal. He handed them a bar of soap and they stripped, jumped into the canal, and enjoyed a refreshing and cleansing swim while some of Liu's men took their filthy clothes inside to be washed. The soldiers left three yellow robes on the bank for them.

The locals were intrigued to see foreigners swim. Most Chinese could do little more than dog paddle, thus they laughed and pointed when Kay, Tommy, and Bill did the Australian crawl, sidestroke, and back stroke. Soon, they had a gallery of folks, men, women, and children watching them from the bank. They were naked and their robes were laid out on the bank. When it was time for them to get out, they waited for the spectators to leave; nevertheless, none attempted to go, but stood motionless on the bank gawking at the foreigners. Kay, less self-conscious than his friends, finally got out of the water followed by Bill and Tommy. Their hairy arms, legs, and chest seemed to amuse the Chinese, and the women and children placed their hands over their mouths and giggled at the sight of the three naked and hirsute foreigners. They dressed in the yellow robes laid out for them then went back into the farmhouse, and lay down on the cots set up on verandah. Sleep soon came, a wonderfully deep, peaceful sleep!

They awoke some hours later to a sumptuous meal of roast pork, chicken, rice, cabbage, and sweet desserts. For the first time in years, they couldn't eat another bite. After eating, they had another nap on the verandah that lasted until sundown. They were three happy men! That evening, they spent several hours with their newfound friends recounting the story of internment in Lunghwa and escape into the Shanghai delta country.

Captain Liu explained that it was one hundred and eighty miles to Changshan with many mountains between here and there. Their escape to freedom would be arduous and quite dangerous.

Captain Liu mapped out a travel plan for them. He said that their strategy should be to continue on to Yushan as in their original plan, then on to Tienkoshan and Sichang, Kunming and the Burma Road to India. If they were lucky, they could make their way to an American air base at Kanchow and catch a plane to Kunming where the British or Americans might fly them over the hump into India. In any case, it would be a long hazardous twelve hundred-mile trek across China to Kunming. The Chiang Kai-shek guerrillas would help them along the way, passing them from one guide to another until they reached Tienkoshan. From there, the Americans would help them escape into India through Kunming. Captain Liu had already alerted the forward posts that the escapees were coming. He had everything under control and the details seemed well organized.

Captain Liu's wife, a beautiful girl of Eurasian extraction, was living at the post with her husband. For her to stay so deep within Japanese held territory was very dangerous; yet Mrs. Liu said that she would never leave her husband's side and they could face any danger together. Kashing and the Japanese garrison were only a few miles away, and skirmishes between Liu's troops and the Japs were constantly going on in the surrounding countryside. She steadfastly insisted that wherever Liu would go, so would she. Mrs. Liu was very intrigued with Bill's li-lo, and was thrilled when he insisted on giving it to her. Kay thought it best not to carry his Luger pistol, especially now that they were in guerrilla hands. Captain Liu had admired it, so Kay gave it to him in appreciation for his help.

Liu was an excellent amateur photographer. He owned an expensive Ziess camera and had a well-equipped dark room with an enlarger and all the chemicals necessary to develop film and make prints. He took very professional pictures of them, then developed and printed the photographs before they went on. Kay, Bill, and Tommy signed the prints and Liu gave each of them a copy.

September 2, 1944, In the Taihu Lake countryside

Captain Liu arranged a yulohing and a guide, Lieutenant Wong Nu Ling, to take Kay, Tommy, and Bill the thirty miles to the next post. Captain and Mrs. Liu accompanied them for the first five miles. Kay was delighted to be escorted by Liu and his wife on an unforgettable sampan trip. The canal was covered in lily pads with Lotus flowers in full bloom and the surrounding countryside was truly beautiful. Emerald-green rice paddies interspersed with cabbage, bean, melon, and sugar cane fields flanked the canal. The horizon to the west was commanded by snow-capped mountains.

L/R: Bill Henry, Captain Liu, Kay Pate, Tommy Crosthwaite, and Coolie in Sampan, Sept 3, 1944

As the yulohing glided silently down the canal, Liu advised everyone to be very quiet and the only sound to be heard was the swish-swish of the boatman's "yuleh" or long oar. Two miles from the guerrilla post, the canal merged with the main canal that led directly into Kashing. Liu cautioned them to lie low in the sampan, put on their coolie hats, and remain silent. Japanese soldiers could be anywhere. They rowed a half-mile down the main canal to a place that was within sight of the rooftops of Kashing then entered a side canal that led away from the main part of town.

Liu told them that one of his men worked in the Japanese garrison post in Kashing, and provided daily reports of Japanese troop activity. Liu was aware of every movement the Japanese Army made in this area. Every time the Japanese patrols ventured into the countryside, Liu's troops would ambush them. These attacks had been so effective, that the Japanese soldiers no longer ventured more that a mile or two into the surrounding countryside. He explained that this was why the guerrillas could feel safe maintaining a post within a few miles of a major Japanese Army garrison. The Japanese were practically held captive in Kashing and their supplies were running low. The guerrillas blew up the last supply train that tried to make it into Kashing on the spur line. Soon the Japanese would retreat from this area, perhaps all the way back to Soochow, and "good riddance to them," Liu added.

They had completed the first five miles of the trip when it was time for Liu and his wife to return home and leave them in the care of Lieutenant Wong. As they said their good-bye's, Liu pressed CRB $2,000 (about 40 cents U.S.) into each of their hands.

"For cigarettes or other little delicacies that you might wish to purchase along the way," he said.

Kay, Bill, and Tommy waved until their sampan rounded a bend and Captain Liu and his wife were hidden from view. Kay commented that a finer chap than Captain Liu didn't exist. After another few miles, they tied up at a small landing and Wong called out to a nearby farmer to get them two fresh "yuloing" or rowers. The boatmen from the first leg of the trip began the long walk back on the towpath to their homes. Several times along the way they repeated this exchange of yuloing. The guerrillas had efficiently organized this underground transportation network.

That evening they came to a village along the banks of the canal, and climbed out of the sampan and walked to the local teahouse. The locals at the teahouse were impressed that Kay could speak Chinese. Foreigners were a rarity in these parts, and any foreigner who could speak Kyangsher dialect was considered unique. Kay had a long conversation with them, and the Chinese were captivated by his story. They considered anyone who escaped from the Japs to be heroic and gained "much face." The locals' hatred of the Japanese was deeply rooted.

Several men related their own stories of Japanese brutality. One fellow showed Kay his deformed fingers. The Japs had inserted bamboo splinters under his nails, then systematically broke every one of his fingers because he shorted them on his forced quota of rice. He had done so because it was all that he had to feed his family. Another man had five daughters and told how the Japanese soldiers had raped four of his little girls, the youngest only seven, then stripped, killed and butchered the oldest girl when the child resisted their advances. The man cried as he told his story. Another farmer related how his family had been burned to death inside their farmhouse as he worked in the fields. Other stories of Japanese Army barbarity to the Chinese peasants were too horrible to relate. Seldom do the Chinese show emotion, but several men in the teahouse were openly crying.

Kay could never understand the unjustifiable savageness and disregard for human life apparent in these Japanese soldiers. He had worked for many years in Japan and had gained the utmost respect for the Japanese people who were kind, considerate, and ethical. Before the Japanese military took over the government of Japan, a more hardworking, industrious and trustworthy nation was not to be found. Such stories of bestiality and cruelty were, to Kay's experience, uncharacteristic of Japanese behavior. Nevertheless, Kay's experience in Lunghwa at the hands of the Japanese guards was similar to that of these farmers. The Japanese felt that anyone who allowed himself to be captured was contemptible, and the Chinese were considered a subhuman race, not worthy of life.

Kay could never rid himself of the vision of the man and woman shot to death and left hanging on the barbed wire fence in Lunghwa or the wanton murder and starvation of fellow prisoners. For him this experience remained a recurring nightmare. He felt that something very evil must take possession of the souls of otherwise humane and moral people when placed in a position of power. They soon come to regard their enemies as inferior and undeserving of humane treatment. For the Japanese in China, such loathing and disregard for human rights extended to enemy soldiers as well as farmers, coolies, and even captured foreigners. Other examples of shameful conduct are not unique in the history of humanity; in fact, it could be considered typical in wartime. Examples abound, including the Germans toward Jews, Serbs and Croats, Turks and

Greeks, Muslim Sunni and Muslim Shiites, European exploitation of American Indians, and American trader's enslavement of blacks. It would seem that every society has something in its history for which to be ashamed. It simply shocked Kay that the Japanese, who were otherwise such gentle, kind-hearted folk, had succumbed to such contemptuous evil. Kay resolved to limit his hatred to the Japanese Army and military rulers and did not include the Japanese people, whom he knew to be better than this. He doubted that the Chinese would ever see it his way.

The farmers offered tea, biscuits, fried watermelon seeds, and never ending talk. One of the women placed a plate of "wong tong," literally "yellow sugar" on the table. Wong tong is an unrefined cane sugar pressed into slabs and then cut into fingers so that it is easy to eat. It was a welcomed treat and they made pigs of themselves by gorging on it. Following the afternoon tea, they got back into the sampan and several miles downstream from the teahouse, the boatmen paddled the boat into a narrow canal that led to another farmhouse where they were treated to a dinner of chicken and rice.

After dinner they sat outside on the verandah and talked until dark. Lieutenant Wong was a wonderful chap, and spoke excellent English. He had been born in San Francisco's Chinatown and educated at the University of California at Berkeley, earning a degree in Political Science. Seven years ago he made his way to China to help Chiang Kai-shek in his struggle against the Japanese. He had been involved in the "China Incident" in 1937 and was wounded three different times. His family still lived in San Francisco where they owned a restaurant. After their enjoyable visit, the fugitives finally bedded down for the night on rattan mats draped with mosquito netting.

September 2, 1944, Chekiang Province

In the morning, they were called to a breakfast of rice cakes covered with sugarcane syrup and pears. Kay had no idea where they found pears, as he had not seen pear trees (or any other fruit trees) anywhere along their travels. Nonetheless, the pears were sweet, delicious, and thoroughly enjoyable. Wong said that it was necessary for him to go into town to arrange the next part of their journey, and until he returned, they were to lounge around the farm. Kay felt quite safe with the guerrillas and Chinese farmers and they lounged on the banks of the canal for three hours until they were startled by the sudden appearance of six armed men on the towpath. Kay jumped to his feet with his heart throbbing in his chest and berated himself for being so careless. He only relaxed when he recognized the smiling face of Wong among the men and learned that he had returned with their escort for the next phase of the trip.

They left about 5 p.m. and walked down the canal bank toward a larger boat that Wong said was waiting for them on the main canal. Lieutenant Wong walked with Kay, Bill, and Tommy along the towpath and his troops were walking about fifty yards ahead of them, when they suddenly broke into a run. Kay looked around for soldiers, but there were none. He asked Wong why his men were running. Wong grinned and said Kay would soon know, and that he should keep walking until they reached the spot where the other men began to run. When they arrived, Wong also broke into a run and the Kay, Bill, and Tommy followed the Lieutenant's example. When Wong suddenly stopped after a hundred-yard sprint, Tommy was the first to notice a very putrid and foul odor that almost made him lose his lunch.

Wong explained that this was where they attacked and sank a Japanese patrol boat the previous week. The boat was outfitted with two .50 caliber machine guns, one mounted fore and the second aft. As the Jap soldiers sped up and down the canal, they delighted in shooting at anything or anyone that moved along the banks. Men, women, children, dogs, water buffalo, it did not matter to the trigger happy Nips. They had killed many innocent villagers with this game of death. Last week after the son of the village elder was killed by a Japanese patrol boat; the guerrillas had set up a trap. They stretched a slack half-inch thick steel cable a few inches under water across the fifty-foot wide canal and secured it on both banks. When the patrol boat came roaring down the canal, they pulled the cable taunt to lift it a few feet above the water. The cable beheaded four of the soldiers as the boat sped underneath. Then they shot the remaining three soldiers, tied rocks to each and left them to rot on the bottom of the canal. Finally, they sank the boat into the mud at the bottom of the canal. The Japs combed the area for their missing comrades and boat, but could not find either and the bodies remained to putrefy in the canal.

"We bathe and wash in this canal, and seven dead Nips wouldn't do much to improve the water quality, so we eventually dragged their rotting bodies out of the water and dumped them into that field. The stinking Jap corpses will make good fertilizer!" Wong added, almost spiting the words out in disgust.

Kay wandered back a few yards and peered over the levee into the melon field beyond. Indeed, there were seven naked dead Japs in the field, each one thrown into the field to decompose among the rows of melons. On the muddy canal bottom close to the bank, he could make out the outline of the gunboat.

They arrived at the main canal, boarded the waiting boat with their escorts, and silently slipped into the waterway. The only signs of life in the serene countryside were the farmers trudging home along the towpaths after a long day's work in the fields. Occasionally they passed a joss house filled with prayerful fishermen and farmers. Wong explained that several of those open-air temples were hundreds of years old. They glided beneath several large motor car bridges, most of which were missing their central spans. The Chinese guerillas had blown them up to render them useless to Japanese transports. The farmers had placed sturdy bamboo walkways across the missing central spans to be used by Chinese pedestrians, wagons, and carts.

As the sun set, they pulled into a small creek that led to a large farmhouse. Armed guerrilla soldiers were everywhere, some with captured samurai swords strapped to their sides. It was evening mealtime, so they were invited to sit at the officers' table as the special guests of Lieutenant Moh Ven Loong, the Chiang Kai-shek Army Commander for this region. Lieutenant Loong was in full Chungking army uniform. That day he had returned from his superior's headquarters and "had to dress for the occasion." It didn't seem to concern him that Japanese were all over the province and he was dressed in full enemy uniform.

Lieutenant Moh looked very young, perhaps in his twenties. Much too young, Kay thought, to carry such a responsibility as

Province Commander. Nevertheless, Chinese age can be very deceptive and it would have been very impolite to ask such a personal question as age. Soon after they were introduced to Lieutenant Moh, who also spoke excellent English, he confided that he had graduated from MIT in Boston with an engineering degree in 1929. He was certainly much older than he looked. It was surprising how many of the Chungking army officers had attended universities in the U.S.

After dinner, Kay, Tommy, and Bill bade farewell to Lieutenant Wong as he prepared to return home, and climbed into one of three sampans waiting for them. The other two boats were filled with Moh's troops, and Moh climbed into the boat with Kay and friends. It was a clear moonless night and the stars stood out as though suspended on a dark velvet tapestry. The Milky Way painted a white path across the sky, and the bright star near the horizon betrayed itself as Venus. Kay could not remember ever having seen it look so bright. Lieutenant Moh mentioned that he was an amateur astronomer, and pointed out a moon-size faint patch of light.

"That is M31, the Andromeda nebula," Moh instructed. "Actually, it is not a nebula at all but an entire other galaxy similar to the Milky Way, yet two million light-years away."

Kay was amazed that he could see something so far away in space and time with only his naked eyes. He pondered the "two million light years" distance, realizing that the light he now looked at started its journey to earth two million years ago, long before people existed. It was like looking into a time machine.

The boats slipped down a very narrow canal partially covered by a canopy of willow trees. Tommy started to hum an English song and Lieutenant Moh broke out singing the words in English. Kay and Bill joined in and when it was finished Kay said to Moh,

"Isn't it dangerous to be singing in English in this countryside?"

"Oh, don't worry about that," Moh chided, "the yellow bellied Nips don't dare venture outside the cities after dark. They are scared stiff of us."

Without question, that was the truth! The guerrillas were in full control of the Kashing countryside, and had the support of the local populace. Indeed, Kay felt very safe in the care of these folks. They continued singing as they drifted along the canal for another half-hour. It was wonderful to hear familiar tunes again. Kay relished the jubilant Scottish songs sung by Bill and Tommy, and good old English tunes such as *It's a Long, Long Road to Tipperary*, *Keep the Home Fires Burning*, and *Keep Right on 'Til the End of the Road*.

They eventually tied up to a dock and walked down a narrow path until they arrived at another farmhouse where they were challenged by a sentry. Although this was Lieutenant Moh's headquarters, they were not allowed to pass until he was challenged and recognized. Once inside, they sat around and talked as Lieutenant Moh's soldiers took down doors and placed them on the verandah to make beds for their guests. They were to encounter these "door beds" throughout their travels in China. To make sleepover guests comfortable, it was quite common to suspend a door on blocks a foot off the floor, then place a straw mattress or "foo-tong" on top and cover it with mosquito netting suspended from the ceiling. These temporary beds were quite comfortable and considerably better than the wet ground and rocks they were accustomed to sleeping on since escaping from Lunghwa. Kay was dog-tired, and would have fallen asleep on an Indian nail bed, but the door bed and foo-tong were much appreciated.

September 3, 1944, Guerrilla Headquarters

They arose early the next morning and followed Lieutenant Moh to the village teahouse, the main gathering place for locals. Lieutenant Moh introduced them to everyone, young soldiers, farmers, fishermen and bearded elderly men alike. There were no women or children present, so Kay assumed this was the equivalent of an English gentleman's club. Wishing to mingle with the locals, Kay sat down at a table occupied by an elderly man who he assumed was the village "elder" or mayor.

The man who was sitting by himself was dressed in a flowing white robe and looked very wise and distinguished. His weathered face and humped back spoke of a long life of hard work, yet it was his deep-set, dark eyes that captivated Kay. The man looked old yet his eyes shone with a youthful sparkle. A long stringy white beard extended from his chin to his chest. He leaned across the table and in a barely audible whisper began to ask Kay questions in broken English. He asked for details of their escape, how it was that they had hid from the Japanese for two weeks, and how they had found Lieutenant Liu's headquarters.

"How you do this?" he asked.

Kay said that someone had been looking after them, and it might be God.

"Which god?" the old man asked.

Kay was taken back by the man's question. "Which god?"

"Well," Kay answered, "there is only one God, but I do not know Him."

"Christian God?" the man persisted.

"Yes, I guess if it was God it would be a Christian God," Kay replied.

"And you not know Him?" the man asked.

"It is more correct to say that HE does not know me," Kay muttered sarcastically.

"You wrong. God knows you," the man said sadly shaking his head.

After a moment of strained silence, the man broke into a broad smile and said, "I am Christian, and many others in village too. Come, I show."

The old fellow stood up and shuffled out the door of the teahouse with the aid of a twisted walking stick. Kay said nothing to his companions as he obediently followed the old gentleman out the door and down the dirt street to a small church situated beside the village square in the heart of town. They went inside. It was still early morning; nonetheless, the interior was adequately lit by single shaft of multicolored light that burst through a round stained glass window above the ornate altar situated on top of a small platform. Several dozen rows of wooden benches were arranged on the stone floor of the nave. A small red lamp flickered next to a veiled box placed in the center of the altar.

"Is this church Catholic or Protestant?" Kay asked. The old man looked at Kay as though he had asked a nonsensical question.

"Christian!" he answered matter-of-factly. "Christian, not Buddhist."

"You kneel and pray. Get to know your God!" the old man commanded as he slipped into a pew and knelt on the cold stone floor.

Kay did as instructed, but he had little experience with prayer.

"How should I pray?" he asked the old man.

"From the heart," the man answered mater-of-fact.

"I don't know God. I have been thinking about Him a lot lately, but since I don't know what he is like I don't know where to find him." Kay said.

"God is wherever you look, in the village, in this church, in those men back in the tea house, and even in Lunghwa," the man said.

"My wife, Lil, knows God. She finds him in her Bible. I have looked in that book, but I see only words, no clear description of God," Kay lamented.

"Oh, He is there. You not find God by only looking at words. You look at words and not see."

"Observe this window," the man exacted as he pointed to the beautiful stained glass window over the sanctuary. "If you look too close, you see only pretty pieces of colored glass, yet look from here you see beautiful picture. Likewise, you not find God if look too close, better you look at whole picture from distance."

That made sense Kay thought. Perhaps he expected to find a God he could grasp and examine, and that was wrong thinking.

His prayer started with a "thank you" for watching over them and ended with a plea for his, Bill and Tommy's continued safety and their wish to be reunited with their families. There was something special about this old church, a kind of warmth and peacefulness that was impossible to describe. Kay felt it permeate his body as surely as he felt his own breathing. After a few minutes, the old man rose and shuffled out of the church. Kay followed him into the bright sunshine.

"Priest-man come each month and pray for village," the old fellow said. His eyes sparkled even brighter as he spoke. "But, God in building every day. God outside too. God everywhere you look. It good that you pray to Him."

They returned to the teahouse, where Lieutenant Moh, Tommy, and Bill were sipping their third cup of green tea and eating biscuits.

"Where have YOU been?" Tommy asked when he saw Kay

enter the teahouse.

"Church," Kay answered.

"Church? What church?" Bill asked.

"The one in town," Kay said.

"Doing what?" Tommy persisted.

"Praying with this old man," Kay responded pointing to the gentleman behind him.

"What old man?" Bill asked somewhat amused.

Kay turned around, but the old fellow was not in the teahouse.

"The old guy I sat down with when we came in!" Kay said, now a bit exasperated. "He was behind me a minute ago."

Bill looked closely as if to examine him for some sign of illness.

"You came in alone!" Bill exclaimed. "There is no old man."

"The guy I was sitting with at that table when we first came in," Kay insisted, now quite annoyed.

"Well," Tommy said in a concerned voice, "I really didn't take careful notice, but it seems to me that you sat alone over there, which I thought was peculiar behavior at the time! If there was an old man, I certainly didn't see him."

Kay searched Bill's face for some sign of support, but he just looked confused by Kay's abnormal behavior. church...prayer... old man? What was happening to Kay? Perhaps the stress of their escape had finally gotten to him.

Lieutenant Moh just sat silently by with the annoying, inscrutable Chinese smile of a Charlie Chan. Kay was clearly annoyed with his companions, but decided to drop the subject. Bill and Tommy had probably not noticed the old gentleman. Kay chalked it all up to the tension of the past two weeks. Forget it! But then again...

They lingered and rested three days at Moh's headquarters while he arranged the remainder of their trip. Runners handled all communications between outposts. They could not take a chance on radios, for the Japanese could triangulate on transmissions. Telegraph or telephone lines did not exist in the countryside. Consequently, it took days to get word to and from one outpost to another or back to Chungking.

September 7, 1944, Lieutenant Moh's Headquarters

On the afternoon of the third day with Lieutenant Moh, he told them that everything was now arranged for their transportation to the next outpost and they would be leaving that evening. One of his soldiers guided them about four miles down the path to another canal-side farmhouse, where Lieutenant Moh said that a boat would be waiting for them. However, there was no boat at the farmhouse, best described as a hovel. It was one of the most tumbled down, dirty, thatched-roof farmhouses that they had seen in this part of China.

The guide talked with the farmer for a while, then disappeared without saying a word. They sat in the darkened farmhouse not knowing what the score was. Since they were not offered anything to eat, they shared two cans of chipped beef from Bill's backpack. When the guide finally returned, he said that a boat would not be here until morning and suggested they find a spot in the house to sleep. They were offered no mats or bedding, so they curled up on the dirty floor.

Without the benefit of mosquito nets, the insects had a feast. The hungry critters seemed to prefer English blood to that of the soundly- sleeping Chinese farmer. Between the hungry mosquitoes and rats scurrying about the filthy floor, it was a very uncomfortable night for them. They were overjoyed when dawn finally broke and their guide returned. He instructed them to wait in the farmhouse courtyard, yet offered them no breakfast, lunch, or even hot tea while they waited.

By 3 p.m., the anticipated yulohing still had not arrived, and the guide seemed at a loss as to what to do next. Finally, he suggested they all return to Lieutenant Moh's headquarters and find out what went wrong with the plan. Kay did not like backtracking, yet there was no other choice. This had not been a very auspicious start to Moh's travel plans for them: no boat, no sleeping arrangements, and no food. When they arrived back at headquarters, the only person around was a fellow who looked more like a bandit than a soldier. The guide explained why Kay and friends had returned, but the man acted disinterested and would not respond to Kay's questions. He would not look Kay in the face and made him feel quite uncomfortable. After repeated questioning, he finally explained that Lieutenant Moh and his soldiers had gone on a raid and Kay and friends had best lie low because Japanese were all around. They dared not even venture out to the teahouse, and spent the rest of the day sitting on benches inside the courtyard.

Toward evening, two uniformed Nationalist soldiers came into the courtyard and shook hands with the fugitives. One of the men was tall and thin with a Mauser pistol strapped to his belt. The other man introduced himself as Major Cheng Sui. Major Cheng was short and bald with a pencil-thin mustache and a sparse chin beard. Kay immediately liked this fellow. He was very outgoing, friendly, and warm. Major Cheng explained that he was the Nationalist Intelligence Officer for the entire district and was returning from a visit to all his outposts. He knew who they were and had already heard their story. He explained that he was on his way back to provincial headquarters, and would be glad to take them along with him.

Relieved to be on their way again, they walked a few hundred yards along the canal to Cheng's beached sampan and climbed in. They were surprised later when the sampan tied up at the same hovel where they had spent the previous night. However, this time things were quite different. Several coolies hurried around to set up door beds and mosquito netting for each of them. Before retiring, they were treated to a dinner of whole baked duck, cabbage and rice. It was a simple dinner, but one of the most delicious that Kay had ever had while in China. The duck was so well cooked that it fell apart with chopsticks. It was stuffed with all sorts of goodies. This was certainly different treatment than they received at the same house the previous evening. This night they slept soundly on their door beds protected from hungry insects by mosquito nets.

September 8, 1944, Chekiang Countryside
After breakfast, Cheng said they would have to wait for night to move on. He warned that there were many Japanese moving throughout the area, including patrol boats that would make it unsafe to be on the main river or pass through towns in daylight. They kept busy by wandering around the farm, feeding the ducks and chickens, and watching the farmers harvest rice. Cheng came by later that afternoon and warned that his scouts reported that a

Japanese patrol was headed their way. They quickly packed up their things, and led by Cheng, scurried down the path and hid in a reed patch. Minutes later a Japanese patrol of a dozen well armed soldiers marched by the farmhouse and down the path, passing not more than twenty yards from their hiding place. The soldiers marched by in a very loose formation, laughing and smoking as they went, and thankfully paying little attention to the reed patch. Cheng said that last week the same patrol had shot the young son of one of the villagers for no reason. The Japanese considered such action as sport, a sort of relief from boredom. "They would get theirs," Cheng promised, and indeed Kay heard two days later that Lieutenant Wang and his men killed the whole bloody lot of them in an ambush on the Tai River.

They had an early dinner, and later that afternoon began their sampan trip down the canal with Cheng. Although Cheng's sampan was much larger than the other sampans, it was still very crowded. Besides Kay, Tommy, and Bill, the other passengers included Major Cheng, his Aide, the Aide's wife, and an old woman and young boy who were traveling to visit the woman's son at Cheng's headquarters. In addition, six coolies sat quietly in the bottom of the boat among several bundles that took up considerable room. The other two sampans, one in front and one behind, were filled with a dozen well-armed men. The three boats moved very quietly down the canal that ultimately merged with a large river, a tributary of the Kin Kiang that Cheng said eventually flowed into Taihu Lake.

The sun had set, yet in the twilight a considerable amount of boat traffic still moved along this large river. Junks, barges and walla wallas (motorized tugs) with barges in tow shared the river with sampans of various sizes. Boats heading downstream kept to the middle of the river where the current swept them along at a good pace. Those boats heading upstream were forced to struggle against the current and therefore stayed close to the banks where the river flow was slowest.

The construction of the barges was curious. Prows rode high above the river, whereas the sterns were only inches out of the water. Along each side of the craft from bow to stern, a narrow running board was set out over the water. Three or four coolies on each side stabbed long poles into the river bottom and then walked the plank from front to back pushing the boat against the current. When they arrived at the stern, they pulled their poles out, carried them up to the prow, and repeated the task in endless succession. The coolies sang as they worked their poles in mindless repetition. Gangs of coolies struggled along the towpaths as they pulled larger barges upstream with long ropes. A few steam-powered tugs were towing two or more barges, and as they chugged upstream, they belched thick black smoke from short smokestacks.

Cheng's coolies pulled their boats upstream with long hemp ropes slung over their shoulders. Progress against the prevailing current was frustratingly slow until the countryside flattened and the river slowed perceptibly. At this point the coolies climbed back on board and powered the yulohing with the long sweeps. Closer to the city of Wuchen, the countryside eventually gave way to a more built-up area, with several huts and houses grouped together along the banks. Cheng's flotilla glided silently by a few small villages with only a dog here and there to announce the boats' passing.

There was no one up and around in the several small villages alongside the river, nevertheless Cheng chided everyone to be very quiet. The Japanese soldiers usually did not come out at night; nonetheless, there might be a few Chinese puppet troops around who could report their movements to the Japanese. The guerrillas despised these puppet troops who were in the pay of the Japanese. They considered them traitors who had thrown in with the Japs for selfish reasons. Cheng called them "Dunghoak" a name in Chinese politely translated as "pond scum." The river eventually merged with another even larger river flowing northward toward Taihu Lake.

Towards midnight, Major Cheng told them that they would soon be passing through "Hell Gate." The ancient town of Wuchen straddled the river, and to protect it from floods, a mile long twenty-foot high moss-covered wall had been constructed along both banks. The river, which was one hundred feet wide, now narrowed to only twenty-five feet as it entered the city, which made the passageway look like a long deep canyon. Japanese pillboxes guarded the entrance and exit of the walled canyon, and a fortified bridge connected the east and west portions of Wuchen. It would be ticklish business to slip unobserved through Hell Gate.

They followed the example of the soldiers in the other two sampans and donned their coolie hats. Cheng told them to hunker down in the bottom of the boat and pretend to be asleep. Fortunately, the nearly full moon was hidden behind thick clouds and only dim lights came from the un-electrified city. Together, the three sampans in their convoy were certain to attract attention if spotted by the Japs, so the three boats separated and glided silently one at a time into the "canyon." The oarsmen greased their "sweeps" so that they would make a minimum of noise.

Candlelight filtered through small windows in the pillbox at the canyon entrance and cast yellow shimmering reflections on the water. A hundred yards into the canyon two sentries with torches were patrolling the bridge. Cheng unholstered his pistol, and his Aide and the other soldiers released the safety of their rifles. They hoped for no trouble from the Japanese, but if trouble came, they were determined that there would be more dead Japs in the river than Chinese guerrillas. They glided silently through the canyon, barely daring to breathe as they drifted under the bridge, but not even one of the boats were challenged. Once beyond the second pillbox and safely away from Wuchen, everyone relaxed. Kay lay down on the bottom of the sampan, rolled up his sweater for a pillow, and fell asleep.

September 9, 1944 Outside of Wuchen

It seemed to Kay that he had just closed his eyes when Major Cheng was gently shaking him awake. The sun had risen over the rice paddies and everyone but Kay was sitting up.

"Time to wake, Pate hsien-sheng," Cheng said.

Kay yawned, stretched, and sat up. The Major looked at Kay and grinned.

"Either you have a very clear conscience, or have no fear of the Japs," Cheng chuckled.

Kay noticed that Major Cheng sat cross-legged in the boat with his pistol in his lap. All the other soldiers sat likewise with their rifles cocked and ready.

"Are you expecting trouble?" Kay asked.

"Perhaps not," Cheng replied, "usually the Nips go back into the cities at daybreak, but there are some patrol boats in the area, and we would be no match for their 50 caliber machine guns."

Just as he finished saying that, they could hear the dull throb of an approaching gunboat, however it was hidden from their view by a bend in the river a hundred yards ahead. Fortunately, a narrow reed and bulrush-lined canal merged with the river just a few yards upstream. As fast as they could paddle their sampans, they slipped quietly into the small canal and drifted a few yards into the four-foot high clumps of bulrushes, flushing a flock of noisy ducks in the process. The ducks flew directly across the bow of the gunboat as it roared past them. The speeding gunboat raised two-foot waves that almost capsized their frail boats.

"That was very close!" Major Cheng exclaimed, "it was fortunate that these bulrushes were nearby, and that the ducks distracted the Nips. Had the bastards looked towards the bank, they surely would have spied us. What luck!"

Bare shoreline and small clumps of grass were all that decorated the riverbanks for hundreds of yards up and down the river from the little side canal and patch of bulrushes they had ducked into. There were no other side canals to slip into or even a bush to hide behind in all this distance. They were indeed very lucky to be near the reeds when the patrol boat roared by. Nevertheless, Kay did not think luck was responsible for such good fortune. He wanted to tell Cheng that God was looking after them, but he didn't want to explain such a comment at this moment. He quietly said another prayer of thanks.

As they rounded the bend, there was a sudden sharp crack of a rifle and a bullet splashed into the water just a few feet in front of the first sampan.

"Stop and identify yourselves," a Chinese soldier yelled from the bank as a band of soldiers climbed to the top of the levee. Cheng yelled back that they were Chungking soldiers and the man should stand down.

Back came the Chinese equivalent of, "Oh yeah, you and who else is going to make me?"

"Are they Puppet troops?" Bill nervously asked Cheng.

"No, I think they are guerrillas from the next province," Cheng replied.

The warning shot gave everyone quite a fright, but Major Cheng beached his sampan and got out to parlay with the soldiers. He was correct; they were guerrilla soldiers from the next province who hadn't initially recognized Cheng and his troops. He complimented the soldiers on their watchfulness, and they all bowed and grinned. Kay and Tommy stayed in the boat while Bill climbed out to attend nature's call in the tall bulrushes. The soldiers stared at Bill as he passed by but said nothing, nor did they ask Cheng any questions about the foreigners he had in tow. More Chinese discretion!

CHAPTER FIVE

Headquarters

September 10, 1944 Lake Tamil

They traveled all-night and about 8 a.m. paddled up a small creek and moored next to a large cargo yulohing secured to a dock. Tommy had pressing business to attend to, and rather than wait until the sampan was fully tied up, he tried to jump from the boat to the dock and missed his footing resulting in a dump into the muddy water. Kay and Bill had a good laugh at Tommy's clumsiness, yet none of the Chinese thought this accident was the least bit funny. Quite the contrary, they all looked away as if to empathize with Tommy's embarrassment. Tommy climbed out of the muddy river and hurried dripping wet over to a bamboo grove. Kay and Bill climbed out of the boat and went into a farmhouse where breakfast had been prepared for them.

After breakfast, they resumed the sampan journey and about noon, the river merged into a wide lake that Major Cheng called Lake Tamil. The lake was several miles wide and the coolies rowed toward a large pine- covered island located about two miles off shore. On this island was the imposing headquarters of the "Taipan" or "head–guy", General Chang Bang-fee of the Nationalist Army. General Chang met them at the dock and introduced himself. General Chang commanded all guerrilla troops in the Chekaing Province and was a nephew of Generalissimo Chiang Kai-shek himself.

He was a very trim handsome man just under six feet tall. An army cap embroidered with the Nationalist China medal to indicate his position covered his head. He wore a well-pressed uniform with bullet belt and highly polished boots. He looked quite young to be a general, yet as they had learned, the age of Chinese people can seldom be correctly judged. General Chang led them into the main building of his headquarters. The camp had been converted from an estate that once belonged to Generalissimo Chiang Kai-shek's family. They sat down on comfortable high back chairs at an ornately carved, teakwood table as coolies served the usual ceremonial tea before lunch. General Chang, who spoke excellent English, questioned them about their escape from Lunghwa and their trek across the Shanghai countryside. He was most interested to learn about cities and towns that were controlled by the Japanese and which were not, and specifically the location of airfields, prison camps, and munitions dumps. They told him all they had seen and heard; however, Kay suspected that the general hadn't heard anything from them that he didn't already know.

He proudly boasted that his troops, about eight thousand strong under his command, had great success against the Japanese Army. The Japanese, stretched thin fighting the Americans in the Pacific islands and the British in Southeast Asia were gradually losing ground in China. Chang Kai-shek's forces had driven the Japanese out of most of Honan, Hupeh, and Hunan Provinces, and were now on the verge of liberating the city of Nanchang to the south. He told of the American victories at Guam, Wake and Iwo Jima Islands, and of the British victories in Burma (Myanmar) and Malayia (Malaysia). It appeared that the Nips were on the run everywhere. This was exciting and welcomed news. Perhaps the war would be over in another year or two, but this would not be soon enough for Kay and friends. They were determined to make their way back to their families in the states, come hell or high water, and they had already experienced plenty of both.

That very day, Major Cheng received some bad news that sent him hastening home. His youngest son, about five, had died suddenly while he was away. Kay offered his condolences and Major Cheng was given leave to hurry home to be with his family. General Chang said he would take care of the escapees while Major Cheng was on leave, and prepared beds for them in his upstairs office

General Chang offered to take them into the nearby city across the lake, Shih-Chung (Zhichang). Anxious to see the surrounding countryside, the escapees accepted his offer and they were rowed across the lake to a dock on the opposite shore, then walked about two miles into the city. There were no Japanese soldiers in Shih-Chung. General Chang's troops had driven them out after a fierce battle some months back, but the Japs burned and sacked parts of the city before they left. General Chang wanted to show off the reconstruction projects underway, mostly funded by the British and American governments and private charities. Construction seemed to be ongoing throughout the city.

A large cathedral in the center of town was missing most of its red tiled roof, and workers swarming over rickety bamboo scaffolds labored to repair it. General Chang explained that this was a "Christian" church, and the Japs had dynamited the interior. The explosion blew out the stained glass windows and destroyed most of the roof. Every bit of stained glass had been carefully recovered from the rubble and was laid out on the bare floor of the church as artisans reconstructed the precious windows. Chang went on to explain that most of Shih-Chung citizens were Christian. The Chinese pastor often spoken out against Jap atrocities committed in his parish. Before they blew up the church, Japanese officers murdered the pastor and nailed his corpse to the front door. [As the war concluded, the Japanese officers responsible for this atrocity were captured in Soochow, tried and hanged by the Nationalist Government.] Now that General Chang's troops had freed the city from Japanese control, an American missionary was reportedly on the way to take the martyred pastor's place, and the parishioners wanted the church to be finished before he arrived.

Chang emphasized that if the Japs ever tried to retake the city, the townsfolk would fight to the death rather than allow any Nips into Shih-Chung, and the citizens were well armed and prepared to defend themselves. Chiang Kai-shek's plan for repatriating China was to defeat the Japanese army city by city, and then after a city was repatriated, arm the citizens and make them responsible for defending it. This was the present status of Shih-Chang, where every man carried a weapon of some sort, even while he worked. Most had carbines or pistols, and some even shouldered tommy-guns.

General Chang openly expressed his contempt and hatred for the Japanese army, and no one could blame him. Everywhere they went in the city, folks would stop and bow to General Chang. It was clear that he was revered as a liberating hero in these parts.

There was no large machinery at the construction sites, no cranes, no cement mixers, and no "dozers." No power tools were evident either, for the city had no electricity. In fact, few cities in interior China and almost no rural areas were electrified before the war. All work was accomplished by hand with picks and shovels, pulleys, ropes and hammers. Bamboo scaffolding and brute human strength substituted for cranes. Very few trucks or buses operated in the fuel-poor city. With no gasoline available, the few trucks and buses they did see were either fueled by grain alcohol, or by a coal generator. The coal generator worked by heating coal in a container and burning the resulting methane. Workers swarmed over the various construction projects like bees around a hive.

It was a very hot day, and the canal that flowed alongside the town walls looked inviting. Kay, Bill, and Tommy slipped off their shirts and trousers and jumped in for a swim. Soon, dozens of men, women and children gathered on the banks to watch them swim. As before, the Chinese seemed fascinated with the Englishmen's swimming techniques. They giggled, and pointed at the Englishmen's hairy bodies. It was a bit embarrassing, but Kay, Tommy, and Bill put on a show for them.

A traveling tent circus was visiting town, and after their swim, General Chang treated them to the show. Chang was a "guest of the city" and certainly did not have to pay to enter the tent. No one would have asked him for admission, but to save face he gave the proprietor CRB500 (about ten cents, U.S.) for each person. Inside the tent, shafts of sunlight shone through countless unpatched tears and holes and daubed the center ring with natural spotlights. The center ring sandpit was contained by a low wall surrounded by wooden bleachers. Every seat in the tent was close to the action and every seat was taken. The troop manager led General Chang and his entourage to a row of ground level highback upholstered chairs, evidently reserved for dignitaries, and designed as the best seats in the house.

The show consisted mostly of acrobatics. Tumbling, juggling, knife throwing and magic tricks were featured. Three trained panda bears performed various tricks, and three white Siberian tigers did the bidding of a trainer. Colorfully costumed dancers pranced about the ring to the accompaniment of a three-piece Chinese orchestra. These musicians were not particularly talented and did nothing to improve Kay's opinion of Chinese music. One thing Kay never grew to appreciate in his years in China, was Chinese music. He called it "orchestrated noise."

The many children in attendance especially enjoyed the show, squealing, laughing, and clapping continuously. It amazed Kay that in the midst of a war and Japanese occupation, such a troupe of traveling entertainers could make a living. The audience seemed to enjoy every minute of the performance.

After the circus, they went shopping in the downtown portion of the city. It was like a huge flea market, crowded with hundreds of tables and stalls each loaded with every item imaginable for sale. Multitudes of exotic cooking smells and a pall of hazy smoke drifted over the marketplace. Vendors attempted to attract the attention of shoppers by waving their arms and shouting that they had this or that for sale. They reminded Kay of the "bull pen" in the Chicago Futures Market. Unrestrained children ran down the street and in and out of the various stalls. Many of the stalls sold small honey cakes and other baked goods. Other stalls and tables were covered with all descriptions of fried foodstuffs and fresh vegetables, melons, fruit and baskets of grain. Cages of live chickens, ducks, geese, and even a few dogs were offered for sale. Piles of fresh-water shrimp and fish of all descriptions lay filleted in pans awaiting purchase for the evening dinner table. Hordes of flies swarmed about the tables and covered the food so that the sellers spent most of their time chasing them off with large hand fans to allow potential customers to inspect their goods.

Several tables were brimming with samurai swords, knives, daggers, pistols, rifles, and even a .50 caliber machine gun, no doubt captured from the Japanese army. Kay still had the CRB2,000 that

Liu had given him, and spied a beautifully carved ivory handle dagger for CRB750, complete with a handsome leather sheath. He purchased it for the asking price, but later General Chang suggested that he should have bargained the owner down somewhat and not paid such an exorbitant price. Kay figured that fifteen cents U.S. was bargain enough for such a beautiful and useful knife, but Chang said that it was expected for buyers to negotiate a price, and somewhat of an insult if a buyer did not attempt to do so.

General Chang bought packages of dried fruit, hard candy and honey cakes. They walked together along the paved canal pathway that led back to the dock and exchanged foodstuffs. The weather was gorgeous; however, an autumn chill blew in from the lake as the sun dipped below the horizon. The path topped a canal levee that led from town to the lake. The levee wall was raised only a few feet above the canal and rice paddies and was constructed from blocks of granite so intricately laid end-to-end that not even a piece of paper could have been inserted between them. After a leisurely walk of less than an hour, they arrived at Lake Tamil boat landing where one of Chang's soldiers was waiting in a sampan to row them over to headquarters.

September 11, 1944, General Chang Headquarters

The next morning, General Chang took Kay, Bill, and Tommy on an inspection tour of his headquarters. They visited the barracks, officers' quarters, and various training areas of the camp. Chang's troops assembled in the parade field surrounded by the barracks for inspection. Chang was very particular about the care of weapons, and as he inspected the troops, he meticulously inspected each soldier's weapon. If he spied even a millimeter of dust, he thrust the weapon back into the poor soldier's hands and yelled something in Chinese that even Kay could not decipher.

Although the camp was well camouflaged to look like a normal Chinese farm, Kay was amazed that such a facility was right under the noses of the Japanese Army. From the mainland, the island was accessible only by boat. Chang kept a well-armed gunboat moored at the dock and staffed a twenty-four-hour observation tower to thwart any possible Japanese attack. Chang took them to his quarters and introduced them to his wife, a very young and beautiful Eurasian woman who warmly greeted them. The General took pride in showing off his collection of Japanese samurai swords displayed in his ground-floor office.

That evening at dinner, Chang told the fugitives that their travels must be delayed for several days, as his informants warned that there was considerable Japanese activity in the countryside between Lake Tamil and the Chekiang Mountains. It would be too dangerous to travel across Chekiang Province until this activity died down. However, it would be safe for them to go to Linghu in the morning. Linghu was the largest city in the vicinity, across the lake and about eighteen miles down river from camp. Chang had business there, and he assured them that there were no Japanese soldiers in Linghu or the countryside around it. In fact, Linghu was in Chiang-Kai-shek army control. This would be a big outing for them, about a five-hour trip by sampan. The General introduced them to his adjutant, a Major Ling who was to accompany them to Linghu.

September 12, 1944, Linghu

Early the following morning after breakfast, Bill, Tommy and Kay went down to the dock to board the sampan along with General Chang, his wife, and Major Ling. Two other sampans filled with armed soldiers were ready to escort them. Major Ling had a square bundle under his arm. When Kay seemed curious about Ling's bundle, the Major took off some of the brown wrapping paper and revealed a bundle of cash. Ling said that there was CRB150,000 inside! Kay asked him why he had so much cash.

"Pate hsien-sheng, do you know where we are going?" Ling asked.

"Sure, we are going to Linghu," Kay answered.

Ling smiled. "Well, this bundle is for shopping and a day of pleasure."

Ling, Tommy, Kay, Bill and General Chang and his wife climbed aboard the middle sampan along with three armed soldiers and two coolies to row the sampan.

Around noontime, they arrived at the Linghu dock and went into the city to the local teahouse, where they were introduced to the local "number one," General Chen Dah Yoh. General Chen had a personal bodyguard of six soldiers each armed with tommy guns. Kay asked why bodyguards were necessary if there were no Japanese soldiers in Linghu. Ling explained that to "keep face." this was necessary for such a big General. After all, Chan reported directly to Chiang Kai-shek himself.

"This is expected!" Ling said with an air of finality.

They were served a scrumptious lunch, and the usual Leh-Chu (Chinese wine) was poured. General Chen asked Kay if he drank wine, and he said that he would enjoy some wine, although he occasionally preferred beer. The General said something to one of his soldiers who scurried out of the teahouse. Ten minutes later, the soldier returned, poured a bottle of U.B. Beer into Kay's glass, and set a second and third bottle in front of him. Kay overheard the soldier tell Chen that this was the entire stock of beer in Linghu. Surprisingly, the beer was chilled. Chinese hospitality at its finest and Kay drank all three bottles.

Afterwards they visited a barbershop for a haircut and shave, the first professional grooming they had since they were imprisoned at Lunghwa. Bill was amazed that there would be a barbershop in Linghu. When General Chen entered the shop, all four chairs were occupied, but as soon as the customers saw the General and his entourage, they all jumped out of their chairs and offered them to the new arrivals.

A scruffy beard that could hide tomorrow's lunch covered much of Kay's face. He was delighted to have a shave and haircut. Tommy's salt and pepper beard was matted and his unkempt hair made him look like a wild man from Borneo. He was glad to be rid of his beard, but kept his mustache. Bill did not have a lot of hair on his head or face, but a haircut and shave was definitely needed. All during their visit to the barber, General Chen's bodyguards stood guard outside. Kay thought there was more to this than the necessity for the General to "save face," so to speak. Kay wondered why the guards looked so uneasy and suspected Chen had not told them everything.

After their visit to the barber, all three looked and felt like new men. General Chen and his wife took them to a haberdashery, where he purchased new shirts and pants, a lightweight zipper-jacket and leather hiking boots and wool socks for each of them. The General said that they would need such clothing and footwear to cross over the mountains. The guerrillas were not only providing food and accommodations, now they were clothing them as well. How wonderful and generous these people were to three British civilians.

After they returned to camp, Kay developed a pounding headache and upset stomach. He felt too miserable to do anything but lay on his cot between trips to the lavatory. Neither Bill nor Tommy was sick, so Kay suspected that his illness was due to the Chinese beer. He regretted drinking all three bottles; however, by the next morning he awoke feeling one hundred percent better. This was the only time on the whole trip that Kay was sick. Unfortunately, Bill and Tommy were not to have such good luck.

One day merged into the next as they waited to resume their journey. General Chang said that the Japanese Army was still very active along their proposed route and unfortunately, they would have to wait. Each day, the three of them would walk a mile or so down the canal towpath that bisected the island to a camelback, stone bridge that spanned the canal. From the top of the bridge they could look out across the rice paddies and Mulberry fields of the island to the snow-covered Chekiang Mountains or "Mountains of the Moon" that dominated the southwestern horizon.

This particular bridge was special. With a blue sky above and the clear water flowing underneath with fish visible in the shallows, it became a favorite spot to visit each day. The countryside was so peaceful and serene and the people so friendly that they fell in love with the Tamil Lake area. Often they asked to be taken by sampan across the lake and walked the path into Shih-Chung to visit the local teahouse, where they soon became regular celebrities. Kay wished that some day he could bring Lil and Darryl back to this very spot and introduce them to the people of Shih-Chung and the beauty of the surrounding Lake Tamil countryside.

Bill woke one morning not feeling very chipper and visited the General's doctor, Dr. Tung, who gave him some injections. Dr. Tung knew Kay's family doctor in Shanghai, Dr. Hu, who was a first class doctor. Dr. Tung said that he had studied under Dr. Hu at the Paulun

Hospital in Shanghai; therefore, Kay knew that Dr. Tung must be a first-class doctor. Tommy also developed a fever during their stay at Tamil and visited Dr. Tung. He diagnosed that Tommy had a case of recurring malaria. Tommy thought he had probably contracted this parasite while in prison camp in the Philippines, yet this was the first severe bout he had experienced with the disease. Malaria is an insidious disease and it would continue to infect Tommy at various times throughout their journey and for many years to come. Dr. Tung gave him quinine and sulfanilamide, but the drugs did not seem to help much. Tommy would be fine during the day, but each evening he developed a fever and chills and could only lie in bed with several layers of covers over him. It was fortunate that this illness developed at General Chang's headquarters rather than on their flight from Lunghwa. Had Tommy been sick in the delta, it would have been difficult for them to make any headway at night.

At General Chang Bang—fee Headquarters September 11, 1944
L-R: Bill Henry, Kay Pate, Gen. Chang, Tommy Crosthwaite,
Major X

After the visit to the barbershop and in new clothes, the three escapees looked like well-groomed civilized Brits again. General Chang had his personal photographer travel to camp to take their pictures with the General and his staff. The photographer showed them pictures he had taken of the Murray-Kidd fugitives when they visited this same place weeks earlier. He gave them a copy of these pictures along with those he took and developed of Kay, Bill, Tommy, General Chang Bang-fee, and Major X. Major "X" was an interesting, if somewhat enigmatic fellow. Kay called him Major "X" because he never gave them his Chinese name. He was slightly rotund as Chinese go, and never wore a uniform, preferring the loose pajamas worn by rural Chinese. Kay guessed that he was a member of the communist faction operating in Kwangtung Province. Kay's supposition was based on a few comments the Major expressed in praise of Mao Zedong, along with his Cantonese dialect and aversion to wearing a Nationalist officer's uniform.

The photographs became treasured souvenirs of their days with the guerrillas.

They each wrote letters to their families while at camp, but had no way of mailing them. One of the General's spies frequently infiltrated Kashing and even Shanghai on occasion. He offered to take their letters with him to Shanghai and mail them to their relatives in the U.S. He even claimed that he could smuggle a letter from Kay to his mother in Lunghwa. Kay was relieved that Lil and his mother would finally know that he had made it safely to sanctuary.

September 16, 1944

The fugitives had been guests of General Chang for six long days and it became apparent to the General that his wards were not only anxious to move on but seemed bored. As it was still unsafe for them to continue their trip southwest across Chekiang Province, he invited them to accompany Major Ling and Major "X" on a planned raid north toward the city of Soochow. Tommy was still recovering from his bout with malaria and was not yet fit to travel thus he remained in camp. Kay and Bill were each issued Czech Bren guns with an extra twenty-five round curved clip.

Anxious for adventure, at the first hint of dawn they climbed into a sampan with Major Ling, and accompanied by forty-five solders in six other sampans paddled across Lake Tamil. The pre-dawn morning was crisp and the fading stars shone bright despite the faint glow of the morning sky. Kay looked toward the sunrise in the east and caught a green flash of light just before the sky changed to the orange-red tint of the emerging sun. As the sun rose over the hills, it tinted the wisps of tule fog rising off the lake with a reddish hue. The flotilla passed a dozen sampans, each with two fishermen. Some fished with long bamboo poles while others dipped large nets into the limpid water. The smell of decaying algae and fish assaulted their nostrils as their sampans reached the shore-line then paddled north up the delta of the Tamil River toward the lake country of Lake Taihu, a forty mile wide lake due west of Shanghai. Hundreds of small lakes, many interconnected by canals, dotted the Taihu countryside. They paddled along the canals from lake to lake until noontime, when they beached their boats and marched across open fields toward the small town of Luhu, where Major Ling intended to attack a Japanese ammunition depot. They broke up into two platoons, an advance party consisting of a dozen soldiers led by Major X, and a larger contingent commanded by Major Ling. Major X and his troops marched down a dry riverbed a few hundred yards in front of Major Ling. Bill and Kay remained with Major Ling and his troops. The riverbed was cluttered with room size boulders and defined by steep banks on either side. As Major X and his troops rounded a bend, they were met head-on by a Japanese patrol of a dozen men. The Japanese soldiers, unaware of the larger contingent of guerrillas following behind, opened fire with sub-machine guns as Major X and his soldiers ducked behind boulders and returned fire.

Upon hearing the gunfire, Ling shouted a charge and the guer-rillas ran toward Major X and his soldiers shooting at the Japs as they went. When they saw Ling's troops, the Japanese realized that they had blundered and now were greatly outnumbered. They turned and sought refuge in a group of boulders fifty yards upriver from the guerrillas. Kay and Bill ducked behind a large boulder as bullets and ricochets flew everywhere. Not wanting to miss any of the action, Bill kept peeking around the boulder.

"Bill, keep your damned fool head down," Kay warned as a Jap bullet whizzed passed Bill's head and hit the boulder just above Kay sending shards of granite flying in all directions. Bill ducked back down and apologized for his recklessness.

Ling directed five of his troops to go back down river climb up the bank and fire on the Japanese from above. When the snipers opened up on the Japs below them, the Japs broke and ran for additional cover further up the river. Kay watched in horror as Bill bolted from behind their boulder and ran after the retreating Japanese soldiers. He charged down the gully like a mad man, jumping from river rock to river rock, Bren gun blazing as he went. It was like a scene from some John Wayne war movie. Four Japanese soldiers felled by bullets from Bill's gun or from the snipers above fell headlong into the riverbed. Severely wounded, they lay dying as their blood soaked into the sand. Bill soon came upon the withering, gasping soldiers, pointed his gun at them, and opened fire until he had expended all remaining rounds from his Bren cartridge. Ling's troops charged past Bill, chased down the remnants of the Japanese patrol, and shot every one of them.

Kay caught up to Bill who remained standing over the Jap soldiers with his smoking gun in hand. The soldiers stopped twitching and lay in an ever-increasing pool of blood. Greatly disturbed by a side of Bill he didn't realize existed, Kay was unable to say anything but placed his hand on Bill's trembling shoulder.

"God damned rotten son-of-a-bitch Nips!" Bill mumbled. "I hope you all rot in hell!"

Major Ling walked back from the scene of carnage upriver and gawked at the still shaking Bill, who remained standing with his weapon still pointed at the dead soldiers.

"Lower your weapon," Ling commanded, "The dunghoak are all quite dead."

Bill followed Ling's command but remained standing over the dead Japs as if in a stupor.

Kay looked into Bills' blank face.

"Bill…are you all right?"

"Yeah, I'm alright…just getting even for some of those Lunghwa beatings."

Until this moment, Kay had not realized how much hatred Bill carried in his heart for Japanese soldiers. Those scabbard beatings had really effected him, much more than Kay had ever imagined.

Ling decided that it would be unwise to continue marching down the riverbed, and ordered everyone up on the bank. If the Jap patrol had been on the high ground when Major X came across them, Ling's troops could have been cut to ribbons.

They cautiously approached the town of Luhu, where a garrison of Japanese soldiers was reported bivouacked. From a small hillock west of town, they could clearly see the cement block building that housed the ammunition depot. Less than twenty yards away from the depot was a gray two-story barrack. Ling gathered his troops in a grove of trees one hundred and fifty yards from the depot and instructed Major X to take three soldiers with explosive filled back-packs, sneak up to the building, place the explosives next to the walls and light the fuses. Major X did as he was commanded and several minutes later returned to the grove.

"Everyone take cover," Major X said in Chinese. Kay understood the command, but Bill, not understanding Chinese remained standing until Kay pulled him down. A few seconds later the first backpack exploded, followed closely by a second and then a third. Kay looked through the trees as a large mushroom cloud of black smoke enveloped the depot. Then a brilliant flash of light was followed by a concussion that sucked the air from his lungs. Cement blocks from the building rose hundreds of feet into the sky and then rained down through the trees crashing dangerously close to Ling's troops. Like ants escaping from a disturbed anthill, Japanese troops ran through the archway leading into town and toward the burning remnants of the depot and barracks. Ling gave the order to retreat to the dry riverbed. The forty-five guerrillas made such a clamor as they crashed through the grove that only the confusion of the Jap soldiers prevented them from discovering Ling and his troops. Kay thought it would have made more sense to conduct this mission with a dozen troops rather than the forty-five that now ran back toward the riverbed. To Kay's utter amazement, none of the Japanese soldiers came after them. Kay surmised their ears were ringing from the explosion just as his were, and they were probably disoriented and unable to figure out who had caused the explosion and in which direction they had escaped.

It was imperative that the guerillas make a hasty retreat back to the sampans, as the explosion was certain to bring Japanese airplanes looking for the perpetrators. As they paddled across one of the small lakes a few miles from Luhu, they heard the drone of approaching aircraft.

"Here they come," Ling warned. "Take cover in the reeds alongside the shoreline." Fortunately, the lakeshore was covered by tall tule plants and bulrushes that provided adequate cover from the airplanes. They hid in the bulrushes as wave after wave of Jap Zeros flew over them at treetop level. Unable to spot the sampans, the airplanes continued toward Luhu. As soon as the drone of the Japanese airplanes faded, they paddled across the lake and into a canal that emptied into a larger lake, but one that was choked with weeds. This lake had no cover whatsoever, and had they been on this lake when the Japanese flew over, they certainly would have gained the attention of the Japanese pilots.

One hour later, while in the middle of a large lake just a few miles from the Tamil River that would lead them back to Lake Tamil, the Japanese airplanes returned. Ling shouted a command that Kay did not understand, but everyone stopped paddling, donned coolie hats and took hold of bamboo fishing poles. Bill and Kay did likewise. Several airplanes broke off from the main squadron and flew toward them. They made several close passes as Kay braced for the inevitable strafing that he was sure would follow. Yet, their masquerade as innocent Chinese fishermen successfully fooled the Japanese pilots, and after several flybys, the airplanes rejoined the main squadron.

Ling's armada arrived back at headquarters around dinnertime. General Chang met them at the dock, and told Ling that he had heard through his "bamboo grapevine" that they had successfully blown up a major weapons depot and the ensuing explosion had killed several dozen soldiers garrisoned in the barracks down the street from the depot. It was very satisfying to know that they had done such good work.

September 19, 1944, Lake Tamil Headquarters

The next day, a month to the day since the escapees cut the barbed wire at Lunghwa, General Chang said it was now safe to resume their journey, and suggested they do so that very evening. So much had transpired in the intervening month; their escape from Lunghwa, hiding in the rice paddies, all the close calls with the Japanese, the miracles and the wonderful help given to them by the Chinese farmers and missionaries, finding the guerrillas, and the hospitality of General Chang Bang-fee and the raid on Luhu. Through all this turmoil, their real protector had been the Almighty, who had steadfastly remained with them and for this, they would be forever grateful.

The fugitives warmly thanked Ling and General Chang and his wife for their hospitality and kindness. Kay, Bill, and Tommy along with their two new guides piled into the middle sampan of three in the convoy. The other two boats were filled with armed soldiers. As Kay shook hands with the General, Chang pressed CRB2,000 into his hand for each of them.

"For incidentals along the way," Chang said in Chinese. "God go with you."

Then Chang handed Tommy a brand new torch (flashlight) and Bill a Swiss Army pocketknife.

Kay pondered the adventures of the past month as their yulo-hing glided across Lake Tamil and toward the main river delta that emptied out of the lake. He said a prayer of thanks to God for their delivery to these good Chinese soldiers. It all seemed like a bad dream. Tommy was sick again so he curled up in the bottom of the sampan and they covered him with a thick wool quilt that Ling had lent him. They worried about Tommy and the strenuous journey that they were about to undertake. He would need all his strength to make it, and Kay prayed that the quinine and sulfa would give him some relief from the malaria. Despite their vow back in Lunghwa that should any one of them be unable to continue, the other two would go on without the disabled member, neither Kay nor Bill even considered leaving Tommy with General Chang. After what they endured together as a team, it was "all or none."

As they crossed the lake, the snow-covered Chekiang Mountains or "Mountains of the Moon," only twenty miles southwest of Lake Tamil were clearly visible. The mountains reflected in the water and shimmered in the fading twilight. Beyond these mountains lay the great central Chinese interior, Changshan, Chungking and Nationalist China.

The Yangtze River that flowed across Szechwan Province and cut a deep canyon (Three Gorges) through the mountains as it rushed from Tibet to the ocean would have been a good route to take to Chungking, but travel upriver was not only difficult but also heavily patrolled by Japanese gunboats. They had long since decided not to go to Chungking and would now proceed instead across Chekiang Province to Yushan through Changshan. However, they faced the challenge of how to cross over the Chekiang Mountains that loomed before them. Kay had no idea how this would be done, for the mountains looked forbidding. Nevertheless, the guerrillas had a plan. Kay was comfortable to leave things in their capable hands, and God's of course.

CHAPTER SIX

The Mountains of the Moon

September 20, 1944, Loshechen

As dawn broke, they found themselves on the outskirts of Loshechen, a city that had been recently cleared of Japanese troops. The sampans plied the town's waterways and finally docked at the far end of town, where one of General Chang's representatives, Lieutenant Sui Sang, met them and led them to a "safe house" where lunch was served. While at lunch, Kay overheard his guides and Lieutenant Sui arguing about money. It seemed that the money necessary for their trip had not yet arrived, and they would have to stay overnight until it was delivered in the morning.

Lieutenant Sui and an escort took them to an open-air theatre that evening. Kay had once attended a Chinese play, and knew that they go on, and on, but had forgotten how mind numbing the performances could be. The banging of cymbals, honking of horns and squealing Chinese violins continued throughout the entire performance. The typical Chinese costumes were intricate and very beautiful, but the play went on non-stop for five solid hours. Tommy and Bill, neither of whom understood Chinese, had enough after two hours and asked the escort to take them back to the safe house. However, out of politeness Kay remained with Lieutenant Sui until the play ended. Neither Bill nor Tommy was feeling very well, and their apologies were quickly accepted. The play finally concluded in a soul-destroying fanfare, which was none too soon for Kay. Although interesting, one of these plays is enough to last a lifetime, and now Kay had experienced two. When he arrived back at the safe house, Bill and Tommy were soundly asleep on their door beds. One of the escorts had given Tommy an opium pill, which had done wonders for him. Kay climbed into his bed with the "music" from the play still ringing in his head. He didn't sleep very well that night, and was up at dawn.

September 20, 1944, Tehtsing

After breakfast, the pledged money appeared and they shoved off in a single sampan with two new guides and two coolie rowers. They rowed toward the town of Tehtsing, arriving there around noontime and tied up at the dock. The guides said they had some business in town, and Kay and his friends should wait at dockside until they returned. They sat on a waterfront bench and watched the coming and goings in the harbor. It was a very busy place, with many freight barges and sampans waiting to be loaded and unloaded. When the guides had not returned after two hours, Kay took a short walk into town to search for them. He finally found them shopping in the town marketplace. Each guide was loaded down with several packages. They evidently had been shopping while their charges waited for them at the dock! Kay was very annoyed with such thoughtless behavior and suspected that these two were spending the travel money on a shopping spree. These two were certainly not up to scratch in the guiding department, as Kay was to discover later.

Kay went back to the dock and fetched Tommy and Bill for some lunch at a local restaurant. The word had gotten around town that there were foreigners visiting and soon after they sat down to eat, the restaurant filled with Chinese, who stood around and gawked as the foreigners ate lunch. The crowd just stood there, first on one foot, then the other and stared and stared. No one said a word, not even to each other.

In the middle of their meal, a well-dressed elderly man came over to their table and asked in Chinese if he could join them. Kay invited him to do so and offered to share a spot of tea and biscuits. The man did not introduce himself and unlike most Chinese, asked many questions. Kay was reluctant to share important information with a total stranger and politely evaded his probing questions. They explained that they were businessmen from Shanghai on their way to Changshan, and were only passing through Tehtsing. Seemingly satisfied, the man wished them well, got up from the table and bowed, then left the restaurant. Their guides passed him as he left the restaurant. They had finally finished their shopping spree or ran out of money and had come to join their charges for lunch. They explained later that the man was actually the Taipan or Chief of Police of the city, which would account for his inquisitive nature. The police officer made Kay quite nervous, as he had been warned that there were many Wang Ching-wei soldiers in Tehtsing. He was concerned that the Taipan might be in collaboration with them. Kay told the guides that they had best leave, but they just smiled and continued eating apparently without a care in the world. Kay motioned to Bill and Tommy to leave the restaurant and they began the walk back to the harbor.

"The hell if we should wait for these two gadflies to leisurely eat their lunch. For all we know, the local Wang Ching-wei solders are looking for us," Kay said.

They were passing through the town plaza on the way back to the dock when they heard a commotion coming from one of the cobbled side streets. Bugles blared and people murmured as a procession of a dozen Chinese soldiers dressed in ceremonial garb and proceeded by six buglers marched down the street. The soldiers led two barefoot prisoners, a young man, and a young woman, toward the city square. Each was dressed in long white gowns, their hands were tied behind their backs, and they were blindfolded. The unfortunate prisoners were tethered with ropes around their waists and placards hung about their necks proclaiming their crimes. Kay was unable to decipher the Chinese characters on the placards, but one looked like the character for bandit. Everyone on the street shifted to one side or the other to make a path for the procession. The soldiers carried long swords and looked very grim. Their hapless captives stumbled down the street as one of the soldiers struck them on their backsides to hurry them along. As they passed by, the woman looked especially frail and could have only been a teenager. The man also looked very young.

Had any of them been fully aware of what was to come next, he and his companions would have made a hasty retreat back to the dock. However, curiosity got the better of them and they joined a crowd of men, women and children gathering about the plaza as the poor unfortunates were dragged to the center of the square and forced to kneel. One soldier pushed the woman's head down exposing a long graceful neck and gathered her long hair as a second soldier with a broadsword stepped forward. With a swish of the sword and a dull thud the woman's head rolled onto the ground. The execution was quickly repeated and the man's head rolled beside hers. One of the soldiers picked up the bloody decapitated heads by the hair and displayed them to the crowd that stood in hushed silence.

Kay, Bill, and Tommy were stunned by the public beheadings and totally shocked to witness such a grisly incident. Tommy choked back his lunch. Bill commented that life was cheap in China. Kay looked away from the gruesome scene and noticed a soldier giving him a close look-see. Such scrutiny made Kay feel very uncomfortable, and he entertained the notion that some of the soldiers in the crowd could be puppet troops. He instructed the guides, who had caught up with them and seemed to be enjoying the beheadings, to get them out of town as fast as possible. Loaded down with packages, the guides could only trot back to the dock and the escapees arrived back at the dock way ahead of their guides. The coolies who had remained dockside climbed aboard the sampan with Kay, Bill, and Tommy and waited for the guides to arrive. When they finally did, there was barely enough room in the sampan to accommodate the guides and their many packages.

The coolies rowed away from the city, down the waterway that coursed lazily westward for thirty miles until it merged with a major river that the guides said flowed north past Huchow, and into Lake Taihu. It was twilight as the coolies struggled upstream toward the city of Anki located alongside the banks of the river. As they approached the outskirts of Anki, their guides warned that the Japanese controlled Anki and they should put on their coolie hats and be very quiet as they rowed through the main part of the city. The main bridge connecting the northern and southern sections of Anki was an impressive five span granite structure graced on either end by high parapets. It must have been a very old bridge, because trees were growing from the flood water bastions. Japanese soldiers guarded each end of the bridge, and a sandbag barrier partially blocked the center span. Several soldiers were busy inspecting farm carts and searching passersby at the mid-span checkpoint.

Two soldiers leaned over the railing to give Kay's sampan a closer look see in the dim light. As the flotilla neared the bridge, one of the soldiers shone a powerful light on the lead sampan. Seconds later, the soldiers were distracted by a commotion that had erupted at the mid-span checkpoint. The other soldiers had over-turned a vegetable cart, and watermelons, cabbage and turnips spilled onto the bridge, rolled across the roadway, and splashed into the river. They passed beneath the bridge and out the other side without being challenged.

They rowed along the river all night finally stopping at daybreak at a large villa that once belonged to the provincial governor. After breakfast at the villa, they continued upriver well into the afternoon and eventually the sampan entered a narrow canal barely wide enough to accommodate the boats. One coolie rowed with a "yuloh" or large oar in the stern, while the other coolie guided their sampan by means of a second yuloh in the bow.

After a mile or so, they landed near a Buddhist temple and disembarked. The temple sat on a small hill in the shade of a huge Banyan tree, the largest Banyan Kay had ever seen. It covered almost a full acre of temple grounds that extended well beyond the Banyan into the distance. One of the guides went to a nearby town to purchase the evening meal and returned few minutes later with two coolies each carrying a large high-sided wooden tray protected by a woven hemp cover. Inside were cups of "Ba-oze" (pork chopped and steamed in dough balls with hot spice), a North Chinese delicacy and delicious! They ate their meal under the Banyan tree and the temple priests brought out steaming bowls of rice and green tea to complement the meal.

After dinner, they stretched their legs with a short walk around the extensive temple grounds. The grounds were gorgeous, arrayed with flowers of every description, groundcover, and well-manicured ornamental shrubs. A brook meandered throughout the garden,

finally cascading over large river stones, and splashing into a colorful carp-filled pond covered by purple, white and red Lotus flowers.
Four flat-stone paths wound around the grounds finally terminating
at each corner of the temple located in the center of the gardens. It
was a marvelous Chinese garden and one to be remembered.

Kay walked up one of the paths leading to the temple, took off
his canvas shoes, and climbed the eight steps that led into the structure. It was dark inside, a stark contrast with the bright sunlit garden
outside. The temple smelled of incense, and when Kay's eyes
adjusted to the dim light, he gazed upon a large golden Buddha that
dominated the center of the temple. The corpulent Buddha sat
cross-legged on a raised platform covered with red silk cloth. It was
an imposing statue, about fifteen feet high and looked down on Kay
with an inscrutable, erudite smile. Kay lit an incense stick and
placed it on the platter in front of the Buddha. He stood there gazing
at the Buddha until Tommy called to him from outside.

"Come on Kay, its time to go!"

Kay bowed, said a quick prayer, and joined the others waiting
for him outside. The sun was setting behind the temple, which now
took on a golden glow in the fading sunlight. Although a good motor
road ran from Anki all the way to Yutsien, it was heavily patrolled
by the Japanese. From this point forward, the journey would have to
be on foot, cross-country and away from busy, well-patrolled roads.
The goal was to arrive at a safe house in the foothills by midnight;
about a twenty-mile walk westward from the temple.

The coolies suspended the guides' many packages on bamboo
poles across their shoulders and everyone walked single file along a
narrow crosscountry path. The countryside was a checkerboard of
Mulberry groves interspersed with small rice paddies fed by countless small creeks and canals. After walking at a quick pace for over
an hour, the path suddenly came to a blacktop highway. This was
the main highway between Soochow and Hweichow; both important Japanese-held cities. The guides warned that considerable
motorcar traffic used this route and they should expect Japanese
patrols at any time. Sugarcane fields bordered the road, so they
waited hidden by the cane while one of the guides hurried across
the highway to a secluded spot where he had a clear view up and

down the highway. To prevent ambushes, the Japanese had cleared all trees and vegetation from the sides of the highway forming a swath fifty yards wide on either side. In addition, deep drainage ditches paralleled both sides of the highway. The escapees were faced with a one hundred and thirty-yard dash across the no-man's land, across the highway and two ditches all in highly visible open space. The idea was to wait until the guide indicated the coast was clear, then one by one each person was to make a mad dash for the safety of the cane field on the other side of the highway.

The guide remained motionless in the cane field across the highway as a convoy of Japanese trucks passed by, followed by several motorcycles, and then more trucks. Less than a minute later, several more Japanese trucks sped down the road from the opposite direction. This indeed was a very busy highway. They waited patiently for a signal from the guide. Finally, he stood up and waved for the first and second ones to come across. Bill ran across first, quickly followed by Tommy. They both disappeared into the cane field on the opposite side just as another Japanese truck came speeding down the road. Kay waited for his turn, and when the guide signaled, he ran across the ditches and blacktop to the cane field just as a motorcycle came roaring down the road. He made it into the canes and breathlessly waited and prayed that the motorcycle driver had not spied him. Thankfully, the cycle roared past without even slowing. Finally, it was the coolies turn, and loaded down with all the guides' bundles, it would take longer for them to cross. Traffic continued to pass in two or three minute intervals. Kay was surprised to see so much traffic until the guide explained that the guerrillas had been giving the Japanese a lot of trouble in Nanchang so the Japs were very much on alert. Many soldiers had been reassigned from Shanghai into Hupeh and Chekiang Provinces to help put down the insurgency.

"This is just great," Kay brooded. "As soon as we escape Lunghwa, a major battle erupts in the very province we must pass through, and we now find ourselves right in the middle of the muck."

Finally, the remaining guide and then the coolies were motioned to cross over. As the first coolie crossed the blacktop, he dropped one of his packages right in the middle of the highway and continued running into the cane field. As the second coolie ran across, he bent over and tried to pick up the dropped package, but pair of motorcycles were swiftly approaching and, already burdened with his own load, he couldn't seem to find room for anything else. He abandoned the package and ran into the cane field.

"Damn these guides and their bloody packages, they are going to get us caught," Bill whispered.

The motorcycles came roaring down the highway and stopped alongside of the abandoned package. One of the soldiers bent over and picked it up, tearing off the brown wrapping as he did so. The package contained an army parka, and the soldier held it up across his shoulders to see if it would fit him. As he admired his find, another convoy was approaching, so apparently assuming the package had fallen off a truck, the two motorcyclists speed off down the road.

They all hurried away from the highway, crossed over a wide canal on a camelback bridge, then followed the towpath alongside the canal. The guide said that it was about fifteen miles through Jap infested country before they arrived at the safe house outside Jap held territory. They would have to move fast and be very quiet.

They walked and walked until their legs began to ache. As it grew dark and without his glasses (another breadcrumb left along the way), Tommy had a difficult time seeing the path. They were moving fast, almost at a trot. Narrow trenches crossed the path every so often to allow water to flow from one paddy to the next, and in the dim light, Tommy kept tripping over these trenches. Several times, he ended up on his hands and knees. Kay's night vision was better than Tommy's, so he went in front and whispered "hole" every time they came across one of these trenches. In this way, Tommy was able to keep pace and not trip over a ditch.

A few miles later, the towpath abruptly ended, and a dirt path continued on top of a four-foot high levee. As they walked along, they heard voices drifting from across the canal. In the dim moonlight Kay could make out the outline of Japanese soldiers encamped on top of the canal levee on the other side, only two hundred yards away. Kay could see the glow from Japanese cigarettes, a small campfire, and the flair of an occasional match. Their jabber and laughter floated across the canal. The guides motioned everyone to be very quiet. They breathed a sigh of relief when they were finally beyond the Japanese encampment, yet they still could see and hear Japanese patrols coming and going on the levee across the canal.

The levee path on their side of the canal crossed many narrow creeks and canals that were bridged by narrow catwalks constructed from six-foot long by two-foot wide slabs of granite positioned on top of granite blocks. One of these "bridges" had a gap about six inches wide between spans, and Tommy, unable to see it clearly, put one foot into the crack. His leg and knee jammed into the open space and he broke his finger as he fell forward. Kay helped him out of the gap, but poor Tommy had to hobble along and ignore the pain in his knee and finger. When they came to the next bridge, Kay whispered to Tommy that there was another gap ahead and to take care to avoid it. Without thinking, Tommy took his torch from his backpack and shone it on the bridge ahead of him.

"Put that bloody thing out!" Bill hissed.

Tommy immediately turned the flashlight off and everyone held their collective breath praying that the Japs on patrol across the canal had not seen Tommy's torch. After a few minutes, they realized that there would be no Jap response to Tommy's blunder. Thankfully, the runaways and their guides and coolies had not been spotted. Another small miracle to be thankful for. They climbed down the paddy side of the levee and stopped to catch their breath and have a smoke out of sight and hearing of the Japanese patrols. One of the guides was still very angry about the careless use of a flashlight and softly swore at Tommy non-stop for a couple of minutes. Tommy did not understand even one of these Chinese swear words, yet the guard's anger spoke volumes. In the course of the diatribe, Kay recognized references to many parts of the human anatomy and animal waste. No translation was necessary.

They continued to trot along towpaths and levees for what seemed like endless hours, until about two a.m. when footsore and weary they arrived at the safe house nestled in the foothills. They were overjoyed when the residents told them that the Japanese never came this far into the foothills, so they should relax. The usual door beds covered with futons had been set up for them on the verandah, and Kay fell asleep as soon as his head hit the pillow.

September 21, 1944, Fang-Chia-Tang

Up again at dawn, they washed as their host prepared breakfast, then strolled around the farmhouse property. The farm was located in the foothills of the Chekiang Mountains with a clear view of the checkerboard plateau that stretched eastward into the Shanghai delta country. The foothills were glorious, so different from the ubiquitous rice paddies and fields in the plateau below. Behind the farmhouse, terraced rice paddies climbed high up the hillside in row after row like gigantic steps. Trees dotted the slope in small groves along with large stands of bamboo and tall pampas grass. Water plunged from terrace to terrace and down cobblestone creeks plunging in misty waterfalls into the valley below. The sun attempted to rise over the mountain peaks but was shrouded by a haze of morning mist that refracted the rising sunlight into a rainbow of subtle colors. On a nearby terrace, a water buffalo strained to drag a wooden plough through the thick paddy mud, his master encouraging the animal's efforts with a long pole. Trailing the water buffalo and his driver, several women wearing large coolie hats planted young rice plants in the newly created ditch.

The closest village to the farm was Fang-Chia-Tang, and the farmer claimed that this village was in "No-Jap China." Evidently they had crossed over the border the previous night, and were now in Guoimndang. The soldiers they ran into the previous night were probably a contingent of border guards. From now on, there would be no Japanese soldiers or a possible bullet in the back or head to worry them. Well, not quite, the farmer warned. The cities of Hweichow to the north and Chuhsien to the south were still controlled by the Japanese Army, and Japanese patrols occasionally ventured deep into Guoimndang. They all would have to remain alert to this possibility.

After breakfast, they met Captain Tran of the Nationalist Chinese Army. He was to escort them on their next leg of the trek to the city of Yutsien. Captain Tran had considerable difficulty arranging for bearers, and raised quite a ruckus with the two guides, who should have gone into the village to hire coolies earlier that morning but had slept in. They pleaded with Tran that they had no money remaining with which to pay bearers. The captain refused to accept this excuse and berated them, for he knew that General Chang had given them sufficient funds for the entire trip. He demanded an accounting of the funds, but the guides were unable to do so. Kay remained silent throughout this dispute, although he had dark suspicions about the shopping spree the guards went on in Tehtsing. Except for the meal at the temple outside Anki, the food the guides purchased for them was limited to rice, cabbage and bean curd, or "coolie food" as Bill called it.

The packages that the guides had purchased on their shopping spree were piled in one corner of the room. The captain demanded to know what these bundles were and to whom they belonged. When the guides feigned ignorance, Captain Tran asked Kay if he knew anything about the packages. Kay simply said that the packages belonged to the guides. Captain Tran angrily tore open one of the packages and new clothes and trinkets fell out. Their guides were caught red handed, and finally admitted that they had purchased these packages in Tehtsing. The captain booted each of them in the rear and promised that General Chang would hear of their conduct, and the General would appropriately deal with such scoundrels personally. Then he turned to the farmer and asked him to distribute the packages to the poor folks of Fang-Chia-Tang.

They began the journey into the mountains with the guides, Captain Tran, and fifteen of his troops. Rather than hire additional porters, Tran made the crooked guides help the two coolies carry all the provisions, including Bill and Tommy's backpacks. The hike into the mountains was strenuous, up and down one hill after another, and the narrow path was covered in shale and shards of sharp rock. They gradually gained elevation, and stopped after the first hour for a rest and smoke.

Tommy, Bill, and Kay were not in top physical shape. Tommy was experiencing another bout with his fever and Bill's swollen knee and broken finger were giving him lots of pain. The blisters that Kay had developed between Szeking and Sunkiang were exacerbated by the previous night's forced march. They were painful and Kay was worried that they might become infected. When he took off his shoes to rub his sore feet, Tran noticed Kay's blisters, and took a small tin out of his backpack and rubbed a white salve on the wounds. Kay did not know what this medication was, but over the next few days his blisters healed miraculously. The fugitives were still wearing the same canvas shoes that they had worn since their Lunghwa escape.

Tran looked at their canvas shoes and said, "Shoes no good for mountains!"

They all changed to the socks and hiking boots that General Chang had purchased for them in Linghu. Kay chided himself for not changing shoes before they started into the mountains. Had he done so, his blisters probably would not have become worse.

They arrived at a large village where they stopped for lunch, then marched on for the entire afternoon, passing through the city of Huang-Pei. At dusk, they came to a large farmhouse that was the designated rest stop for the evening. A small stream ran alongside the farmhouse, and although the water was ice cold, they bathed, washed their clothes, and soaked their tired feet. Afterwards they felt quite refreshed and after supper had a good night's sleep.

September 22, 1944, Yutsien

The next day's hike into the mountains was arduous. The path was steep and narrow but despite their infirmities, they had to tramp on. Bill and Tommy were holding up progress, so the captain and three of his troops went on ahead to arrange for their next stay, leaving Kay and his friends in the care of their guides and the remainder of the troops. When they passed through the next village, the guides stayed behind to arrange for some "business" and said that they would catch up. Kay, Bill, and Tommy trudged on, accompanied by Tran's troops. The path climbed even higher into the mountains and seemed like it would never end. After a few hours, they were beginning to wonder how the guides would ever catch up with them when they sped by in sedan chairs. General Chang had said that when they arrived in the mountains, he had given the guides sufficient funds to hire sedan chairs for all of them. Kay assumed that the guides were broke as they had claimed, and could not afford such a luxury. Evidently the guides, undeterred by the reprimand from Tran the night before, were again pocketing funds by only hiring sedan chairs for themselves. Such behavior was certainly not typical for Generalissimo Chiang Kai-shek troops; nevertheless, these two scoundrels needed to be dealt with.

Kay decided not to confront the crooks, and would save his complaints for Captain Tran. On several occasions that day they caught up to the guides as they gave their coolies a rest beside the road. Two miles short of the village where Captain Tran had arranged to meet them; the guides sent their coolies back and marched along with everyone else into the village. Captain Tran met them at the village teahouse, where dinner was prepared. Kay, Bill, and Tommy staggered into the teahouse and collapsed onto a bench. Tran's soldiers looked equally exhausted, yet the guides looked remarkably fresh. This anomaly did not escape Captain Tran's attention, and he asked why it was that only the pair of scalawags weren't tired. They did not have a good answer, so he turned to Kay and asked what was going on.

Kay suggested to Tran that he should ask them about the sedan chairs. Tran became quite angry, made the pair strip down to their underwear, and searched their pockets and backpacks. He discovered almost CRB32,000 hidden in their pants and jackets. They had been holding out on everyone including Captain Tran. Such dishonesty and stupidity was about to cost them dearly. Tran placed them under arrest and the local constable locked them up in the village jail for the night. The next day Tran ordered four of his soldiers to take the pair in handcuffs into Yutsien to be dealt with by the local magistrate. Kay recalled the pair of thieves beheaded in Tehtsing Square, and hoped that such severe punishment would not befall their guides, although in his estimation they were no better than pond scum.

They arrived about 7 p.m. at the hotel in Yutsien where Captain Tran had arranged lodging for that night. Tommy was in bad shape, suffering with chills and a high fever, so they gave him a dose of quinine and immediately put him to bed. Although Kay and Bill were tired, stiff as ramrods and aching all over, they met Captain Tran and a young second lieutenant downstairs for dinner. The lieutenant was to guide them onto the next destination, Tangchaiwan. Captain Tran intended to remain behind and lodge charges against their two guides. Kay never caught the Chinese name of the young lieutenant, but they referred to him as "Charlie" from then on because he reminded Bill of Charlie Chan of Hollywood fame. Captain Tran gave Charlie the CRB32,000 he had confiscated from the dishonest guides. Charlie could only speak a few words of English and his Chinese dialect was neither Kyangsher nor Cantonese, thus their conversations were limited and Kay had to interpret for Tommy and Bill. Nevertheless, Charlie was a good traveling companion whose main interest was to look out for the well being of the three Brits.

September 23, 1944, Tangchaiwan

The next day, thirty-four days out of Lunghwa, Charlie arranged for rickshaws for the four of them, and they were on their way. They passed through the city of Hochiao and didn't stop the entire day except every hour to give the coolies a rest and to relieve themselves or have a smoke. They were met by General Ho Yang Ling when they arrived at the Government Rest House in Tangchaiwan. General Ho was the commander of all troops in eastern Chekiang Province, and as was the custom, he hosted them at dinner that evening. General Ho did not speak English, and his Chinese dialect was difficult for Kay to understand, but despite this impediment they managed a friendly and relaxed conversation.

He introduced them to the secretary of the government offices, who spoke excellent English and explained that they were to rest and stay for three days as the General's guests in Tangchaiwan. He arranged quarters for everyone at the guesthouse, and said his guests were to have ground floor accommodations, as the upstairs rooms had more bedbugs. Charlie accompanied them around town for the next three days and was a cheerful and welcomed companion.

Tangchaiwan, although not very large, was the first city they visited that was electrified and even had a daily newspaper. Kay purchased a paper and read the war news to his companions. It was mostly good news for the Allies and everyone but the Japanese and Germans could see that the end was in sight. It would just be a matter of time until the Americans invaded Japan, yet Kay knew that the Japanese people would never surrender their homeland to the Americans without a terrible and bloody fight. Every inch of Japan would have to be taken, and hundreds of thousands of lives would be lost in the process. Here in China, the fight would not be as terrible. Chiang Kai-shek was gaining strength and would eventually push the Japanese Army back into the South China Sea. The American Navy had severely crippled the Japanese fleet in the Battle of the Philippine Sea in June 1944, and the Americans held Guam and Okinawa.

September 24, 1944, Tangchaiwan

General Ho invited Kay, Bill, and Tommy to visit his villa in the hills above the city where he intended to host a dinner in their honor. That afternoon they traveled to his home with Charlie as their guide. The villa was a beautiful, red-roofed home located on a bluff that overlooked the entire city nestled in a valley about four miles wide. The red- tiled roofs of Tangchaiwan homes spread out from the banks of a wide river that flowed from rugged mountains and meandered through the valley, past the city and to the foot of the bluff. Deep pools of blue-green water were fed by stretches of white water that cascaded alongside the ancient walls of the city. Groves of fruit trees and green fields of cabbage, barley, melons, and rice carved a checkerboard pattern into the valley. The valley was girdled by cloud-shrouded mountain peaks that jutted high into the deep blue sky. It was a picturesque sight, and one that Kay would never forget.

General Ho met them at the large oak front door and ushered them into his living room where he introduced them to his officers. They expected typical Chinese chow, yet got quite a shock when they entered the teak- paneled dining room. A long dinner table was spread with a white linen tablecloth and set with European cutlery, crystal wine and water glasses, and ornate ceramic hand-painted dinnerware. General Ho introduced Kay, Bill, and Tommy to his staff and invited them to sit down to a meal unmatched in excellence by any four-star restaurant in New York or Paris. After dinner, women served coffee and through an interpreter, General Ho asked Kay to recount their adventures from the time they were thrown into Lunghwa to their arrival in Tangchaiwan.

Kay retold their adventures in lurid detail, pausing occasionally to allow the interpreter time to translate. He included in his story descriptions of the horrors perpetrated by the Lunghwa prison guards. He narrated their escape and days sloshing through the rice paddies of the Yangtze River delta. He expressed his gratitude for the help of Chinese farmers and townsfolk and the guerrillas of Chekiang Province, with special admiration for General Chang Bang-fee. When he finished, there was a round of applause and General Ho summarized Kay's expression of gratitude through the interpreter.

"Well this is to be expected, after all we are allies and the Chinese country folk have always been known for their hospitality."

General Ho then recounted his involvement in the "China Incident," the second Sino-Japanese war in 1937, and the atrocities the Japanese committed in Nanking. He was especially bitter about how General Wang Ching-wei betrayed Generalissimo Chiang Kai-shek and set up a collaborationist government in Nanking. He also expressed concern about the communist Chinese under Mao Zedong in the north and Mao's troops in Kwangtung Province, and said that the communists could not be trusted. Infighting between the Communist Chinese guerrillas and Nationalist Chinese forces headquartered in Chungking impeded the ouster of their mutual enemy, the Japanese. Had these two forces been able to unite and cooperate, the occupying Japanese could have been forced out of China long before the U.S. forced the Japanese to an unconditional surrender in Tokyo Bay. However, such teamwork was not to be, and after the war was over infighting resulted in Mao Zedong forcing the Nationalists from Mainland China to Formosa (Taiwan).

The young officer who acted as interpreter translated as best he could, but the subtleties and political issues did not make much sense to the three Brits, even when properly translated.

After dinner, they retired to the parlor for cigars and conversation. General Ho explained that from here to the next post, he would provide new guides as Charlie was to return home in a few days. He said that the route as planned by General Chang needed to be revised. The change was necessary because of recent activity of the Japanese Army that was trying to take over parts of Kiangsi and Hupeh Provinces.

General Ho looked very serious and spoke softly to Kay.

"Tojo does not realize that he is finished in China. Out of desperation he has ordered his army to take all of China and gave them only seven weeks to do so. Nippon's military commanders in Tokyo are fools and liars. They tell their Emperor Hirohito that the war is going well for them when it is not, and they hide from him the many defeats that his forces have suffered. Even with ten times the number of troops they have presently deployed, Tojo could not occupy all of China. Moreover, what will be the Japanese response when the Americans invade Japan? It is no secrete that those folks are preparing to do so, and quite soon. My American contacts claim that such an invasion will result in the loss of over one hundred thousand American lives, and over a million Japanese. The Japanese will fight for every inch of their homeland, and it will be the bloodiest invasion in all history. I think both Emperor Hirohito and President Roosevelt want to avoid such bloodshed, but it seems inevitable. The Japanese people will never surrender to the Americans, unless of course they agree to let the Emperor continue to rule the country. I hear that the Americans have a plan to avoid invasion, but I don't know what that would be."

The hour had grown late, so Kay thanked General Ho for a most enjoyable evening, and they returned to the guesthouse.

September 26, 1944, Tangchaiwan

They said good-bye to Charlie as he prepared to return home. Charlie had been a good companion, and did not seem to mind his nickname. When Kay asked his Chinese name he replied, "Please, just call me Charlie." He never did share his Chinese name with them.

While at breakfast, they met their new guide, Captain Cho, a captain in the military police, and his two aides. Cho, who was only a little over five feet tall, explained in broken English that he had attended an English school in Peking and was very honored to be assigned as their guide.

Tommy had a raging fever that morning and was in no shape to travel, so Captain Cho suggested they have a rest day and perhaps Tommy would be well enough to travel in a day or two. Bill's knee kept him at the hotel, but Kay and Captain Cho kept busy by visiting the Tangchaiwan teahouses and the market place. As they sipped tea at one such establishment, Cho asked Kay if there was anything he would especially like to do. Kay replied that he would like to visit the famous museum and tea garden in Tangchaiwan, where he had been told there was a dragon on exhibit.

Cho smiled, nodded, and led Kay through the cobblestone streets to a residence surrounded by a high brick wall near the commons. From the outside, the residence didn't look very much like a museum and tea garden, but Kay rationalized that perhaps once inside the wall it would look more like he expected. Cho pulled on the cord and rang the bell, and soon a robed woman opened the gate and led them inside the courtyard. Even from inside, the place still didn't have the look of a museum and tea garden. A middle-aged woman met them in the entryway of the stone house and led them into the sitting room where she indicated they should sit down and wait.

The sitting room was unusually ornate. An intricate Chinese rug covered the floor, heavy red drapes lined the windows, and the overstuffed divan and sitting chairs were covered in red upholstery. Kay was very uncomfortable. This house certainly did not look like what he expected. He looked over at Cho who was sitting with a smug smile on his face. He was about to question him about this place when the woman returned with three beautiful young women in tow. This house was certainly no Chinese museum.

"Captain Cho," Kay whispered, "you have brought me to a brothel!"

Cho looked perplexed. "Pate hsien-sheng, is this not what you asked to do?"

"No!" Kay said emphatically, "I wanted to visit the museum with the dragon!"

Cho blushed. "Oh, so sorry. Your Chinese not good. Dragon and woman companion sounds much alike. Perhaps I misunderstand, but we are here now. Make choice or you offend the madam."

Kay did not know what to do. The three ladies dressed in silk kimonos stood before him patiently waiting for Kay to choose one of them. All three were beautiful and he did not want to offend them, yet he was not about to go to a room with one of these young women. It was not his style to break his marriage vows, yet he needed to save face.

"Tell the madam that there was a misunderstanding," Kay

pleaded, "All I wanted was a bath and a massage."

Captain Cho had a few words with the madam, who laughed and motioned Kay to follow her. She led him into a tiled room with a large step down bath and handed him a bar of soap. Kay undressed and one of the young ladies came into the room with a bucket of warm water and began to wash Kay's back. When he was all soaped up, another woman appeared with another bucket of warm water that she poured over him, then led him into the next room with a spa filled with very hot water. It was so soothing to soak in that bath. All his aches and pains seemed to melt away. After a few minutes, the madam appeared with a kimono, and then led Kay into a room where two women gave him a massage that left him feeling like a limp dishrag. It was wonderful! Kay dressed and returned to the sitting room where Cho was waiting for him. Cho wore an inscrutable smile as Kay entered the room, but said nothing until they were back outside on the street.

"Does Pate hsien-sheng still want to visit the museum and see the dragon?" Cho asked

Kay said that he did, so Captain Cho led him down twisting cobbled streets to a large building on the outskirts of town. The museum, a former Chinese Emperor's summer palace, was constructed from large pink sandstone blocks. The gardens surrounding the building were truly beautiful, adorned with miniature fruit and bonsai trees, and a multitude of flowers and ornamental shrubs. Cho led him past the gardens and up the marble steps that led into the museum. The museum interior was remarkably ornate. Intricately woven oriental area rugs partially covered the lustrous mahogany floors, and the walls were paneled with teakwood and adorned by large intricate tapestries. The museum did not smell musty as Kay expected, but a pleasant fragrance of jasmine permeated the rooms. The curator met them in the lobby, and Cho told him that they wanted to see the dragon. The curator bowed and led them into a large room, a former palatial ballroom. The largest glass chandelier that Kay had ever seen hung from an ornate ceiling covered in frescoes. In the center of the room was the fossilized skeleton of a large lizard-like creature. The body was about twenty feet in length and five feet in girth, supported by four stumpy legs. A tapered tail extended another ten feet behind the main torso, and a large toothy head sat atop a long extended neck. While in college, Kay had taken a course in paleontology and immediately recognized the "dragon" as a dinosaur, inaccurately constructed from the bones of several different extinct species. Other inaccurate reconstructions of dinosaur bones were probably responsible for Chinese dragon myths.

Cho and Kay toured the remainder of the museum. On display were many artifacts from the Ming Dynasty, including gorgeous silk clothing and exquisite vases and bowls of all sizes and shapes. Superb pottery and paintings were housed in glass covered cases throughout the museum. Kay's attention was drawn to one particular display case filled with intricately carved jade daggers and embossed swords and scabbards, and another with samples of minerals that included fist size gold filigree nuggets and precious and semi-precious gem stones. One case displayed a beautiful green emerald the size of a golf ball, a light blue topaz of similar size, and a large, fist-size purple garnet. Each uncut gem was the largest Kay had ever seen.

One of the strangest exhibits was that of a bizarre fish preserved in a large liquid filled glass aquarium. The fish was about ten feet long and three feet in girth, with rough black skin and the usual accouterment of fins. At first glance, Kay thought it was a sturgeon or a shark, but on closer inspection it was obviously neither. While the body resembled that of a sturgeon, a huge mouth full of long sharp teeth in an enormous head said otherwise. The dagger-like teeth overlapped and crisscrossed each other as they do in a nurse shark. Kay, who was an amateur ichthyologist, knew quite a bit about Pacific Ocean fish and said that this fish was certainly not a shark or any other identifiable denizen of the deep. Kay attempted to decipher the Chinese characters on top of the glass case, which announced that this animal was caught in the Hwang-Hai (Yellow Sea), near Yu-Chan Island in 1933. If this was not a clever fake, it was of a species unknown to Western science.

After the tour, they were served tea in the garden teahouse, then returned to the guesthouse in time for dinner.

CHAPTER SEVEN

A Secret Mountain Base

September 27-28, 1944, Hochiao

Tommy was feeling better the next day, yet still suffered from the effects of malaria. Captain Cho decided that the escapees needed immediate medical attention, Tommy for his malaria and Bill for his knee. In addition, ugly festering sores had developed on Kay's legs from the dozens of Mulberry thorn scratches he received in the delta, and without therapeutic attention, they could become serious. Cho suggested that they backtrack sixteen miles from Tangchaiwan to Hochiao and go to a place "up in the hills," where there was a "hush-hush" American secret post with several doctors. An American post here in the Chekiang Mountains. This seemed improbable to Kay, but Cho knew this province well, and Tommy badly needed to see a real doctor.

The next morning, Kay was ready to go but both Tommy and Bill had developed fevers. Fever or not, they had to travel back to Hochiao and up into the mountains to the American post. Cho provided horses from the Tangchaiwan Calvary unit, and they mounted up along with four other soldiers and rode to Hochiao. Kay, Bill, and Tommy were experienced riders and as such were delighted to have good mounts for the trip to Hochiao and the mountains. The thought of walking any distance again was daunting, especially considering Tommy and Bill's condition. Kay said a prayer of thanks that these two had not become this ill while they were in the Shanghai delta area fleeing from the Japs. It would have certainly slowed them down and not gone well for the trio.

The horses were small, but strong and carried each of them with ease. The path from Hochiao into the mountains was steep, precipitous, and narrow, only two to three feet wide in some spots. Covered with loose shale, it wound up the mountainside on a series of dizzying switchbacks, and in some places, one misstep would have resulted in a fall over a sheer cliff of over two hundred-feet. Thankfully, the horses were sure-footed and carried them up the mountain in relative comfort, although after several hours in the saddle, Kay complained that he would take his next meal standing up. When they arrived in a small village, Kay asked an old woman shucking corn by the side of the path how far it was to the American post. She answered that it was about six li (two miles).

Not far, although later Kay swore that "three li of the six was straight up." The path became so steep that they were forced to dismount and guide the horses up the mountainside. A rickety-looking bamboo bridge spanned a deep twenty-foot wide chasm, and there was a Chinese soldier carrying a tommy gun guarding the portal. The guard sprang to attention when he spotted Captain Cho. Cho explained that the soldier belonged to a detachment of troops assigned to guard the American post, and that they were very close to the end of their climb. Because of his damaged knee, Bill was having an especially difficult time climbing up the steep path and was thankful that their objective wasn't much further. As they rounded a bluff, the mountainside opened to the foot of a large box canyon. In the back of the canyon and in front of a group of buildings stood a tall flagpole flying both an American and Nationalist Chinese flag.

The post headquarters was located in an ancient Buddhist temple that had been built into a deep natural niche etched into a two-hundred-foot high cliff. A large verandah built onto the temple steps commanded a superb view of the valley below. Several Caucasian men were sitting in wicker chairs on the verandah, and as Cho and his entourage approached, two of the men rose and rushed down the stairs to greet them. One officer introduced himself as Dr. Collella and the other as Sgt. Ricrillo. Kay briefly explained that they were escapees from a Shanghai prison camp and were badly in need of medical attention. The doctor was shocked to see three "Brits" in these parts, but assured them that they could attend to their medical needs. Sgt. Ricrillo led Kay, Bill and Tommy into the post and introduced them to the camp commanding officer, Commander Arthur P. Black USN, who was also a medical doctor. They were introduced to Lieutenant Commander Jarabak, Lieutenant Commander Walker, Lieutenant Commander Devers, all USN and Lieutenant McGaha USMC. None were dressed in uniforms and each wore a plain khaki shirt, pants, and baseball cap.

Kay observed that these doctors were a well-knit, highly functional unit and more like a band of brothers than military officers usually were. Commander Black was a gentleman among gentlemen. Before the war, he had been a professor of medicine at the Rockefeller Peking Union Medical College, and he was a first-rate doctor and surgeon. He was most gracious to them, provided excellent medical treatment, and attended to their every need. He and his staff made them feel part of their family.

Dr. Black examined Tommy, dosed him with Atabrine, and put him to bed immediately after they arrived. His temperature was 103.6 degrees at the time. Bill had a bad case of dysentery, a dislocated knee, and a broken finger. The doctors splinted his broken finger, and drained and bandaged his swollen knee and gave him some medicine for the dysentery. Dr. Black treated Kay's festering leg sores with salve and gave him a shot of penicillin, an American anti-bacterial medication previously unheard of in China. Other than his infected leg sores, considering what he had been through, Kay seemed in fine shape. Even his foot blisters were healing with no sign of infection. He did have a couple of teeth that needed filling, and Lieutenant Commander (Dr.) Jarabak USN and a dentist promptly filled them. Imagine finding first-rate doctors and dentists at a secret American outpost in the middle of Japanese territory in 1944!

The temple had been cleared of all religious paraphernalia to allow the Americans to convert it temporarily to their needs. The monks moved the altars and other religious items to a nearby smaller temple. The Buddha was a large, ten-foot high bronze statue and much too heavy to be moved, so it remained, as did a huge copper gong that hung from a three-foot diameter teak log and must have weighed tons. The temple floor had been converted to a dining and meeting room and it was engaging to see these Americans eating with the large Buddha smiling down on them as they ate. They were all very respectful of their surroundings, and a monk said a blessing and rang the gong before each meal was served.

The temple backed up against an embankment with just enough room for a small garden and fifteen-foot wide pond lined with moss covered granite blocks. A brook splashed over a retaining wall and into a cistern next to the temple. A bamboo pipe delivered a continuous stream of ice cold water from the cistern to the pond. The pond was used for communal bathing and washing, but the water was too cold for Kay's taste, so he took a sponge bath with hot water from the Kong just outside the temple. The Kong was a fifty-gallon drum heated by firewood and filled from another bamboo waterline.

Next to the temple/dining room, the monks' former quarters had been converted into barracks. Twenty American officers and two dozen enlisted men lived together at the post, along with three dozen Chinese soldiers commanded by a Colonel Lee. The Americans were bivouacked in one of the buildings, with the enlisted men upstairs and the officers downstairs. The Chinese occupied the barracks next to the temple. The barracks included a meeting room and parlor. After meals, everyone retreated to the verandah to lounge in wicker chairs and enjoy the cool breeze that blew in from the surrounding mountains. The view of the valley from the verandah was magnificent. Kay could see all the way across western Chekiang plateau toward Tibet and the snow covered Himalayas to the southwest.

While relaxing on the verandah one evening, Captain Cho related the story of his encounter with Major Doolittle and his crew after their bombing raid over Japan in 1942. The raid had been designed as a one- way trip. Without enough gasoline to return to their home base on Guam, Doolittle intended to crash land the B-17's in Guoimndang. Soon after Doolittle's airplane crashed, they were surrounded by Captain Cho and a dozen of his Chungking troops. In the darkness, neither the Americans nor the Chinese Nationalists recognized each other, so a firefight erupted. Captain

Cho finally detected that Doolittle and his crew was speaking English, not Japanese, and called for a cease-fire.

"Who are you?" Captain Cho asked in English

"Americans!" Doolittle answered. "Who the hell are you?"

"Chinese!" Cho yelled.

They jumped over the ditch and dike that separated them and embraced each other as if they were long lost comrades. Doolittle gave Cho a pearl-handled .45 Colt pistol as a present. By now, Captain Cho only had three bullets remaining for his treasured pistol. He was unable to find .45 caliber ammunition anywhere in Guoimndang. Commander Black had several boxes of .45 bullets and gladly gave Cho a couple of boxes. Most of the Chinese weapons used .32 or .38 ammunition, so Cho was very grateful for those bullets.

The post was electrified by a gas-driven electric generator that operated from six until ten each night. How the Yanks managed to get their hands on a supply of gasoline was a mystery, for this was the first gasoline Kay had seen since leaving Lunghwa. Since there were no roads from the valley to the outpost, motor vehicles could not be used to transport supplies. Everything from gasoline to food and medicines had to be brought up on the backs of coolies or horses along that precipitous path from Hochaio.

The three Brits never knew what the military mission of this American outpost was, and its secret purpose remained a mystery. Kay knew better than to ask questions only intended to satisfy his curiosity. The hospital was complete with a fully equipped operating room and two recovery wards set up in a building next to the American barracks. A few guerrilla soldiers were recovering in each ward. Yet, such well equipped medical facilities were certainly not the main purpose for an outpost so remotely located and inaccessible by motorcar. Kay guessed that the true purpose was to spy on the Japanese, but that did not explain why the Americans had located such a well-equipped hospital deep inside enemy held territory.

A 100-foot transmission tower loomed over the compound from a hill to the side of the compound, and a room upstairs in the American barracks housed a sophisticated radio room. After the evening meal, everyone retired to the verandah and listened to the news from radio station KGO in San Francisco or the BBC. The broadcasts were piped from the radio room to a speaker box located on the verandah. It was wonderful to hear Allied news, and the news was very encouraging. The Allies had invaded France in June, and Hitler was busily defending the Fatherland. The American and British forces in the Pacific were pushing the Japanese back to their homeland, island by bloody island. The Americans had defeated the Japanese fleet at Leyte Gulf in the Philippines, and the British were making progress in Burma and Indonesia. Indeed, the war news was good.

There were no obvious defensive weapon emplacements on the grounds of the camp. There were no machine guns, pillboxes, or the usual ack-ack guns surrounded by piles of sandbags. Other than the well-armed Chinese troops, there was no protection from a possible Japanese attack by ground or by air. The lack of road access from Hochaio was an effective deterrent to a ground attack from the Japanese and the high mountains that surrounded the post made an attack by air unlikely. The Americans and Chinese felt that they could successfully repulse any attack should the Japs discover the base.

The white dome of an observatory was especially enigmatic and seemed inappropriate if the purpose of this base was to spy on Japanese activities. Located on a little hill at the entrance of the box canyon, the site had a commanding view of the crystalline sky above and western Chekiang Province below, yet the mountains behind the base obstructed any view to Japanese held territories in eastern Chekiang Province. Kay thought this especially paradoxical. If you wanted to design a location for a spy base, why choose one where a major portion of enemy territory was obscured by a mountain.

One evening, Dr. Jim Benning, an astrophysicist with whom Kay had become friendly, invited Kay for a tour of the observatory. The main instrument consisted of a clock-driven equatorial mount supporting a 22-inch reflector telescope. There were panels of electronic instruments along the walls with all sorts of switches, dials, and flashing lights. Dr. Benning never explained their purpose. There also was a darkroom in a small shed adjacent to the observatory equipped to develop and print photographic plates. Dr. Benning aligned the scope to Saturn and invited Kay to peer through the lens. The planet was a brilliant yellowish-white ball with its rings and the Cassini gaps beautifully distinctive. Titan, a Sarturanian Moon, was visible as a brilliant orange-yellow star next to the planet.

Kay conjectured that his original guess as to the actual mission of the outpost was correct. Although the site was impractical, the purpose had to be surveillance given the remote location high in the mountains selected to ensure safety and good viewing of western Checking province. The presence of so many top-notch doctors, scientists, and high ranked officers specializing in diverse technical fields was enigmatic, as was the presence of a well-equipped observatory with a telescope designed for astronomical rather than terrestrial observation. Much of this base was completely paradoxical.

Kay and Tommy wrote letters to their wives, and Dr. Black promised to post them. He enclosed a note along with Kay's letter; but he wouldn't let him read it. Bill's wife was still in Japanese-held Shanghai, so of course he could not write to her. Bill trusted that the message sent through General Chang had reached her, and she would know that he had successfully escaped Lunghwa and was trying to get out of China.

One thing that the Commander had at his fingertips was plenty of up-to-date intelligence. One evening he spread maps out on the table and helped Kay plan a route across Kiangsi, Hunan and Kweichow Provinces. He suggested their goal should be the American air base near Kanchow, about four hundred miles distant, where perhaps they could catch a flight to Kunming and then on to India. Captain Cho gave Kay a map of Kiangsu and Chekiang Provinces printed on a silk cloth about two-foot wide by three-foot long. The map could be folded up and placed unobtrusively in a pocket. Should it become wet, it would not be damaged. Someone from Doolittle's group had given the map to Captain Cho. The Flying Tiger pilots all carried such maps in case they were shot down inside China.

It would be a long and arduous trip for the escapees, over mountains, through passes and across the Chinese interior. There was an underground network set up to help fugitives out of China, and the escapees would be passed from one guide to another along that route. Dr. Black warned them that there was still a lot of dangerous territory ahead and suggested that each of them should carry a weapon. The borders of Guoimndang were ill defined, and the threat of Japanese attack from the air was always a possibility. In some Provinces and cities in the interior such as Ichang, Hangkow, Yochow, and Nanchang were still under Japanese Army control, and Japanese expeditionary forces made forays into Guoimndang from time to time. In addition, bandits and Chinese puppet troops still controlled large parts of Guoimndang. Few parts of China could be considered "safe."

The city of Changshan in southern Chekiang Province was just outside Japanese occupied China, and nearby was the city of Kiangshan, where they could catch a train to Shangjao or beyond. Despite the efforts of Chiang Kai-shek to rid the country of bandits, they still roamed freely about the countryside. Commander Black sent a radio message to the American airbase at Kanchow alerting them to expect the three Brits. It was up to Bill, Kay, and Tommy to get to Kanchow with the help of the Chinese Army underground network. He took the trio into the armory and encouraged each of them to choose a pistol. Kay chose a .45 Colt, a pistol with which he was well familiar. Bill and Tommy chose .38 Smith & Wesson's. Kay jokingly asked the armory sergeant if they could have tommy guns.

He replied, "Sure, you can have anything you want, but after a hundred miles packing one of these babies around you will regret your choice."

October 2, 1944, Chekiang Mountains

General Ma, who commanded the western portion of Chekiang Province, sent his regrets that he could not meet with them personally, and on the day of their departure, Colonel Lee arranged for a going away breakfast, where he presented each of them a Chinese military cap inscribed with their names. Kay's read,

"To K.M. Pate from General Ma, Chekiang, 2 October 1944."

Everyone in camp came by to wish them well. Dr. Black gave Kay CRB10,000 and told him to use it for whatever was needed and if anything was left, please exchange it for U.S. dollars in Kunming and send it to his wife in the U.S. He was giving Kay his own money. They never used any of this money and later sent Mrs. Black

$37 U.S. as instructed. Because Tommy was still very weak, Dr. Black hired a sedan chair and two coolies to take him to Shunan. Kay would never forget the hospitality of these Yanks, as well as the warmth and generosity of the Chinese.

[Many months later, Tommy and Kay quite unexpectedly ran across Dr. Black in New York City, and this time took HIM to lunch and relived old times.]

CHAPTER EIGHT

Across Chekiang to Kiangsi Province

They had been at the American outpost for three days and four nights. Captain Cho said that it would take four or five days to walk to the next large town, Shunan. Thankfully, he knew of a shortcut through the mountains that would take only three days. This sounded like a good plan, so they said goodbye to their newfound friends and followed Cho up the path that led into the Chekiang Mountains.

Within two hours, they were huffing and puffing their way up the steep mountain trail. Up, up, up into the misty fog they climbed. The dampness penetrated their clothing and soon everyone was quite chilled and forced to put on their new jackets. It was amazing how well the coolies managed on these narrow, steep and rock-strewn paths. They not only carried their baggage and packs, but comfortably managed Tommy in the sedan chair. Tommy for his part was frightened and could only close his eyes and sit still in his sedan chair as his porters climbed the precipitous trail that skirted several deep ravines. The only thing between him and a fast trip to the bottom of those chasms was a whole lot of empty air. He was thankful that the fog that crept into the mountains partially obscured his view of the abyss.

Kay and Bill only packed their pistols, yet they huffed and puffed up the path while the coolies just loped along with their heavy loads and without apparent effort. Kay was never comfortable with heights, and therefore was even more grateful for the fog than Tommy was. Had he been able to see clearly to the bottom of the dizzying drop-offs, he would have been terrified. The whole day consisted of climbing up one mountain pass and down the other side only to climb up another, and down again. The mountains were covered by pine and bamboo forests that extended to an obvious demarcation line above which nothing grew except grasses and scrawny bushes. This was in stark contrast to the valleys that were overgrown with vegetation and choked with thick brush.

The perilous footpath clung to the mountainsides and wandered through the valleys in a seemingly endless, serpentine course. It eventually arrived at a small, unnamed village high in the mountains. They stopped in the village for a smoke, and to let the coolies rest. At first, the hamlet seemed deserted, but soon a few villagers cautiously glanced at the strangers from behind doors and out of windows. Then the children, more courageous or perhaps more curious than the adults, gathered around the travelers. Wide-eyed and inquisitive, they stood at a distance and stared and stared. Eventually the bolder ones began to look through Kay and Bill's rucksacks and pilfered small items. Captain Cho frisked them and made them drop the stolen items, then brusquely chased them off with a stick. Kay chided him for dealing so harshly with the children, but Cho defended his actions by explaining that if he did not do so, and rather sternly, the troop would be forced to leave the village with nothing but the clothes on their backs. Kay wished he had something to offer the children but he had nothing to give them.

Rice paddy terraces, a marvel of ingenious engineering and human labor, climbed up the mountains on either side of the valley. Water collected from countless mountain springs fed stone and brick aqueducts, which emptied into the uppermost terrace, then flowed from terrace to terrace until finally reaching the valley floor where it watered the farms through a series of ditches.

This was a very poor part of the country and completely isolated from the rest of China. In the village, several men sat on a bench playing a game of Mah-Jongg with ancient worn cards. They didn't even have the modern wooden tiles as those Kay used in Lunghwa. The three friends visited the local market to purchase something to eat, but the stalls were mostly empty. Kay found a single pear at one stall and Tommy found a lone biscuit. Captain Cho talked to one of the sellers and he disappeared into a house and soon reappeared with several steaming ears of corn. These ears were the largest Kay had ever seen, and they were delicious.

Still high up in the mountains, they arrived at another village around 6 p.m. and Captain Cho arranged for their overnight stay in a hostel. As supper cooked, the proprietor set up the usual door beds. They were so tired that after eating they retired and immediately fell asleep.

October 3, 1944, Ki-shui

Cho woke everyone at 6 a.m. and after packing, they were again back on the trail. This high mountain country was truly gorgeous, thus Kay couldn't help stopping now and then to gape at the vista and catch his breath.

Whenever he did so, "Let's go" Tommy would chide him with, "Come on, let's go! This isn't a bloody conducted tour of scenic spots you know!" Easy for Tommy to say from the comfort of his sedan chair.

This day was much as the last one, first up one mountainside on a switchback, narrow path, then down the other side only to be confronted by another mountain to climb. Again, Kay was surprised at the stamina of the Chinese coolies. Even Captain Cho seemed winded, but despite their burdensome loads, the coolies looked like they were on a recreational stroll.

Finally they descended from the high mountains into a broad valley and arrived at the town of Ki-shui, which had a Military HQ and a branch office of the government. Next to the government building was the mayor's office. The mayor offered the fugitives lodging in the rooms above his office, and showed them upstairs to their rooms to freshen up for dinner. As dinner was prepared, Kay and Bill took a walk through the beautiful one-acre semi-tropical garden behind the government building. It was filled with exotic plants and flowering bushes, some that Kay had never seen before. A brook meandered through the garden and sloshed into a small pond filled with colorful carp. Several exotic and brilliantly colored birds fluttered about the garden. Kay was unable to identify many of them, with the exception of some Magpies and Ravens. Such a garden flourishing high in the mountains in early Fall seemed out of place, yet when Kay marveled at the unseasonable garden at dinner that night, his host explained that this valley had a moderate year-round climate, and seldom experienced snow or freezing temperatures. He pondered what happenstance of geography could cause such an anomaly, yet the evidence was undeniable that this place was indeed extraordinary.

October 4, 1944, Shunan

The going was much easier after leaving town at 9 a.m. the following morning, and despite their soreness from the strenuous climb up and down mountain paths the previous two days, they made excellent progress. The trail followed a whitewater stream that eventually merged with a large river that flowed from the mountains into a broad verdant valley. In the valley foothills, the trail joined a cobbled road that passed through the valley and forked at a bend in the river. The right fork continued following the river deeper into the valley. They chose the left fork that ended a few miles later at a riverbank. In the distance across the river, they could see the walls of a city Cho identified as Shunan. There was no bridge spanning the stream; however, a ferry built from bamboo poles strapped together and stretched across the decks of three sampans carried them to the opposite bank where the road resumed and led to the city gates.

Shunan is an ancient city built on the banks of a tributary of the Fuchun Kiang. The Fuchun flowed alongside a tall age-old wall constructed with river stone and covered by green moss. The high-water mark formed by floodwaters on the wall was six feet above the existing riverbank. Before the wall was built some fifteen hundred years ago, yearly floods must have devastated the city.

Captain Cho said that only three months ago, the Japanese Army was firmly entrenched in Shunan, but had withdrawn east to Yenchow and now the city was under Nationalist control. They went into the city and found the Nationalist government buildings. After checking in at the magistrate's office, they spent the remainder of the day wandering about Shunan buying candy and cakes in the various bazaars, and finally ending up at an inn where they rented a room for the night.

The city magistrate insisted that he host them at dinner that evening. The restaurant he selected was built on the riverbank just outside the city walls. A stone dike protected the restaurant from the high waters of spring runoff. Dinner was served on the riverside verandah where they ate and watched the constant parade of boat traffic ply the Fuchun. Steam-driven tugs pushed rusty barges against the sluggish but insistent current. Junks and sampans loaded to the waterline also worked their way up and down the river. Many of the barges and sampans were towed upstream by gangs of coolies laboring along the towpath. They played tug-of-war with the river current, straining against ropes placed over their shoulders. Other boats were poled up river by on-board coolies. The magistrate said that the Fuchun Kiang merged downstream with the Tsientang Kiang, then flowed past the city of Hangchow into Hangchow Wan (Bay).

Kay was foot sore and Bill and Tommy were still recovering from their illnesses. He asked the magistrate if transportation, a rickshaw for instance, could be arranged for the next leg of their journey to Changshan, eighty miles from Shunan by road.

"But of course," the magistrate replied, "but not a rickshaw. Bus transportation has already been arranged for you at the request of Captain Cho."

The magistrate said that a bus traveled from Shunan to Changshan three times each week. The bus was scheduled to leave in the morning, and he said that they should be ready to go by 8 a.m.

That evening Captain Cho took them to visit a small American outpost just outside the city walls. The post was staffed by three Americans and commanded by a British logistics officer, Lieutenant Stilwell. Stilwell had been in constant radio contact with the American base in the Chekiang Mountains, and Commander Black had informed him that Kay and his friends were on their way to Shunan. The Shunan outpost was hidden in a former Lutheran church and school that had been partially destroyed by the Japanese. They had done little to restore the property, and it looked uninhabited. The lack of restoration was deliberate for it was very dangerous to be located on the fringe of Japanese controlled China, and the less they did to call attention to the facilities the better. The Japanese Army had invaded Shunan three separate times in the past eighteen months, and each time the Americans had escaped with the help of local guerrillas. Lieutenant Stilwell said that other Americans were on their way to relieve him and his staff, and it would be none too soon to suit him.

October 6, 1944, Changshan

They were waiting at the central square the next morning when the Changshan bus fueled by methane gas derived from a charcoal generator chugged down the street. The driver turned off the engine and busied himself refilling the generator with fresh charcoal. The magistrate said that an escort would not be needed on this portion of the trip, so they said farewell to Captain Cho and thanked him for his expert guidance through the mountains from Tangchaiwan. The magistrate asked one of the senior soldiers on the bus to look after the trio and instructed Kay to check in with the magistrate in Changshan when they arrived. The bus was ready to go, but the methane-fueled engine was not. After vigorously cranking the hand crank several times while uttering a stream of Chinese swear words, the driver finally managed to tease the obstinate engine into life and they were on their way.

Once across the river on the scow-ferry, the bus coughed and sputtered down a cobblestone road that soon turned to dirt. Kay felt fortunate that the weather was dry, for the deep ruts in the road indicated that in a rainstorm the road would become a muddy quagmire. The driver seemed to know the road and his bus, slack steering and all. On straight stretches, the bus got up to forty-five miles per hour leaving behind a trail of brown dust. The driver made several stops along the way to let passengers on and off, then shut off the motor at a village rest stop to refill the coal generator. Since there was no gasoline in this part of China and coal was ubiquitous, the innovative charcoal generator was used on all trucks and buses.

It was wonderful to speed along the road and watch the countryside pass by, knowing that each hour of bus travel was equivalent to days of walking. The road climbed into the mountains where some sections of the route hugged cliffs with a sheer drop of several hundred feet and no barriers to prevent an accidental fall into oblivion. The bus chugged up the steep inclines, then sped down the winding, narrow road with squealing brakes and the unforgettable smell of burning brake lining. Kay sat in a window seat where he could look out at the passing countryside, but this soon proved to be a bad choice. With white-knuckles, he held fast to the seatback frame in front of him, peered into the deep ravines beside the road, and prayed.

To save fuel, it was the habit of Chinese drivers to coast down mountain roads. The driver seemed competent, but rather than remaining in gear downhill and let engine compression hold the bus back, he would take the bus out of gear and ride the brakes until acrid brake smoke poured out from each wheel. At the bottom of one steep hill, a water buffalo decided to cross the road right in front of the speeding bus. The brakes by now were too hot to slow the bus and the driver swerved just in time to miss the animal. A collision with this animal would have done considerable damage to the bus and its occupants. Several chickens and ducks were not as fortunate as the buffalo, and a few ended up plastered to the bus radiator grillwork.

Hwabu (Suian) was the first sizeable town they came to and as the driver pulled to a stop in the center of town, he announced there would be a forty-five minute rest stop. Kay watched the driver take impaled birds from his radiator and place them into a sack, probably intended for his cooking pot that night. They walked around the city to stretch their legs, and garnered the typical Chinese stares everywhere they went. Yet, no one could blame them. Three foreigners dressed in American clothes, compliments of Commander Black, wearing Chinese Army hats and with pistols strapped to their side were a sight sure to arouse the curiosity of local residents. The townsfolk didn't know what to make of the trio, and Kay did nothing to enlighten them. The Chinese unabashedly stared and stared. As the three browsed the marketplace, another bus arrived from the opposite direction and stopped alongside the Changshan-bound bus. Kay was astonished when a dozen American service men climbed off the bus, but no more amazed then they were to see Kay, Bill and Tommy.

"Hello fellows," Kay greeted them with a smart palm out salute.

A young lieutenant hesitantly returned the salute not quite sure how to take three chaps who were definitely not military but had saluted him in typical British style. He finally stammered, "What are you Brits doing in this part of China?"

Kay explained their status and as it turned out, these officers were traveling to the American outpost in Shunan to relieve Lieutenant Stilwell. They had a long talk and exchanged information about the road ahead until the buses were ready to leave. They wished each other a safe journey, boarded their respective vehicles and headed off in opposite directions.

The provincial capital city of Changshan appeared around a curve about 3:30 p.m. They crossed a large river, the Ku Kiang, and drove into the city. This was the end of the bus line, so Kay and his friends went off to find the local magistrate. A ten-minute walk brought them to a series of imposing government buildings that encompassed the magistrate's Yamen (compound).

The armed sentry at the gate snapped to attention and gave the trio a snappy salute as they passed by. They entered the main building and the assistant magistrate welcomed them, then led them inside, and made them comfortable in a waiting room in one of the buildings. In another side room, Kay noticed a transceiver manufactured by E.W. Langdon & Co. of Shanghai. He had done business with this company in Shanghai. He was surprised to see first-rate equipment in such a remote place. There was also a telephone in the room, the first Kay had seen outside of Shanghai.

About 5 p.m. the magistrate entered the room, introduced himself and asked if they would like to meet the European "priests" who ran a mission in Changshan. Indeed, they would be delighted to meet the priests. He led them several blocks away from downtown Changshan and past a beautiful park. The mission was a group of red tiled buildings on the other side of the park, and when they arrived, they met the "priests", a Miss Duncan and Miss Reynolds of the China Lutheran Mission Society. The women were very amused at the magistrate's description of their priestly status, but explained that they were simply missionaries of the Lutheran church and as such were not ordained, "yet" one of the women playfully added. The women were charming, and invited them to a spot of tea, then insisted they stay for supper. They explained that they had been stationed at this post for over ten years, but due to persistent rumors that the Japanese were about to invade Changshan, Lutheran Church officials ordered them to evacuate. They planned to travel via motorcar to Kiangshan where they could catch a train to Shangjao and then a bus to the American airbase near Kanchow. From Kanchow, they expected to be airlifted to Calcutta through Kunming. Captain Black had laid out this same plan for the escapees, but this was the first news that the train was actually operating as far as Shangjao.

Miss Duncan invited Kay, Bill, and Tommy to join them in their journey to Kanchow. Unfortunately, it had also been arranged that the women were to be escorted by a Major from the B.M.M., who was not due to arrive for another three or four weeks. It was hundreds of miles to Kanchow from Changshan and a reliable escort and motorcar would certainly make the journey safer. Kay felt that they could not sit around Changshan for almost a month, so he declined the women's generous offer. They had a pleasant dinner and visit with the missionaries, and then walked back to the magistrate's Yamen about 10 p.m.

October 7, 1944, Kiangshan

The following day the magistrate provided them with four sedan chairs, one for each of them and one for their new guide. Their destination was Siang-tan (Kiangshan), about twenty-two miles southeast of Changshan as the crow flies but twice as far by a road that climbed far up over the mountains. They hoped to travel from Kiangshan to Shangjao on the Chekiang-Kangsi Railway. Kay wondered why the magistrate didn't arrange passage for them on a junk or a sampan up the Ku Kiang to Kiangshan, but later discovered that in the past few days several Japanese patrol boats had been spotted patrolling the river.

The magistrate told them that the first part of the road was very rough, but it would "get better" after a few miles. As they negotiated the road, Kay wondered if "get better" meant it would improve or become even worse. The road climbed up one ridge, then down into a narrow valley then up another ridge. They walked the steep climb up and down the mountainside and rode the sedan chairs on the flat stretches. As before, the road was narrow and covered with loose shale and sharp flint rocks that they could feel through the soles of their shoes. It was difficult to see how a motorcar could negotiate such a rut strewn and rocky trail, yet it was marked on Kay's silk map as "motorable."

By noontime the road ended at a small village where they stopped for a lunch of eggs, noodles and bits of fried pork in a jiang-yu (soybean) sauce. It was delicious and they each enjoyed two full bowls. The better road to Kiangshan began at this village. The term "better" is simply an opinion, and as far as Kay was concerned, this road could only be described as primitive, perhaps someday to become better. Under construction to accommodate two-way motor traffic, the road included several newly constructed bridges and several others that were under construction. One recently completed bridge spanned a gully over one hundred yards wide. The bridge cut at least a mile off the distance to Kiangshan, for without it they would have had to detour around the gully. On the other side of the bridge, coolies armed with pick and shovel worked the roadbed in the mid-day heat while an endless procession of workers carried river stones from a mountainside quarry to be used for walls intended to line either side of the roadway. All construction in this part of China was done by hand labor and thousands of coolies labored tirelessly on similar projects. Seldom did Kay see machinery of any kind, except in the largest cities.

They arrived in Kiangshan mid-afternoon and found the local magistrate's Yamen. This time their reception was far from cordial. The magistrate was out of town on business, so they were turned over to his assistant, who seemed annoyed that he had to deal with these foreigners. Kay had a difficult time understanding his dialect and had to depend on the guide to explain everything to the assistant. However, once he understood who they were and that they had escaped from the Japanese, his attitude completely changed. He was willing to do anything in his power to help them. He promptly arranged for their lodging and a dinner was to be given in their honor that evening. Then he took them on a shopping trip into Kiangshan. Tommy loved cigars but had not seen a cigar for months. While wandering about Kiangshan he discovered a tobacco shop and bought a fistful of the smelly things. Kay and Bill bought several packs of Shanghai-manufactured *Pirate* and *Ruby Queen* brand cigarettes. Chinese cigarettes were high in nicotine and tar, but most satisfying.

The evening in Kiangshan was one of the cheeriest and most memorable for Kay and his friends since their escape. Dinner was served at 7:30 p.m., preceded by several rounds of rice wine. Kay was not much of a hard liquor fan, but he did the polite thing and kept up with the others. After several rounds and by the time the main course of bird-nest soup, green turtle stew and shark-fin broth was served, his head was spinning. Kay found the meal not at all to his liking and probably would not have eaten much of it except that after the rice wine he needed something solid on his stomach.

Despite his many years in Asia, there were certain foods that Kay avoided whenever possible. Kay felt those dishes such as bird-nest soup, shark-fin broth and turtle dishes of all kinds were best left to the locals. Kay smiled and choked down his meal. Everyone else thought the meal was delicious.

The guests that evening included their new guide, Captain C.C. Tong. Captain Tong was a graduate of Texas A&M, spoke excellent English, and was a swell chap and companion. Before the war, he worked for Texaco, first in Texas, and then in Canton, and had been fighting the Japanese since 1937. The magistrate's wife and small daughter and son were also at the dinner that evening, and afterwards Kay went out into the courtyard to play with the children. The youngsters warmed up to him immediately as they played a game of tag and climbed the larger trees in the courtyard. Kay thought the children were delightful, and the playtime and his ability to interact so comfortably with the children rejuvenated him.

CHAPTER NINE

Travel by Train.

October 8, 1944, On the train to Shangjao

Captain Tong arranged for their passage by train to Shangjao, scheduled to leave Kiangshan at 7 a.m. the following morning. Kay and his friends awoke at 5:30 a.m. and at 6 a.m. began the two-mile walk to the train station. Captain Tong did not seem in a hurry to get to the station on time, and a few blocks from the station, he stopped at a teahouse for breakfast. Kay grew concerned as the 7 a.m. departure time approached and asked Captain Tong if they should not hurry on to the train station.

"Not to worry," Tong answered, "the train will not leave until important guests such as yourselves are on board."

Important guests? They were simply three Brits of no particular importance, yet Tong's nonchalant behavior was apropos. The train was waiting for them when they arrived at the station at 7:30, and immediately after they were on board and were shown to their compartment, the train chugged out of the station.

Before the war, the Chekiang-Kiangsi railroad extended fifteen hundred miles from Hangchow across the south China interior all the way to Kunming. Japanese bombs had reduced the line to a scant one hundred miles from Chuhsien to Shangjao. For the first few miles of the journey from Kiangshan, the train climbed slowly up into the mountains, rocking back and forth on uncertain tracks and chugging along at a top speed of fifteen miles per hour. Captain Tong commented that derailments were common, and Kay pondered this as the train crossed deep gorges on wooden trestles. The engine huffed and puffed alternate series of acrid black and white smoke. On the flat portions the engine belched white smoke and sped up to about thirty miles per hour. The coal-burning steam engine and coaches were once used on a British Indian railway and the facing lion's emblem was still visible on the sides of the coaches. All along the line, hundreds of coolies labored with pick and shovel to repair sections of the single-track roadbed. Despite their efforts, the rail line was in such terrible shape that the train lurched back and forth worse than a ship in a typhoon.

By mid-morning the train chugged into a large railway station, and Tommy and Kay climbed off to stretch their legs. Kay noticed the station name sign over the platform. The Chinese characters connoted Yu-shan, the very destination that Kay had originally plotted on the map before escaping Lunghwa prison! Kay had selected this particular city as their destination because he had heard that there was an American airbase nearby. His information was a bit off. The Allied airbase near Yu-shan had never been completed because it could be reached from Japanese airfields.

General Chang Bang Fee was aware of this and had mapped a different route to the U.S. airbase near Kanchow. They now stood in the very heart of the city that Kay had promised Tommy and Bill they would reach. Was this a coincidence, or was it due to something else, perhaps Almighty guidance? Kay was convinced that the hand of God had been on them from the very moment they planned their escape, and this was just another signpost of His succor.

After leaving Yu-Shan, the train passed over several wide rivers on newly constructed, steel archway bridges. One of these bridges spanned a swift river six hundred yards wide. The skeleton of the previous steel-structure bridge lay in twisted ruins in the middle of the river, as a gang of workers and several barges labored to remove the navigational hazard. Alongside the tracks lay the rusting ruins of several engines and coaches blasted to smithereens by Japanese bombs. The Chinese simply had pushed the wrecks aside, repaired the rails and bridges and continued train service. American P-51 airplanes based in Kanchow had discouraged recent Japanese air attacks, to the extent that the Chinese could now safely work on restoring the Chekiang-Kiangsi rail line all the way to Kunming.

By mid-afternoon the train arrived in Shangjao. The train station lay in ruins, destroyed by Jap bombs, and the railway that would have once taken them all the way to Kanchow was out of service. They disembarked on a temporary wooden plank platform, as the coolies collected their baggage.

Captain Tong led them through the cobbled streets of Shangjao toward the magistrate's Yamen. The city was old and quaint, and several blocks in the main section of town had sustained heavy damage from the Japanese bombing raids. The resulting rubble was quickly removed from the streets after each raid and piled in heaps on vacant lots to allow commerce to continue undeterred. The main street was lined with countless shops and stalls that sold everything imaginable, from ducks to octopus and automobile parts to guns. The walk to the Yamen took about a half-hour and when they arrived they were seated and the staff brought warm towels, pots of tea, and fried watermelon seeds. Soon, the magistrate, a very small dapper man impeccably dressed in a blue suit offset by a bright red tie, entered the room and warmly greeted everyone. Captain Tong explained that they were in a hurry to get to the Kanchow airfield. The magistrate agreed that haste was essential, for the Japanese had launched a new offensive throughout Kiangsi Province and recently the Kanchow airfield had been attacked. It could be closed down any day now.

"It is most unfortunate that you missed the weekly bus to Kanchow," the magistrate sympathized.

He offered to make a few phone calls to see if other transportation could be arranged.

"In the meantime, I can take you to the British-American headquarters just two hundred yards beyond the Yamen. The British and Americans officers have been expecting you," the magistrate volunteered.

They walked over to the red-roofed former Christian mission that was now the joint British-American military office. Out front, large British and U.S. flags flew on either side of a Nationalist

Chinese flag. They entered a small bungalow immediately behind the mission as an American officer and a NCO jumped to attention.

"Hello Old Chaps, we've been expecting you," the obviously British officer exclaimed. "It's jolly good that you arrived safely!"

The officer introduced himself as Lieutenant Schelyer and the NCO as Corporal Hogan. Kay was startled to be greeted so warmly by a fellow citizen, and it made him feel welcomed and important. Lieutenant Schelyer explained that this was an advance base of AGAS (Air Ground Aid Section), a branch of American Intelligence. Schelyer and Hogan were assigned to AGAS to help rescue and aid U.S. and British aviators who had been forced to bail out or crash land in China. The AGAS office had helped many other British and American fugitives such as Kay and his friends escape from China to India.

Schelyer put them up in the mission and asked Kay to write detailed reports of Lunghwa, their escape through Chekiang, and the places they visited. Kay had kept detailed mental records of those cities occupied by Japanese troops, airfields, various Japanese encampments and troop movements, and this was a good opportunity to commit his observations to paper. Lieutenant Schelyer gave Kay a small bound diary that Kay could use as a daily journal of their travels.

October 9 and 10, 1944, Shangjao

Kay spent the next two days typing these reports on one hundred and twenty pages of paper. He also drew detailed maps and diagrams of Lunghwa Prison, the Shanghai countryside, and Jap positions he had noted. Later, the Allies used Kay's intelligence to conduct several successful raids on Japanese military targets. In the meantime, Lieutenant Schelyer worked to arrange transportation to Kanchow, three hundred and fifty miles away by road. The bus to Kanchow ran only once a week, and it would be five more days before that bus was due to leave again for Shangjao. He discovered by radio that an AGAS jeep was due to arrive on the 11th from Denchi on its way to Kanchow. The American officer in charge and his driver said that they would be pleased to take the escapees along with them to Kanchow.

CHAPTER TEN:

Jeep Trails

October 11, 1944, Yingtan

The next day, the jeep arrived bringing their American guide, Lieutenant R.C. Scott of Pasadena, California. Fueled by grain alcohol, the jeep made a terrible noise as it thundered and backfired down the street and finally pulled to a wheezing stop in front of the Yamen. Kay came out to the street to meet the car and its occupants. The jeep looked like it was on its last legs. Dents and primer-covered metal decorated the bonnet (hood) and fenders. Steam spewed from the radiator and wisps of white smoke escaped from the engine vents. A tattered canvas top covered the passenger compartment and the seats were threadbare. Black smoke puffed out of the tailpipe synchronous with the hacking motor.

Bill, Lieutenant Scott, Tommy and Kay with Jeep

The jeep was towing a tarpaulin-covered two-wheel trailer. Lieutenant Scott climbed out of the jeep leaving three other passengers still seated and introduced himself. He was a tall well-built man with a receding hairline exposing a broad forehead. His broad smile and twinkle in his eyes immediately put Kay at ease. They shook hands as the other passengers climbed down from the jeep. Kay was shocked to see that one of the other folks was Uhlich, one of the escapees from Lunghwa. They sat down to dinner that evening and exchanged stories of their escape and travels. Their separate journeys followed almost exactly the same route. Uhlich had remained in China to help AGAS and other fugitives while the other members of his party went on to Kunming and India.

They said goodbye and thanked Captain Tong, who along with Lieutenant Schelyer had concluded his business in Shangjao and was due to take the train back to Kiangshan later that afternoon. From here on out, they would be in the hands of either the Americans or the British military. Lieutenant Scott, who Tommy nicknamed Scotty, was to be their guide and driver to Kanchow. A Chinese general, General Chin, who was going to Kanchow for medical treatment, climbed into the jeep with Kay, Bill, and Tommy. Scotty drove the crowded jeep with his four passengers, Kay, and he in the front seat, and the three others in the back. It would be a long uncomfortable three hundred and fifty-mile trip to

Kanchow. Portions of the road were reported to be barely motorable, and much of it was strewn with rocks both large and small. Due to the heavy rains of the past months and constant truck traffic, much of the road was washboard and covered with potholes. Scotty seemed to know the precise speed to drive so as to minimize the bouncing and skating of the jeep on the washboard road and at the same time avoid the ubiquitous potholes, some large enough to swallow the jeep and its passengers. All this bouncing and weaving did little to lessen General Tong's discomfort. Already suffering from some undiagnosed malady, he was carsick for most of the trip and often asked Scotty to pull over to the side of the road so that he could relieve himself. Kay didn't complain about the crowded jeep or pothole filled and washboard roads, as it sure beat walking.

Lieutenant Scott had made this trip before and estimated it would take them two or three days, so they loaded enough C-rations for five people for five days. In addition, the magistrate had given them four bottles of Chinese wine and a basket of pears, a very kind and generous gesture.

The trailer was loaded with goods designated for the American airbase in Kanchow. In addition, two fifty-five gallon drums of alcohol, tools, and two extra tires and tubes were included. The trailer was limited to one thousand pounds of cargo and by the time all the gear and equipment was onboard, it was considerably over-loaded. The jeep sputtered and banged like a machine gun along the streets of Shangjao, causing quite a commotion as it passed through the narrow city streets. Although the streets were crowded, a horn was unnecessary. Folks scattered and hugged the sides of the street well in advance of their passing.

About ten miles outside Shangjao they came to a wide river crossing serviced by a scow-barge ferry. The fare was CRB $1,000 (about 20 cents). Since the barge was not long enough to accommodate both the jeep and trailer, Scotty unhooked the trailer and drove the jeep onto the ferry. The trailer would have to wait for a second crossing. The barge operator said that he would need CRB $1,000 for EACH crossing, so Scotty paid him CRB $4,000 in advance. The operator took Kay, Scotty, and the jeep to the other side, but Scotty could not get the jeep started again to drive it off the scow, so he raised the hood and began tinkering with the engine. Although he was an engineer by trade, he admitted that he didn't know much about jeep engines.

Kay began poking around the engine as well, and discovered that the battery terminals and cables were badly corroded and worn thin. Some of the cells were without caps and were low on water. The top of the battery was covered with a white powder and the engine carburetor was choked with gunk. The battery and carburetor could be cleaned; however, Kay had no idea where he could find heavy cable wire in such a remote part of China. Kay cursed in frustration. The ferry operator became quite upset when Kay could not get the jeep started. He complained that he was losing fares, although no one seemed to be waiting to be taken across the river on either side. The man whined and griped until Scotty gave him another CRB $1,000 simply to get some peace from his constant complaining.

A crowd of Chinese had gathered on the scow ramp to watch the foreigners struggle with their jeep. It seemed to Kay that a crowd always gathered whenever they stopped. They did the typical Chinese thing of silently standing first on one foot, then the other and silently stare, and stare.

A Chinese man with a weathered face and wearing a Brooklyn Dodgers baseball cap stepped out of the crowd and asked Scotty in Chinese if there was anything he could do to help. Scotty didn't understand the man's Chinese and was startled to see the inscription on the cap, yet he soon recovered from his wonder. He had seen stranger things in this countryside.

"Dodgers?" Scotty asked.

The man seemed puzzled at the question.

"Your cap," Scotty said pointing to the baseball cap, "Brooklyn is my home town."

The man took off his cap and looked at the inscription, but didn't show any semblance of understanding. Kay stepped in and told the man in Chinese that Scotty was an American, and that the inscription on the cap was that of Scotty's home town baseball team in America, The Brooklyn Dodgers.

"Ah so," the man replied with an ear-to-ear grin. "Booook-en Dawd-gers."

He then repeated his question to Kay. "Is there anything I can do to help?"

"Nothing, unless you happen to have two feet of thick copper wire handy." Kay said sarcastically.

The man retreated to his wagon parked on the road and returned with a three foot length of insulated eight gauge braided copper wire. Kay was astounded that this fellow would have exactly what they needed in such a remote place. The man explained that he was a maintenance man for a trucking line and was returning from having repaired a stalled truck when he spotted the stranded jeep. He not only had enough wire, but a good knife to strip off the insulation. They were overwhelmed by this stroke of good luck. Kay made the repairs, cleaned the carburetor and the jeep started up without further difficulty.

The barge owner was still griping as Kay drove the jeep off the barge and onto the ramp. Scotty was paying the maintenance man CRB 1,500 for the cable, when the barge owner came up to him to complain vehemently that the jeep had caused him additional lost business, and demanded further payment before they returned for the trailer. Scotty's patience had worn thin by this time. He had had enough of this fellow. He put his face next to the man's and cursed. It was comical to watch the barge operator, who did not know a word of English, fully understand a string of cuss words barked in a language totally foreign to him. When Scotty ended his tirade about further payment with "no way in Hell," the operator backed up looking as if Scotty had thrust a sharp sword into his belly. The owner returned his own barrage of Chinese cuss words from a safe distance, and was still complaining, mostly to himself as they retrieved the trailer.

"It's a good thing you don't understand Chinese," Kay said to Scotty. "That fellow had a few choice words for you."

"Oh, I understood well enough—it was outrageous—the guy is a crook," Scotty fumed as they drove down the road, "I was not about to let that little SOB hold us up for more fare."

"Well, it was only twenty cents, and he was probably trying to save face," Bill commented from the back seat.

"Well, that was the U.S. government's twenty cents, and besides it is the principle of the thing," Scotty shot back.

"The poor Chinaman probably thinks we are a bunch of cheap bastards," Tommy added.

Two lessons learned, Kay thought. The first is that cuss words need not be translated, and saving face was as important to Scotty as it was to the boatman. "It must be a Brooklyn thing," he thought to himself.

They drove on until dusk, when it began to rain. The jeep only had hand-operated windshield wipers, so Kay operated the wipers while Scotty drove. Scotty was tired and asked if Kay knew how to drive a jeep on bad roads. Kay said that he could drive anything with four wheels, including the Chinese trucks he often drove from Shanghai to Tsingtao. A jeep would be easy compared to those obstinate Chinese trucks and terrible excuses for highways.

Kay was glad to be behind the wheel. He was much more comfortable as a driver than as a passenger. From then on, Scotty and Kay took turns behind the wheel. The jeep bounced and skittered along the washboard dirt road as Kay learned how to operate the jeep and avoid the many ditches and potholes. As night fell and because the headlights were weak and poorly aimed, it was harder and harder for Kay to see all the holes in the road. Apparently, the generator was not adequately charging the battery. It was a moonless night, and in the pouring rain, Kay could barely see the road ahead. They hit one pothole so hard that the General, who was leaning out the side of the jeep to vomit, almost bounced right out of the vehicle. About 10 p.m. they came to the village of Yingtan. They were tired and General Chin said he knew of a hotel in town. They found the hotel, but it was full.

The proprietor suggested they try a Christian mission in town. He thought the missionaries would gladly put them up for the night. The hotel owner jumped on the running board of the jeep and directed them to the mission. The red-roofed mission consisted of a church, an attached school, and several other buildings. It dominated the central part of the village, a surprisingly large compound for such a small town. As they got closer, it was apparent that the church had been badly damaged. Most of the roof was collapsed into the sanctuary. The gray-haired and rotund priest, a head shorter than Kay, was dressed in a black robe and roman collar. He ran outside when he heard the noisy jeep approaching and greeted them warmly. He introduced himself as Father Theunissen. He asked if he could offer them food and lodging for the night. They gladly accepted his kind offer. The priest led them into the rectory and his houseboy served a simple dinner of fish, rice, and tea. The good padre was a Dutch Jesuit missionary who had been in Yingtan since 1929. He told them how he had escaped to the countryside when the Japanese Army invaded and occupied the town. Two months after they took Yingtan, they suddenly deserted the town and the priest returned to find his church in ruins. The soldiers had set a bomb off inside the church before they left.

Pillaging and burning Christian churches seemed to be a Japanese practice throughout China. The Nips had soaked the rectory and the school building with kerosene before leaving, but miraculously they were unable to ignite it and the rest of the mission was spared. After dinner, the good padre showed them to their quarters in the school. Two ground level rooms and a second story room had been prepared for them. One was for the General and the other for Kay and Scotty, and the upstairs room for Tommy and Bill.

October 12, 1944, Yingtan

Kay was awake early the next morning, so he dressed and went outside for a walk. As he strolled around the Mission courtyard, he heard singing coming from within the church. His curiosity aroused, he peeked inside and saw about two hundred townspeople people kneeling in what was left of the bombed-out church. Father Theunissen was saying Mass on a makeshift altar, with the church lit by the sun as it streamed through the collapsed east wall. As soon as the priest spotted Kay, he motioned to come inside. Previously, Kay had only attended one Mass, and that was in Lunghwa. He knew nothing of the service or the meaning of the Latin prayers, but he could recognize the reverence shown by the congregation. Something important was going on, something in which he had been invited to participate.

He knelt down and in his own way prayed with the congregation and stood, sat, and knelt following the example of the congregation.

Father Theunissen gave his homily in fluent Chinese. It was a talk as apropos and meaningful to Kay as the priest's talk about Job had been in Lunghwa. The padre spoke about how God loved each one of them, as a good father loves his children.

"Ask and you shall receive, seek and you will find, knock and the door will be opened to you," the priest quoted the words of Jesus, "for what father among you would give his son a snake when he asks for a fish, or hand him a scorpion if he asks for an egg."

Kay pondered these words as the service progressed. Until his internment in Lunghwa, in his whole life he hadn't asked God for anything. Then, shortly before his escape, he had asked God for a safe journey, and like a good father, God answered his request by guiding his escape to freedom. When the Japs were about to catch them, somehow they escaped discovery. When they had needed food and shelter, it surfaced. When they needed a place to hide, they found it. Even when Kay needed a piece of copper wire, miraculously it was there for them. When they needed medical attention, they were shown to a hidden hospital. Simply good fortune? Well, that was one answer and the one readily accepted by Bill and Tommy, but not an answer that satisfied Kay. Two months ago, a "good fortune" answer would have sufficed, yet no longer. Something was changing inside Kay. He had come to believe that only a kindly father could be behind all their good fortune.

The question that remained in Kay's mind and was most responsible for his lifelong rejection of God, was why God allowed evil into a world that He supposedly cared for. If He was such a loving father, how could He let Hs people suffer so much? Kay was impressed with these simple Chinese country folk, people who had suffered terribly at the hands of the Japanese, yet now they worshiped in a bombed-out church with a reverence and trust as if nothing had gone wrong in their lives. Why was he so fortunate while so many others were *allowed* to endure unspeakable suffering? Interesting that he should use the term "allow." The answer, he contemplated, must lay in the story of Job. God *allowed* good people to suffer, even those who had done nothing to deserve such evil. Evil was not a product of a vindictive God, but something God allowed, extant to test the perseverance and loyalty of his subjects. God doesn't cause evil; it exists outside of God. People designate this or that as evil, but evil is subjective and in the mind of the beholder. For example, rain nourishes the crops, and that is good, but too much rain will wash them away, and that is evil. In the broader picture, rain is neither good or evil, just nature at work. God is *a good Father* and yet we are not marionettes with God pulling our strings as we go through life. Like a good Father, He answers our requests, yet not always in the way we expect. He does not will evil but allows it to exist, sometimes to strengthen our resolve and fortitude. God does not call down pestilence, hurricanes, earthquakes, and evil men to punish us. These are artifacts of nature and the lack of self-control that lurks in each one of us. Our time here on earth is a test to earn our way into heaven. Nothing comes our way unearned. It was all beginning to make sense to Kay.

Later in the service everyone got up and approached the altar, and Kay followed them up to the priest. He gave each person what looked to Kay like a small piece of white bread. When Kay stood in front of him, Father Theunissen placed his hand on Kay's forehead and blessed him, yet did not give him the bread. Nonetheless, Kay felt an inner warmth like he had never felt before. It was at this point that he became certain that he would someday rejoin Lil and Darryl. It was going to happen. He knew it, just as he knew he had traveled here under God's protection. Moreover, God would be with him all the way home.

After services, Kay joined the others for a breakfast of hotcakes and syrup. When they had finished breakfast, they thanked Father Theunissen for his hospitality and piled into the jeep to continue their journey, but the jeep again refused to start. Not a flicker of life! Kay fiddled with the electrical system and concluded that the generator had not adequately charged the battery, which was now as lifeless as rock. Father Theunissen sent an aid to the local Chinese Army garrison to request a truck to give them a push. The truck showed up about noontime and pushed Kay and the jeep down the road for several hundred yards. With a loud bang and cough, the engine finally caught.

Kay returned to the mission, hooked up the trailer, and everyone climbed aboard. He thanked the good priest for his hospitality and gave him CRB5,000 for his mission work. Amid considerable noise and with Kay behind the wheel, they bounced down the cobblestone road toward the mountains beyond. They had been delayed for a half-day in Yingtan and to this point had only completed one hundred of the three hundred and fifty-mile journey. The trip now looked more like three or four days rather than the two or three they had anticipated, yet Kay would have gladly been delayed a full week just to have had the opportunity to meet Father Theunissen and receive his message and blessing.

As the road out of Yingtan wound higher into the mountains, the grade became increasingly steep. There was even less traffic on this section of the journey than on the road from Shangjao to Yingtan. In fact, after traveling for three hours they only met one other truck. Without the jeep's compound-low gear, they would never have made it over that mountain road. Despite its age and condition, the army jeep was purposely designed for such rigors. Still, Kay could feel the machine struggling to carry them up over the mountain. Roughly halfway up one long grade, Kay felt a considerable drag from the trailer. He glanced in the rear view mirror and saw that one of the trailer tires was slowly going flat. He didn't dare stop, for if he did he would never regain momentum. He continued chugging up the road until they reached the summit. By that time, the smoking trailer tire was completely shredded and useless. Considering the rocky road and the overload on the trailer, they felt lucky that only one tire had been destroyed. Kay was forced to shut the engine off to refuel and change the tire. Fortunately, they were on the downside of a steep hill, so after they changed the tire, and refueled, Kay was able to coast down the hill to restart the engine.

The road snaked down the mountainside, eventually delivering them onto a high and wide brush-strewn plateau breached by an enormous gorge, a gorge deeper and wider than any Kay had ever seen. He pulled the jeep over to the edge of the chasm for a rest stop and was transfixed by the panoramic view before him. The gorge reminded him of pictures he had seen of the Grand Canyon in Arizona. Nature had painted the canyon walls with subtle earthen tones of green, brown, yellow, and red. Had Kay known more about geology, he could have better appreciated the natural history written into the sides of the canyon. Layer after layer of limestone, chert, and sandstone superimposed one upon the other, each layer denoting various geological epochs. Eons of geotectonic uplifting and folding had twisted the various layers into weird, undulating stratum.

From their vantagepoint, the gorge seemed bottomless and the only guarantee that the road would eventually emerge from this abyss was that they could see the dirt and gravel road across the gorge winding through countless switchbacks to reach the top of the opposing plateau. It looked like it would be an imposing grade for the jeep to climb.

The drive down into the gorge was as traumatic a ride as one could imagine. Down, down the jeep went into the bowels of the abyss with Kay making liberal use of the compound low gears, the four-wheel drive, and the brakes, which soon began to smoke. He counted no less than thirty hairpin curves, many with skull and crossbones signs strategically placed to warn drivers of the dangers that lay ahead. There were no guardrails, walls, embankments or other barriers on the outside of the road to keep a warrant truck or bus from careening over the precipitous edge and taking an unplanned shortcut to the bottom. Kay continuously pumped the brakes, and several times, he had to stop to let them cool. By the time they arrived at the bottom, the acrid smell of brake lining assaulted their nostrils.

An angry whitewater river cascaded along the bottom of the gorge and flooded across the road. There was no bridge, the road simply plunged into the angry stream, and fifty-feet later emerged on the opposite bank. Bill joked that the heavy hemp rope strung across the river was strategically placed to catch unfortunate passengers swept into the raging river. Scott climbed out of the jeep and gingerly stepped into the river to test the solidity and water depth of the river bottom they would have to negotiate. Using the safety rope, Scott waded across the river to the opposite bank. The crossing was only knee deep for the entire distance, but the water was swift and muddy.

"Come on across!" Scotty shouted over the roar of the river. "It seems like a solid base of gravel and shale, no mud or sand to get stuck in and it is less than two feet deep."

Kay climbed out, checked that all four wheels were still locked in the four-wheel drive position, then put the jeep into compound low, and cautiously entered the river. Water splashed against the upriver side of the jeep and flooded the floorboards, but the high jeep clearances kept water out of the engine compartment. Amid a spray of rocks and gravel, the jeep climbed safely up the opposite bank.

As Bill climbed back into the jeep, he commented to Kay that he thought he smelled alcohol. Kay thought he did as well. They lifted the hood of the jeep and the smell of alcohol was overpowering. Kay could see the precious fuel squirting from the pump and forming a puddle on the ground below the engine.

"We have a problem!" Kay lamented. "The fuel pump has sprung a leak. It was probably hit by an errant rock as we climbed out of the river. At this rate, we will be out of fuel before we get halfway to Kanchow."

"So, what do you suggest we do?" Scotty asked.

"We will have to drive up the road a piece so we can coast down to restart the engine, find a wide spot to pull over, and try to fix the fuel pump," Kay suggested.

They drove up the road about one hundred yards to a generous pullover, and Kay shut the engine down. The jeep came equipped with a tool kit, so Kay was able to remove the fuel pump without a problem. He held the fuel pump in his hand and told Scotty that the pump "was a goner." The pump was a clamshell device held together with eight evenly spaced bolts and sealed by a cork gasket. The upper half of the clamshell had developed a hairline crack that extended across the entire top cover of the pump, and the cork gasket crumbled as Kay disassembled it. The rubber bladder inside was undamaged, but incoming fuel had been squirting through the crack and the disassembly had destroyed the gasket.

"There is no way I can think to fix this pump, and given the amount of fuel that is leaking from it, we will not make it into Kanchow," Kay warned.

"Perhaps we should wait here for a truck or bus," Tommy suggested. "One is bound to come by—*eventually.*"

Eventually could mean hours or days. They had only passed one other truck and a bus since leaving Yingtan. Scotty had driven this road before and didn't think that another vehicle was likely to come by later that day, but perhaps there would be one tomorrow. There wasn't much they could do except wait. They sat around for three hours without a sign of another vehicle. Since there was only an hour left before an early darkness would descend in the deep gorge, Scotty suggested that they walk back down to the river and make camp for the night. They made a fire, spread a tarp out on a flat gravel area beside the river, and began to prepare the evening meal. Scotty commented that the river reminded him of the whitewater rivers in America, and it was probably home to some fish. Fish would be great for dinner, yet Scotty had no fishing gear with him. He unraveled a few feet of yarn from his pullover sweater and found a short willow stick to use as a pole. The jeep toolbox contained several pin size nails, and with a pair of pliers, Scotty was able to bend one of these into a serviceable, but barbless hook. Tommy had opened their last can of tuna to share for dinner, so Scotty took several pieces for bait.

General Chin had been a rather indifferent and silent traveling companion to this point, but seemed very interested in Scotty's attempts to catch fish. He sat on a rock and watched Scotty cast his bait into the swift, roiling stream. He shook his head in disapproval after Scotty made several unsuccessful casts.

"No, no!" the General finally exclaimed, shaking his head in disapproval. He gently took the rod from Scotty's hand and climbed from rock to rock until he came upon a large blue-green pool upstream from camp. The pool was about twelve feet wide, and part of the stream spilled over a large boulder and entered the pool with a roar and spray of foam.

Three casts into the pool resulted in the first fish, a twelve-inch grayling. Three more grayling soon met the same fate. The General smiled at Scotty as they walked together back to camp with the four fish, which they cleaned and cooked over the open fire. Although delicious, Kay thought they were a bit on the bony side.

October 13, 1944 On the road to Kanchow

The sun did not rise in the deep canyon until late morning and not a single bus or truck had passed in all this time. After a good night's sleep, Kay had an idea how he might repair the fuel pump. He gave a piece of chewing gum to each person from a pack that he had bought in Yingtan, and asked them to chew it. He then cut a circular piece of rubber from one of the shredded inner tubes and made a gasket that he placed between the top and bottom half of the pump, then filled the offending crack from the inside with chewing gum. He replaced the repaired pump in the jeep and then rolled back down the hill to restart the engine. The makeshift repair seemed to do the trick, and not a drop of alcohol dripped from the pump.

The uphill road, covered by loose shale and gravel, was even narrower and more treacherous than the road had been leading into the canyon. Several times the wheels spun out as Kay tried to find a lower gear to pull them up the steep grade. He prayed that they would not meet another truck or bus while attempting to negotiate the grade. Kay sounded the horn around each blind curve. Pullouts were rare. Bill had the outside seat and complained that half the time he was hanging out over empty space. He probably was.

Rounding one corner with a sheer rock face on one side and a drop of hundreds of feet on the other, an abandoned lorry blocked the entire narrow road. The rear axle of the lorry was resting on a jack and the left rear wheel was missing. The owner could have moved the disabled truck to one side of the road to allow other traffic to pass, but he had made no attempt to do so before removing the wheel. There was no one around, and it was probable that although the next village was miles away, the owner had gone off to get his tire fixed. Bill and Kay got out of the jeep to examine the possibility of driving around the disabled lorry. There was absolutely no room on the wall side of the road to do so, and barely enough room to creep around on the drop-off side. Bill did not think it possible to do so without falling into the gorge, but Kay felt he could keep the wheels on the road and with proper directions carefully slip by.

Other options were few. They could wait until the owner returned with his repaired tire, which could be hours, or even a day or two. Alternatively, they could back down to the last turnout and then drive back to Yingtan. Neither of those options was acceptable. Kay cursed the lorry driver for his thoughtlessness.

"Damn him! Only a complete moron would abandon his truck

in the middle of the road and make no effort whatsoever to make room for other vehicles to pass by."

"How about if we release the brake and shove that piece of crap over the side?" Scotty suggested.

"Blast! Brilliant idea, but without the fourth wheel we could not move it that far," Bill reasoned.

"I really think we should try to make it around the truck. If Bill and I direct Kay, he could squeeze by." Scotty argued.

Everyone except Tommy agreed that Kay should "give it a go." Tommy pleaded that the jeep would certainly tumble into the gorge, but he was outvoted.

They all got out of the jeep as Kay slipped it into four-wheel drive and compound low, and with Bill and Scotty's directions, began to slowly ease the jeep around the lorry a foot at a time. Even by scraping the side of the lorry, the outside wheels of the jeep were very close to the edge of the cliff, and the trailer wheels which were slightly wider than those of the jeep, were inches from slipping off the road altogether. Kay could only trust that if this should happen, the trailer hitch would break loose and not drag the jeep with it into the chasm. The trailer wheels broke clods of dirt and rock loose from the edge of the road. The rocks tumbled into the ravine below thunderously echoing as they bounced from ledge to ledge. Kay inched the jeep and trailer forward and after five harrowing minutes of listening to Tommy's screams of impending disaster , he finally made it safely to the other side of the lorry.

They climbed back into the jeep and drove several miles to the top of the gorge where they found the lorry driver sitting on his damaged tire beside the road. As soon as the Chinese lorry driver saw the jeep, he jumped to his feet and waved his arms over his head. Kay stopped the jeep and climbed out. He put his face right up to the driver's face and let loose his full vocabulary of Chinese cuss words, starting and ending with the Chinese equivalent of "you moron". The poor man backed away and obviously flustered by Kay's outburst, could not explain why he left his truck in the middle of the road. Kay allowed him to throw his flat truck tire into the jeep trailer, but told him there was no room for him in the jeep, which was the truth. The next village of Nankang was miles away, and as far as Kay was concerned, "even if there had been room in the jeep, the jerk should walk the entire distance." Kay told him that he would leave the tire by the side of the road at Nankang. They took off in a cloud of dust leaving the forlorn lorry driver standing alone beside the road.

Kay continued down the road and stopped once to pump alcohol from the drum into the jeep gas tank. About 8 p.m. that evening they pulled into the city of Nankang. Scotty directed them to an inn where they found lodging for the night. Kay parked the jeep on a side street yet wondered how he would get it started the following morning. Scotty took them to a restaurant a few blocks from their hotel. As they came into the restaurant, they spied six American soldiers in full uniform drinking and laughing as they waited for their dinners. As soon as the Americans saw them enter they invited them to join them at their table, and it wasn't long before they were exchanging stories and jokes and quaffing Chinese beer. They had a very enjoyable dinner and told of their troubles with the jeep and the blocked road. The GIs had parked their six-by-six truck behind the restaurant and offered to help them start their jeep in the morning.

October 14, 1944, Ningtu

The next day the GIs not only gave the jeep a push, but also filled their gas tank and a spare fifty-five gallon gas drum with 100-octane aviation gasoline.

The city of Nankang was situated alongside a large lake that the road followed southward for several miles then continued through a marshy area for several more miles. Eventually it crossed over a large river and entered the city of Nanchang. Beyond Nanchang the road followed the Kan Kiang valley and then climbed into the mountains and through a mountain pass that led to the city of Kian (Ningtu).

They had made good time since leaving Nankang until another tire went flat. It was one of those gradual flats that give no warning until the tire is shredded and in ruins. To compound the problem, they could not find the wheel lug wrench. Lieutenant Scott surmised that they must have lost it when they changed the last flat tire. Kay managed to remove four of the five lug nuts with the spanner wrench in the tool kit, but the remaining nut was on so tight that it was impossible to remove it with that wrench. All they could do was shut off the engine and hope a truck would soon come along and help them. They ate their C-rations and waited for a truck or bus to show up.

Two hours later, a Chinese government truck chugged its way up the road and they waved it down. The driver loaned them the necessary lug wrench, and Kay removed all the jeep and trailer wheel lug nuts and carefully greased each so in the future they could more easily be removed with the spanner wrench. They made Ningtu by dinnertime and stopped in front of the local government run Rest House.

The Rest House was very crowded, but for a price, the innkeeper found room to accommodate everyone. After dinner that evening, Scotty tried to arrange for a tow to start the jeep in the morning, but he could not make the innkeeper understand what he wanted. Scotty asked Kay to talk with the innkeeper, but as far as this man was concerned, Kay's Kyangsher dialect may well have been Hindustani. As hard as Kay tried, gesticulating and using basic Chinese, he could not make the manager understand what he wanted. Out of frustration, Kay asked the man if he spoke French, and voila, he spoke perfect French! He thought they were asking for a tow all the way to Kanchow and was trying to explain that this was not possible, but once he understood that Kay just wanted a tow to start the jeep, he was more than willing to help.

October 15, 1944, Kanchow

After a wonderful breakfast of duck eggs and biscuits, a truck gave them the required tow and the engine started right up again. The jeep ran much better with 100-octane gasoline than with grain alcohol. Kanchow was eighty-five miles away, and there were only small villages between Ningtu and their destination. Before leaving Ningtu, Scotty thought it prudent to get one of the spare tires fixed. One spare tire was shredded beyond repair, and another was split along the sidewall. It would not do to be out on the road without at least one spare tire. Kay had asked the Rest House manager where they could find a motor car repair shop, but he had no idea nor did anyone else they asked. Kay drove up and down the streets of

Ningtu until he spied a bicycle repair shop and spoke with the proprietor. Could he fix their spare tire? Again there was a language barrier to overcome, and the owner spoke neither French nor English. The mechanic looked at the split spare tire and shrugged his shoulders then motioned for them to follow him. He led them outside the shop to a pile of used bicycle and motorcar tires, but none of these would fit their jeep. Kay picked up a tire that looked reasonably serviceable, borrowed a hacksaw and began cutting the tire into sections that he inserted into the inside of the split spare tire and glued them into place with rubber cement. After patching the inner tube with pieces of bicycle tubes, the spare was ready to be pumped up. A bit of a patch job, but it would have to do.

The road from Ningtu climbed high into the mountains toward a pass. The single lane road had few turnouts and again there were no guardrails to protect vehicles from the hundred foot drop-offs around every curve. The road had little traffic to speak of, other than carts and oxen drawn wagons. However, they did pass several trucks and military vehicles, and this made Kay very nervous. Without a muffler, the jeep made so much racket that Kay could not hear the warning beeps of oncoming traffic around the many sharp curves. Kay eased the jeep around each curve, sounded his horn, and prayed that they would not meet a speeding truck or bus. The Chinese drivers had no such concerns. They drove their vehicles at breakneck speed, relying on their horns and brakes to avoid head on crashes. Pullouts were rare, so when they did meet traffic, the uphill auto would have to back up until they either came across a pullout, or a part of the road wide enough for two cars. A few times, he was forced to pull over so close to the drop-off that his outside tires were barely on the road. Tommy shuddered each time such maneuvers became necessary, convinced that their jeep would slide off the road into oblivion. Nevertheless, Kay seemed to know just where the edge of the road was and how to keep all four jeep wheels solidly on the road.

About twenty miles from Kanchow, one of the jeep rear tires blew out, and as Kay changed that tire with the repaired spare, he noticed that one of the front tires had collected a nail and was slowly losing air. All he could do was have Scotty pump that tire up, then drive for ten or fifteen minutes, find a pullout, and pump the tire up again. It took them three hours to drive the twenty miles into Kanchow, and Scotty developed hand blisters from using the air pump. They were all relieved to finally see the Kanchow Bridge and after Scotty pumped the leaky tire one last time, they crossed over the river and drove into town. Kay let General Chin off at the local hospital and then drove through Kanchow. Once outside of Kanchow, Scotty directed them to a side road that led up to the American airfield, which was situated on a plateau several hundred feet about the city.

The airfield was humming with activity. Trucks and jeeps scurried between B-17 bombers parked in long rows on either side of the grass runway. On the dirt tarmac beside the hangar and operations hut were rows of P-51s and P-38s, fueled and ready for action. Ack-ack guns poked out of camouflage netting and machine gun placements up and down each side of the field. Soldiers were busily attaching bombs under the wings of P-38's and loading bombs into the bomb bays of B-17s as they prepared for an impending raid. Several C-47s (DC-3s) taxied to and from the main runway, and Kay counted dozens of these silver birds parked on the tarmac in front of the control tower. It was a thrill to hear the throb of American props cutting into the air and the drone of airplanes circling overhead awaiting their turn to land.

They pulled up to a Quonset hut with a large hand-lettered sign reading "Operations Center." Scotty went inside as Kay examined the jeep and trailer tires. He was shocked at what he discovered. Every tire had cuts and multiple bulges, and none looked like it would hold together for another two miles. Three hundred and fifty miles of ruts, potholes, nails, and sharp rocks had destroyed all six tires as well as the two spares; and it was surprising that they had made it safely to the airfield.

Kay patted the hood of the old jeep as if to say, "Good old boy, you needed glue and chewing gum, but you got us here."

Scotty came out of the Operations Center and invited Kay, Bill, and Tommy to come inside then introduced them to the Officer of the Day, Lieutenant Arnold Jennings.

"Do you think three Brits could hitch a ride to Kunming?" Kay pleaded.

"Sure thing," Lieutenant Jennings said without hesitation, "Lieutenant Scott has vouched for you folks and the U.S. Army Air Corps would be glad to give you a lift. Unfortunately, the last DC-3 for Kunming has already left. Be here at 6 a.m. tomorrow morning and I will arrange a flight out for you."

Lieutenant Jennings instructed his clerk to cut transportation orders to Kunming for the three men and added their names to the flight manifest.

Kay breathed a sigh of relief and said a little prayer of thanksgiving. God was still looking out for him.

Scotty drove the barely functioning jeep and trailer over to the motor pool and borrowed a good jeep, then drove everyone into Kanchow for dinner. Kanchow was an impressive yet atypical Chinese city. The son of Generalissimo Chiang Kai-shek himself was in command, and he had made Kanchow into a model city. Although extensively damaged by Jap bombs, the city was clean, neat and orderly. Burned out buildings and the twisted steel skeletons of former structures stood in stark evidence of the many months of Japanese air raids, yet the streets were clear with the rubble piled high on vacant lots.

The Generalissimo's son, whom the Americans nicknamed "no-nonsense Shek" ran Kanchow with an iron fist. Unlike every other Chinese city that Kay had visited, beggars, prostitutes, gambling, and narcotics were strictly prohibited. The city bustled with people, carts, rickshaws, and motor vehicles. Repair work was going on everywhere, with stacks of lumber, bricks and cement blocks arranged neatly alongside the streets. This was the first time since Shanghai that they observed bulldozers, cranes, and other heavy construction equipment at work. After dinner, they returned to the airfield where Lieutenant Jennings had arranged temporary lodging in the BOQ (Bachelor Officers Quarters).

Before retiring, Lieutenant Scott invited them into the Officers Club for a drink. A group of Yank officers sat drinking at a large table and after greeting Lieutenant Scott, they invited the escapees to join them. These folks had recently been assigned to Kanchow after taking part in the fighting on Guadalcanal in '42 and Kwajalin last summer. Understandably, they were disinclined to talk about their own experiences, yet wanted to hear all about Kay, Tommy, and Bill's adventures. Kay, reinforced by the testimony of his friends, related the entire story from their escape from Lunghwa Prison to the harrowing jeep ride to Kanchow. The officers marveled at their close escapes and laughed about the rigors of jeep travel. The Yanks listened intently to every word, and kept shoving drinks in front of them.

Kay was not much of a drinker, but felt compelled to down at least a few Whiskey and Sours as his story progressed. By the time he finished, he felt quite lightheaded. The Yanks broke into enthusiastic applause, shook their hands, and slapped all three of them on the back. Kay was a bit embarrassed by all this enthusiasm and was unaccustomed to the Yank tradition of backslapping. He felt he didn't deserve such praise, especially from these chaps, some of whom were recovering from wounds. He and his friends had not fought battles, or been wounded by Japanese bullets, or gone through the hell that these soldiers had endured. He begged to differ that they had done little to merit such acclaim.

"Quite the contrary," one of the Yanks argued. "You folks did your part to harass the Japanese by escaping from them. What you folks did took as much courage and fortitude as what we did on Guadalcanal, and for this you deserve our admiration," and that was that.

Toward the end of the evening, an Air Corps Major came into the bar with three leather flight jackets draped over his arm.

"It will be cold on your flight to Kunming and you might need these," he said nonchalantly, as he handed a jacket to each of them.

They were very grateful for the gift of warm jackets. The jackets that General Chang Da Yoh had purchased for them in Linghu were lightweight, intended to fend off the rain rather than provide much warmth.

As Lieutenant Scott drove them to the BOQ, he pointed out the location of the closest air raid shelter.

"The Japs often bomb this airfield, and if you hear the air raid siren or the "crummp-crummp" of bombs and the "bump-bump-bump" of ack-ack guns, get into this shelter immediately," he instructed.

The urgency of his warning was unnecessary. After all that they had been through, no Jap bomb was going to be their undoing! Thankfully, there were no air raids that night and they slept comfortably on their cots until awakened by Lieutenant Scott at 5 a.m.

CHAPTER ELEVEN

By Air to Kunming

✦⟫⟪✦

October 16, 1944, Kanchow Airbase

At sunrise, the airfield was completely socked in with fog and the tower reported "zero visibility." The C-47 they had been assigned to was loaded with cargo and ready to take off. They met with Captain Curtis, who was the U.S. Air Corps pilot on this flight. He told his passengers to standby, as the fog could lift at any moment. It was common for the mist to burn off from the 5,150-foot high Kanchow airport as soon as the sun peeked over the mountains. The passengers and crew waited patiently beside the airplane. In addition to Lieutenant Scott, Tommy, Bill, and Kay, there were six GIs and several Nationalist Chinese officers traveling to either Kunming or Liuhow, the refueling stop in Kweichow Province.

One of the Chinese officers was General Xu, the ranking Chinese Nationalist officer in Liuhow and a cousin of General Chang-Bang-fee. Kay told him of their stay with General Chang and assured him that his cousin was well, then added how grateful they were for the generosity and hospitality Chang had shown them. He showed General Xu the photograph of his cousin taken with Bill, Tommy, and Kay. The General was grateful for the news of his cousin and said that he had not heard from him for several months, but he looked well in the picture.

About 8:30 a.m. the tower reported that the ceiling had lifted to six thousand feet, so the pilot decided to give it a go. Everyone climbed on board and strapped themselves into a seat. The seats were little more than rough wooden boards that folded down from the sides of the aircraft. Since Kay was also a pilot, he asked if he could ride in the cockpit. Captain Curtis offered Kay the jump seat behind the co-pilot, where he had a good view out the front and port side windows. Captain Curtis taxied to the end of the runway and tested each engine before takeoff. White fluffy clouds completely shrouded the 12,000-foot high mountain peaks surrounding Kanchow. The fog on the airfield had not entirely dissipated; but they could now see the windsock at the end of the runway. Captain Curtis taxied to the end of the runway, revved the engines of the C-47 to full throttle, released the brakes and the airplane bounced down the grass runway and into the cloud covered sky.

As they climbed into the thin mountain air over Kanchow, Kay soon understood why pilots affectionately called the C-47 a gooney bird. As they jounced up and down in the turbulent air, the wings seemed to flap much like those of a bird. The mountains surrounding Kanchow thrust their jagged summits five thousand feet above the airfield, and as they circled to gain altitude, the airplane was soon enveloped in pea-soup fog. The pilot couldn't see a thing and it was risky to attempt to return to the field so he continued to fly in tight circles hoping to break through the clouds. The C-47 was unpressurized, and as they passed through twelve thousand feet Kay struggled to breathe in the thin air. It was also bitterly cold, so Kay zipped up his new leather flight jacket and settled back into his seat. At twelve thousand five hundred feet they finally broke through the clouds and leveled off.

Surrounded by several ominous mountain peaks that poked above the cloud cover, Captain Curtis cautiously skimmed the sea of white cotton clouds, and headed for a mountain pass to the west. The pilot radioed the airfield and set a direct course for Liuhow airdrome, which was to be a stopover on the way to their final destination at Kunming. The air traffic controller radioed back that "although he couldn't see them, he could hear their motors, and the airfield was under attack from Jap Zeros." The C-47 was the only aircraft in the air at the time and the control tower warned Curtis "you had better get the hell out of there as fast as a bunny in heat."

Suddenly three Jap Zeros, the red rising sun prominent on their tails and wings, flew out of the clouds directly below. The C-47 was unarmed, slow, and lumbering compared to the swift Zeros. There was no way to outrun them. The Japanese airplanes were five hundred feet below and fortunately had not yet spotted the C-47. The Japanese probably had overheard the warning from the tower and were obviously searching for a C-47. Their airplane would be a sitting duck should it be discovered. To Kay's left an altocumulus cloud billowed high above them and Captain Curtis sharply banked toward the cloud just as a Zero spotted the helpless airplane. Once inside the cloud Captain Curtis couldn't see squat, but neither could the Japs. He set his compass bearing southwest toward Liuhow, then climbed to fourteen thousand five hundred feet to avoid the twelve to thirteen thousand-foot mountain peaks that surrounded the airplane. Without oxygen, Kay struggled to breathe at this altitude.

A few minutes later as they emerged from one cloud and headed toward another, Kay suddenly heard a rat-tat-tat-rat-tat! Two Zeros passed directly underneath with their machine guns blazing. Ping-ping-ping—, three bullet holes appeared on the left wing, just missing the engine. The Japanese whizzed past and began a 180-degree turn for a second pass. Captain Curtis dove into another cloud before the Zeros could make a second run at them and banked sharply to the left.

"We will just have to hide in these clouds until those damn Nips get tired of looking for us," Captain Curtis said. "They won't hang around very long 'cause by now they will be low on fuel and it is a long haul back to their airbase in Hanoi."

He turned to Kay and asked, "Kay, please go back into the cabin and see if everyone is alright."

Kay unbuckled and went back into the cabin. One of the Chinese officers was lying on the floor with Tommy, General Xu and a couple of others kneeling beside him. Kay noticed a pool of blood beside the fallen officer, and several bullet holes in the side of the airplane where the officer had been sitting.

"He's been hit," Tommy cried. "See if the pilot has a medical kit onboard."

Kay went back into the cockpit and the co-pilot handed him a first aid kit. When he returned, Tommy was slowly shaking his head.

"No need," Lieutenant Scott said to Kay, "the poor bugger is dead." Kay recognized the fallen soldier as one of General Xu's aides.

No one else had been hit, although there were dozens of bullet holes all along the left side of the fuselage, right in between Tommy and Bill's seats. It was a miracle that they had not taken a Jap bullet. Scotty was sitting on the opposite side of the aircraft, and there were no bullet holes on that side.

Kay went back into the cockpit and delivered the bad news. Captain Curtis circled inside the cloud for several more minutes before resuming his original course. When the airplane poked out of the cloud, the pilot, co-pilot and Kay craned their necks looking for the Zeros, but did not see them. He then dove into the next cloud and continued to dodge from cloud to cloud for the better part of the next hour, keeping to a zigzag course toward Liuhow. Kay noticed the oil pressure gauge on the port engine was dropping toward the red line. He looked out the side window and saw that the engine cowling was streaked with black oil. About 100 miles away from Liuhow, the portside engine choked and sputtered to a stop, trailing thick black smoke behind it. The co-pilot feathered the engine and threw the fire extinguisher switch.

"God damned stinking Nips got the engine," Captain Curtis swore, "I've been watching it overheat for the past half-hour. Not to worry, this bird can fly on only one engine."

Despite the pilot's assurances, Kay noticed that the altimeter was slowly moving counterclockwise, which indicated they were losing altitude. He went back into the main cabin, explained the situation in Chinese and English, and told everyone to put on a parachute. When Kay returned to the cockpit, Captain Curtis was talking with the tower in Liuhow. Their situation was exacerbated by the fact that the Liuhow airport was at forty nine hundred feet and surrounded by high mountains. At the rate that they were losing altitude, it was doubtful that they would make it over the eighty-five hundred-foot mountains between themselves and the airport. It was going to be close. Captain Curtis sent Kay and the co-pilot back into the cabin with instructions to lighten the load.

"Throw whatever isn't bolted down overboard," Curtis advised.

They opened the large side cargo door and began chucking cargo into space. Several of the Chinese officers helped shove eight pallets of cargo out the door along with sixteen large boxes of ammunition and other supplies.

Kay returned to his seat and looked up at the snow-covered mountain peaks looming directly ahead. They all looked higher than the present altitude of the airplane. Captain Curtis was focusing on controlling the airplane, which was shaking badly and kept yawing to their left. Kay looked out the port window and noticed a gap between the cloud-shrouded peaks.

"Over there," Kay poked the pilot's shoulder and pointed, "there's a pass through the mountains!"

Captain Curtis banked toward the pass and radioed the tower his intentions. The altimeter read 8,100 feet, and the tower reported that the pass they were headed toward was at 7,800 feet. They were losing altitude at 100 feet per minute and at this rate of descent by the time they arrived at the pass, they would be at 7,600 feet, too low to clear the pass. Captain Curtis revved the remaining engine to the redline rpm's and watched the temperature gauge slowly climb. The altimeter held at 7,900 feet as they approached the pass. There were no clouds shrouding the pass but it was covered in tall pine trees.

"Damn," Captain Curtis cried out, "I hadn't figured on 100 foot high pines covering the pass."

The tops of the trees looked dangerously close as they flew over them with only a few feet to spare. Everyone in the cockpit breathed a sign of relief as the mountains gave way and the airport gradually came into view in the valley below. With the remaining engine dangerously overheating, Captain Curtis throttled back and began a slow descent toward the airport runway. He contacted the Liuhow tower for landing instructions.

The tower told him to go around and land on the crosswind runway because the runway he had chosen was obstructed by a wrecked B-25.

"Go around?" Captain Curtis yelled into the mike, "I can't go around, I only have one engine and it doesn't have enough power to go around.

I am going to try to land on the access runway!"

"You do not have permission to land on the access taxiway. There are airplanes parked on either side!" the controller ordered.

The access taxiway was barely long enough for a safe landing and in addition, it was narrow and unpaved. However, they had no other choice but to attempt a landing on it. Kay said a prayer.

Captain Curtis lowered the wheels and flaps and lined up with the taxiway. B-25s lined both sides of the taxiway and on the main runway, a bulldozer was busily pushing the smoking wreckage of a B-25 to the side, but the runway would not be cleared in time for their landing. It would have to be the taxiway or the flooded rice field beside it. The captain had once landed in a rice field and it wasn't pretty. After several cartwheels across the field, he was lucky to come away with only a broken collarbone.

A stiff crosswind caused their airplane to first yaw to the left, then the right. The right wing dipped at an alarming angle and Curtis straightened it out, only to have the left wing dip. He managed to get squared up and throttled back as the gooney bird passed over the pylons that marked the end of the taxiway. They hit rather hard and bounced back into the air, then hit and bounced a second time. After they hit the taxiway for a third time, Curtis managed to keep the aircraft on the ground and stood on the brakes until the C-47 came to a halt within 100 yards of several aircraft parked on the tarmac at the end of the taxiway. He taxied over to a wide spot on the tarmac, braked and cut the starboard engine, which by now was belching copious amounts of thick black smoke. A fire truck pulled up alongside and sprayed white foam onto the starboard engine and the still-smoking port engine. Curtis along with his passengers and crew climbed down from the wounded bird and stood on the tarmac grinning at one another.

"Well, any landing you can walk away from is a good landing!" Captain Curtis proclaimed. Then added, "anyone need a change of underwear?"

A paddy wagon drove up to them and three MP's and a Major climbed out. The Major asked who was the pilot of this airplane.

Curtis saluted and said that he was.

"You are in big trouble," the Major said. "You disobeyed a direct order not to land on the access runway."

"I had no other choice," Captain Curtis said. "It was the access runway or the rice paddy, and the rice paddy did not look too inviting."

Curtis was escorted by the MP's to the paddy wagon

Kay had looked forward to this airplane ride for some time, but such a spectacular one had not been part of his plans. Their airplane was obviously not going on to Kunming, and with Captain Curtis under detention, they marched over to the operations hut to see what other arrangements could be made. Again, luck was with them. A Cargo C-47 was headed to Kunming later that afternoon and the Officer of the Day said that they were welcome to hitch a ride.

Later, Kay went over to headquarters to see how Captain Curtis was getting along. Kay found him in the mess hall. He had been released without any formal charges being lodged.

"I was detained on a bureaucratic mix up, and I straightened it out with the General." he explained.

"I'm not going back to Kanchow," Curtis said, "The word is that the damned Nips have made that airfield temporarily unusable. My outfit is relocating here."

"Well, the best of luck to you," and thanks for the lift," Kay said shaking the captain's hand for the final time.

Kay left Curtis standing there wondering if Kay was being sarcastic about the "thanks for the lift" part. "I'll never figure out Brits!" Curtis mumbled to himself as Kay walked away.

CHAPTER TWELVE

Bureaucratic Red Tape

-+=○⊂=+-

Lieutenant Scott took Kay and his friends over to the Officers
Club for a drink while they waited for their airplane. If ever a
stiff drink was definitely in order, this was the time. They all had a
double Scotch on the rocks, followed by a Sapporo beer. Tommy
asked the sergeant bartender how it was that they had Japanese beer.

The sergeant grinned and said "We took several cases from the
Nips when we took Guam from them last month. Mac (General
MacArthur) had it flown over here. Not bad stuff, but watch out, it
is stronger than that piss-water you Limeys are used to."

Kay was just beginning to unwind from their harrowing airplane
ride, when the Liuhow air raid siren wailed. Everyone in the bar ran
to the air raid bunker located behind the Officer's Club with the
sound of ack-ack guns and the thump-thump of bombs ringing in
their ears. One bomb exploded just 100 yards away scoring a direct
hit on a B-25 parked on the tarmac. The B-25 was loaded with
bombs and the resulting secondary percussions threw Kay onto the
tarmac. Dazed, he picked himself up and stumbled into the bunker.
Kay looked for blood on his shirt and finding none, looked around
the bunker for Tommy and Bill who had been running ahead of him
before the B-25 exploded. He spied them huddled on a bench at the
back of the crowded bunker. Kay pushed through the others in the
room and stood in front of his friends. Bill's mouth was moving, but
Kay could not hear him over the ringing in his ears. In fact, Kay

could not hear anything, yet he felt the concussions from additional explosions that continued to rock the airfield for several minutes. When the "all clear" sounded, Bill grabbed Kay and they stepped outside the bunker. Several fires were burning alongside the airfield. Thick black smoke billowed up from what minutes ago had been a serviceable B-25 and now was just a pile of twisted smoking metal no longer recognizable as an airplane.

Lieutenant Scott ran up to them and yelled something that Kay could not hear. Tommy and Bill followed Scotty and Kay tagged along, not knowing what was up or where they were going. Scotty led them to a C-54 on the tarmac that already had one engine going. Several GIs and Chinese soldiers were climbing into the aircraft, and Scotty, Bill, Tommy and Kay got in line. The pilot was anxious to get off the ground before a second wave of Japanese bombers hit the airfield, and a sergeant stood beside the rear door encouraging everyone to get onboard. Kay found a seat and buckled his seatbelt as the aircraft taxied onto the runway. The C-54 had been partially converted to a passenger aircraft by adding four rows of seats immediately behind the cockpit bulkhead. Behind the passenger seats, pallets and boxes of goods were strapped to the floor and secured to the sides of the fuselage with webbing.

Kay took a front row window seat that had a good view forward of the wing. As the airplane accelerated down the runway, it passed several still smoking bomb craters lining the airstrip. The C-54 lifted off the runway and smoothly climbed into the twilight sky. Scotty took the seat next to Kay and tried to say something to him, but Kay could not make out a single word. In fact, he was barely aware of the drone made by the engines over the ringing in his ears.

As night fell, a full moon brightened the landscape below. The airplane climbed to fourteen thousand feet to avoid the snow capped twelve thousand-foot mountain peaks clearly visible in the moonlight, and after a bitter-cold four-hour flight, the C-54 began a gradual descent into Kunming airport. Kay's hearing gradually returned as his ears adjusted to the increasing air pressure.

To their south, a large lake shimmered in the moonlight and Kay could make out the white cliffs bordering the east side of the lake and a large scar on the mountain above it. Kay pointed the scar out to Scotty who, shouting over the noise of the engines, said that this was Kunming Lake and the scar was the remnants of a huge landslide that had tumbled down the mountainside and smashed into the lake a year ago. The landslide raised a fifteen-foot tsunami that smashed into lakeside buildings on the western side of the lake and drowned dozens of folks. The lights of Kunming glowed beyond the western edge of the lake and an airport beacon light flashed like a lighthouse guiding them toward the runways. Located beyond the reach of Japanese fighters and bombers, Kunming airport accommodated both civilian and military traffic, and was one of the busiest airports in Asia. The pilot circled around the field for fifteen minutes waiting for his "all clear" from the flight control tower, then got in line right behind a B-29 bomber.

The C-54 landed on the brightly lit, paved runway and taxied over to the terminal. The sergeant opened the side door and everyone climbed down onto the tarmac. The Yanks and Chinese soldiers disappeared into the night, but Kay, Bill, and Tommy remained next to the aircraft with Lieutenant Scott, who said a jeep was on the way to pick them up. The jeep appeared ten minutes later and they all climbed in and drove to the opposite side of the airport and the Operations Office. They barged into the dimly lit operations office and Scotty asked the corporal on duty if he could contact Major Wichtrich of AGAS. The soldier said that he didn't know a Major Wichtrich and, in fact, had never heard of the AGAS.

Scotty seemed befuddled and looked again at his written orders, which clearly stated that he should contact a Major Wichtrich of AGAS when they arrived in Kunming. The corporal looked quizzically at the three Brits, who were obviously not military and asked Lieutenant Scott what their business was. Scotty showed his orders to the corporal and explained that the three British civilians had escaped Lunghwa prison near Shanghai, walked across China and were trying to get safe passage to India. The corporal looked over Scotty's orders, smiled and said that a C-54 passenger airplane was due to leave for Calcutta within the hour, and he would immediately cut orders for the three to hitch a ride if he could find the Officer of the Day to sign them. All he needed from them was their passports or citizenship papers.

Naturally, Kay, Bill, and Tommy did not have any papers other than the written transportation orders from Lieutenant Jennings in Kanchow. The corporal said, "sorry, but no papers, no airplane ride out of China". His refusal didn't fluster Lieutenant Scott who knew that his orders required the escapees to first contact a Major Wichtrich before leaving for India. Even if a ride was immediately available, orders were orders! First, they would have to find Major Wichtrich.

A few minutes later, the Officer of the Day appeared and seemed pleased to throw a wet blanket on their travel plans.

"Without passports no one can authorize transportation out of China for you Brits," the OD explained. Then he added with a sly smile, "perhaps your Major Wichtrich can arrange some magic with the local British Consul and encourage them to issue you passports in a hurry. However, I have never heard of a Major Wichtrich and every experience I have had with the British Consul office has been very frustrating. I wish you luck, but you might have better success with the British Embassy in Chungking."

Chungking! Kay had no intention of flying to Chungking for a passport.

The OD made several telephone calls and finally handed the phone to Scotty and said that this fellow could possibly help them. On the line was a Lieutenant Maiser of AGAS. He explained that Major Wichtrich was in India on his way back to the States and had left no instructions regarding Kay, Tommy, or Bill. Nevertheless, he could arrange for them to be billeted and fed here at Kunming Airbase. Perhaps they could straighten things out in the morning. In no time, a jeep arrived to pick them up. It was driven by Master Sergeant Guttmann who drove them the two miles over to the BOQ and officers Mess and arranged for their care. They ate and said "cheerio" to Scotty, who was due to return on a flight to Liuhow later that night. Scotty had been a great companion and a good friend, and they were all sad to part company.

October 17, 1944, Kunming
The following morning Sergeant Guttmann came by and drove them over to the AGAS headquarters where they met Captain

Frank Mullen who had assumed Major Wichtrich's duties. Mullen was an U.S. Army captain temporarily assigned to the AGAS office in Kunming. He apologized for what he called a "major SNAFU" (a Yank anachronism that meant Situation Normal All Fouled Up). Major Wichtrich received his orders to return home and only had a few hours notice to pack and wrap up his duties at Kunming. The escapees' situation was evidently not part of his wrap up process.

Kay gave Captain Mullen the orders from Lieutenant Jennings, and the captain went to work typing out new orders for Kay, Tommy and Bill's transportation to India. He thought they could make it onto a flight to Calcutta the day after tomorrow or perhaps by the end of the week, but first they would have to get the British Consulate in Kunming to issue new passports and exit permits, and this could take, "who know how long". In the meantime, he asked Kay to type out everything he could remember since being incarcerated in Lunghwa. He showed Kay to an office with an old Underwood typewriter and gave him a stack of paper and carbon sheets for the report. Other than that task, they were to make themselves comfortable and wait for further instructions.

They had not yet had breakfast, so they walked over to the cafeteria in the main building on base. As they exited the food line, Kay thought he recognized a man in military garb sitting alone at a nearby table. He took a second look, and he could not believe his eyes. The man was Ray Phillips, a good friend and American business associate who had worked for Globe Wireless in Shanghai, and was often Kay's Bridge partner at the Club. Kay sat down at the table and simply said, "Hello Ray!"

Ray looked up from his sausage and eggs and almost dropped his fork.

"Kay, you Old Bugger, how in bloody hell did you get to Kunming? I thought you were in Lunghwa."

"Well, I was until I cut the wire and escaped with these good friends two months ago," Kay said with a wink.

Kay introduced Bill and Tommy and they ate breakfast together as Kay retold the story of their travels to Kunming, with Bill and Tommy filling in some missing details. Ray's breakfast grew cold as he listened intently to every word of their story. After Kay finished, Ray had some news of his own. He had been repatriated from another prison near Shanghai and shipped out with Lillian and Darryl on the *Teia Maru* to Goa, the Portuguese port in India where the American/Japanese prisoner exchange took place. Lillian and Darryl had found passage to the USA and Ray had taken a commission with the U.S. Army Intelligence Office and ended up stationed in Kunming. This was the first news Kay had received about his family since he waved goodbye to them so many months ago. Lil and Darryl were safe in the USA. Kay was ecstatic!

"I have some more news for you," Ray teased. "Guess who is also here in Kunming?"

"Who?" Kay was in no mood for guessing.

"Your brother-in-law!" Ray exclaimed.

"Sid?" Kay exclaimed, "Sid is here in Kunming?

"None other!" Ray laughed. "He is a lieutenant working for the American Army. You can call him from the AGAS office." He wrote Sid's phone number on a scrap of paper and arranged to meet for dinner later that night at a restaurant in Kunming.

Sid and Ray had worked together for the Globe Wireless Company in Shanghai, and both had been repatriated and shipped out on the same boat as Lil and Darryl. They still played weekly Bridge together at the Officers Club.

"Where...how can I contact him? Kay asked.

"No problem," Ray said. "You can call from the AGAS office."

Ray drove them over to the AGAS office and Kay gave Captain Mullen the reports he had written in Shangjao along with some other documents that Lieutenant Schelyer had entrusted to their care. Before beginning his typing job intended to add the journey from Shangjao to Kunming to his report, Kay called his brother-in-law on the telephone.

"Lieutenant Marco, please," Kay asked the Orderly who answered the phone.

A voice soon came on the line. "Lieutenant Marco here, how can I help you?"

Kay gave him the razzberry, which was a little joke between them.

The line was silent, so Kay repeated the razzberry, louder and longer this time.

"Kay, is that you?" Sid asked dumbfounded.

"It sure is Old Bean," Kay answered.

"How in the Hell—what are you doing in Kunming?" Sid demanded.

Kay explained that he was in the AGAS office and Sid said he would be right over. Kay hung the telephone receiver up, and less than five minutes later Sid came crashing into Mullen's office. He saluted Lieutenant Mullen and slapped Kay on the back. Kay introduced him to Bill and Tommy, and Sid asked if he could take them over to his place. Lieutenant Mullen said the reports could wait, so they all piled into Sid's jeep and ended up at the Officers' Club for a drink.

Before telling their escape story, Kay wanted to hear any news Sid had about Lil and Darryl.

"You mean my sister and nephew? Well, they are in the USA of course," Sid said matter-of-factly.

"Just where in the USA for heaven's sake?" Kay asked a bit exasperated.

"In New York City," Sid answered.

"How about an address?" Kay persisted.

"Hmm...somewhere in Greenwich Village I think," Sid was teasing him, a likely retribution for the razzberry.

Clearly, Kay was becoming agitated with Sid's game.

"You bloody bastard, give me an exact address."

"Oh, 58 West 8th Street, Apartment 6B. They are both doing well."

The mean Old Cuss, taking advantage of a poor refugee! Kay seized both of Sid's shoulders and shook him violently as other officers looked on in amusement. They all laughed, and enjoyed a round of beers before going over to Sid's quarters. They had lots to jaw about too, since Kay had not seen Sid since 1941. They reminisced until almost 6 p.m. when they piled into the jeep and drove to a restaurant in Kunming to meet with Ray for dinner. They talked and talked, drank and ate and laughed together until almost 11 p.m., when Sid took them back to the BOQ. It was the most enjoyable evening Kay had experienced in years.

October 18, 1944 Kunming

The next morning they returned to Lieutenant Mullen's office. Bill wanted to go only as far as India and accept his commission with the R.A.F. there, while Tommy and Kay wanted to fly to the good old USA where their wives waited for them. Could Lieutenant Mullen make such arrangements? Well, it would take some string pulling since they were British citizens, Lieutenant Mullen warned. He said that he had contacted the British Consulate officer, Captain Robinson, who would see them in his office in Kunming before noon. Lieutenant Mullen then drove Bill, Kay, and Tommy into Kunming and dropped them off at the Consulate office.

Captain Robinson was a good chap, who immediately set about to arrange papers for each of them. Technically, although he had never received his commission, Bill was very much in the military since signing up in Shanghai months ago and as such did not need a passport. He had signed up with the British army and was awaiting his commission when Pearl Harbor changed everything. Yet commissioned or not, he was still considered part of the British army. Robinson arranged Bill's military clearance and cut orders for him to take an R.A.F. flight the next morning to Calcutta. He then filled out the applications for new British passports and exit permits from China for Kay and Tommy. Actually, Kay was a Canadian citizen and as such could apply for either a Canadian or British passport, but there was no Canadian Consulate office in China at the time so his application was to the British Consulate in London.

"These passports could take a day or two, or even as much as a week in some cases to come through" Robinson warned. "I will have the attaché cable London today, but it often takes several hours for a response. Check in later today."

He asked Lieutenant Mullen to arrange transportation for them to the USA, but first they would have to travel over the hump to Calcutta where the B.A.A.G., the British equivalent of the AGAS, would be responsible for them. Lieutenant Mullen explained that this might take a bit more doing, so when he returned to his office he sent a Teletype message to Washington asking for permission to arrange transportation to Calcutta for British escapees Kay and Tommy. As Mullen worked on clearances, Kay busied himself that afternoon on the Underwood to update his report. Hampered by his two-finger typing technique, it took several hours for Kay to type out his story.

Later that afternoon Captain Mullen shared mixed news with them. Transportation to Calcutta had been approved contingent on valid exit permits and passports. They would not be allowed into India without this documentation. The B.A.A.G. office could help them obtain American Visas through the American Consulate in Bombay and arrange transportation to the U.S.A, but first British Intelligence in New Delhi wanted to debrief them. This all sounded like a lot of bureaucratic mumbo-jumbo to Kay, yet at least the passports process was under way. He understood that they would have to jump through all the necessary hoops to get into the USA.

Sid phoned and said that he had arranged a reunion dinner of sorts in a downtown Kunming restaurant, and he would be over shortly to pick them up. Before dinner, Sid gave them a brief tour of Kunming. The old name for Kunming was Yunnanfu, which was not only a musical sounding word in and of itself, but it conjured up every kind of colorful picture one imagines of ancient China. The center of Kunming was filled with aged temples, beautiful parks, and ornate public buildings. They visited a museum filled with ancient Chinese art, Ming Dynasty artifacts, and exquisite examples of original Chinese writings and folklore.

Before dinner, they visited the British Consul attaché to check on their passport applications. The attaché shuffled through a stack of papers and said that the passport request cable had not yet been sent. He seemed bored with their application and reiterated that it could take some time to verify their citizenship with London. Kay had a difficult time hiding his frustration and anger over the complete disinterest shown by the Consulate office and this attaché. He stifled a sarcastic comment and politely asked the attaché if he "would be so kind as to expedite their requests." The attaché responded by moving their cable passport request closer to the top of his stack of stuff.

At dinner that evening, they met Ray and several of Kay's

acquaintances from Singapore, including Neil Brown, the onetime manager of the Globe Wireless Shanghai office. Long before dinner was served, drinks were poured. It never failed to amaze Kay how it was considered socially unacceptable not to match drinking partners drink for drink. Kay's limit was usually two drinks; however, his glass was never allowed to go empty. Tommy, a hard-drinking Scotsman, did his part to imbibe socially for both he and Kay, and no one noticed that Tommy was drinking from both his glass and Kay's.

October 19, 1944, Kunming

After an emotional send-off for Bill on his R.A.F. flight to Calcutta, Tommy and Kay went to breakfast at the base cafeteria where Kay ran into another old Shanghai friend, Dee Brown. Dee had been a rowing club partner of Kay's in the Shanghai Skull Club. They were also both civilian pilots, and before the Japanese confiscated all private aircraft in Shanghai, Dee had often invited Kay to fly with him in his Lockheed Lodestar. He had just been promoted to Lieutenant Colonel in the U.S. Army Air Corps. After the customary greetings, back slapping and exchange of stories, Dee looked pitifully at their light summer khaki clothes, the same shirts and pants General Chang had purchased for them in Linghu.

"Those clothes, with the exception of your flight jackets and boots, will never do," Dee proclaimed.

He took them over to the Quartermaster and had them outfitted in GI winter uniforms. The uniforms were used but had been cleaned and came with all the customary enlisted men's insignias and patches. They felt very comfortable in their new clothes, but it did cause them a bit of a problem later that day when they visited the Officer's Club (OC) with Sid and Dee.

The Officer's Club shared the same building with the Enlisted Men's Club (EMC) with only a double door separating the two rooms. The EMC was always more crowded than the OC, and that evening there was a long line waiting to get into the EMC, yet there were plenty of empty tables and no line at all in the OC. Kay and Tommy did not realize what a stir they would create by entering the OC dressed in their enlisted men's uniforms.

When they found a table and Dee and Sid went to get drinks,

226

three officers came over and told Tommy and Kay in no uncertain terms that they had quite a nerve to enter the OC. Kay tried to explain that they were escapees and had just been given the uniforms; notwithstanding, one burley captain would hear none of it. He and his officer friends were about to haul both Brits outside by the scruff of their necks, when Dee intervened. The silver bird on Dee's collar snapped all three officers to attention. After explanations were given, everyone laughed and sat down to toast one another. Neither Kay nor Tommy were allowed to buy a single round the rest of the evening.

Nonetheless, as payment for drinks and acceptance at the OC required them to repeat their escape story for the nth time. By now, Kay had the story down pat, and had created a *Readers' Digest* shortened version. Later that evening, Kay and Tommy were invited to a movie on base by one of their new American friends. It was the first movie they had been to in years, something with Clark Gable and Ginger Rogers. The title of the movie wasn't memorable for either of them, all Kay could remember was that it was a musical, but they were very impressed with the sound track and color. Neither of them had ever watched a movie photographed in color before.

October 20-23, 1944, Kunming

The British Consulate office in Kunming seemed in no hurry to obtain the clearances necessary to issue passports. Kay and Tommy visited the office only to find out that after five days, the request for passports had not even been sent to London. The requests still sat gathering dust on the attaché's desk. Kay complained bitterly, but the attaché, showed no concern for the escapees situation and simply said he would get to it when he could. Kay tried to see Captain Robinson, but he was not in the office, and wasn't expected back for a few days.

Thoroughly frustrated with the attitude of the Kunming British Consulate office, Kay and Tommy returned to the AGAS office to see if there was anything Captain Mullen could do to expedite their paperwork.

"Put a firecracker under their lazy bottoms," was the way Tommy put it.

Captain Mullen said that his office had little pull with the British Consulate, and this was typical of their behavior. He suggested that they might have better luck with the British Embassy in Chungking. He offered to arrange transportation to Chungking on a flight leaving the next day. After obtaining their passports in Chungking, they could then return to Kunming and catch a flight to Calcutta. Chungking had not been part of their escape plans since Lunghwa, but here they were now faced with just such a visit. It seemed better than just sitting around waiting for the British Consular Office to do their job. Captain Mullen said he would arrange for them to fly to Chungking as soon as possible.

That night they attended a show put on by the United Service Organization (USO). The show headlined Pat O'Brien and Jinx Falkenberg, along with several voluptuous showgirls. Kay and Tommy thought it a wonderful show and had not laughed so hard in months.

CHAPTER THIRTEEN

Chungking

❖⟹⟸❖

October 24, 1944, Chungking

Captain Mullen arranged for a flight to Chungking on a mid-morning C-47. He also called Captain Robinson's assistant over at the British Consulate and explained the problem that Tommy and Kay were experiencing with the Consulate office, and in particular with the attaché. The assistant was apologetic, but agreed that the Chungking Embassy had a reputation for competent, fast service in cases such as Kay and Tommy's. He promised to cable the Embassy office copies of Kay and Tommy's passport applications immediately.

The C-47 climbed quickly through layers of cold gray clouds hanging over Kunming and broke into the clear blue sky above. The aircraft was fitted with wartime netting seats hung along the fuselage to achieve maximum payload. Kay was one of the few who had a window next to his netting. The other passengers included a dozen Chinese Nationalist soldiers, five American officers. Kay and Tommy were the only Brits onboard. Crates and packages were held in place by additional web netting. The airplane was unheated and unpressurized, which again made for a very uncomfortable, long flight.

As they circled the city of Chungking, Kay observed two separate landing strips. The main airport was outside the city along the road to Chengtu, while the other was an alternate airstrip on an island in the middle of the Yangtze Kiang. During the spring floods the island airstrip would be under several feet of fiercely swirling water as it rushed headlong toward the China Sea fifteen hundred miles downstream, but this time of the year the island was high and dry. The river was nearly a mile wide, and even at low water the current ran so deep and fast and that if people fell into it, they would be swept away and battered to death. It would not have made much difference to their survival, but few Chinese were strong swimmers. With the melting snow in springtime, the river could rise several feet overnight and sweep away anything or anybody foolish enough to remain on the banks below the high-water mark. Every year the Yangtze claimed the lives of many Chungking citizens.

Because this was the middle of October, and the river was at its lowest point of the year, the pilot had been instructed to land on the alternate dirt airstrip. The pilot was forced to maneuver the C-47 south of the runway to avoid the electric power lines that stretched across the Yangtze River and were directly in the flightpath leading to the island airstrip. No other government would have tolerated such an obvious hazard, but the Nationalists evidently never thought to reroute the power lines. After they landed, a truck came out to meet the airplane and drive the passengers into downtown Chungking. Kay and Tommy were deposited at the British embassy, an ornate building that once was a museum.

They entered the embassy, and the clerk on duty ushered them into the office of the assistant ambassador. He explained that a cable had already been received from London confirming their citizenship and their passports were ready to be issued.

Impressed with such unusual efficiency, Kay commented, "Well, finally we are getting somewhere!"

Although the passports were authorized, the assistant said that Kay and Tommy were required to pay ten pounds sterling each before he could issue them. Kay was dumbfounded! It didn't seem to occur to this numbskull that poor refugees would not have ten shillings, not to mention ten pounds to pay for a passport. This was simply more mindless British bureaucracy. Tommy pleaded that they had escaped from a Japanese prison camp and had only a few

Chinese dollars between them and little means of obtaining the required tax, but the fellow just shrugged his shoulders and repeated, "Sorry, no money, no passport, rules are rules."

Kay demanded to see the ambassador, but his assistant claimed that he "was detained" with other business. Tommy asked if the ambassador was planning to be "detained" tomorrow. His assistant would only offer a "perhaps" in response. Determined to see the ambassador and plead their case, Kay and Tommy found an inexpensive nearby hotel, paid for a room, and then treated themselves to a nice dinner with their remaining funds.

October 25-30 1944, Chungking City

The following day Kay and Tommy visited the British embassy a second time. Kay sat down in the ambassador's outer office and said he would remain there until Hell froze over, or the ambassador agreed to see them, whichever came first.

"What a bunch of bureaucratic numbskulls these people are," Kay fumed.

"And our own countrymen to boot!" Tommy added.

Finally, after a two-hour wait, the ambassador agreed to see them. They explained their situation and pointed out how kind and generous the Americans and Chinese had been. Should they expect less consideration and generosity from their own government? After so much pain and suffering, they now found themselves in their own embassy with government officials who were demanding ten pounds from poor destitute refugees. Did King George approve of such treatment of his subjects? The ambassador was unmoved.

"So sorry, but without payment of the fee I simply cannot issue your passports. Rules are rules, and nothing in my book allows me to give free passports to anyone, even poor blokes such as you," the ambassador said.

More bureaucratic mumbo-jumbo, and if anyone else said "rules are rules," Tommy promised to give them a bloody nose.

Thoroughly discouraged by such inane policy, Tommy and Kay decided to return to Kunming without the damned passports. They thumbed a ride back to the island airport and checked in at the operations office for a ride back to Kunming. They were advised that the first space available on a flight would not be until the afternoon of October 30. They would have to "cool their heels" according to the American transportation officer, and spend a few days in Chungking until a flight was available.

"Why don't you see the city while you wait?" the officer suggested.

"We have no money," Tommy complained.

The officer signed a chit for CRB $5,000 each, which he thought would see them through for the next few days. They thought the Americans were very generous, considering that their own British Embassy had not offered them a farthing.

They thanked the officer, thumbed their way back to the cheap hotel in Old Chungking, and rented a room along with two bicycles. For the next few days, they would become sightseeing tourists, and there was much to see in Chungking.

Chungking was a city of one million people in transition from a town of narrow crowded streets surrounded by an ancient wall, to a major government and industrial city. Spread out for five miles in each direction from the city central park, the metropolis was a bustling center of activity. The Japs had harassed the city with extensive bombing raids early in the war, though by now the damage had been mostly cleaned up and construction companies were busily rebuilding the city. American airbases in the Chinese interior had halted Japanese air raids by mid 1943, and now reconstruction progressed unimpeded.

Chungking was built on and around Mount Chin-pi-Shan, a hilly promontory of red Jurassic sandstone and shale, which reached a maximum elevation of 900 feet above sea level. The promontory was bordered on the north by the Chia-ling River, with the industrial area of Chiang-pei on its north bank, and on the east and south by the Yangtze River. Other hills, southern offshoots of the Hua-ying Mountains, rose beyond the city's outskirts and suburbs.

The Old City of Chungking, still partly surrounded by a crumbling city wall and permanently opened gates, occupied the eastern third of the rocky promontory and covered an area of about five square miles. The south and east slopes facing the waterfront formed the "lower city," while the remainder was the "upper city."

An east–west main thoroughfare ran through the middle of each of these areas, and a third ran atop the spine of the promontory ridge. Cross streets were narrow, meandering, and sinuous as they followed the topography of the hill. Some of the pedestrian streets went up and down in flights of hundreds of steps. Chungking's main business district surrounded the park in the center of the Old City. Kay and Tommy wandered about the business section, then climbed up hundreds of steps to end up eating lunch at a restaurant located on top of Mount Chin-pi.

Across the street from the restaurant was a beautiful Buddhist monastery that occupied the entire summit of the promontory. A high stone wall surrounded the grounds, and two gigantic stone lions that seemed to snarl at visitors guarded an ornate iron-gated entrance. Kay and Tommy were peering at the gardens through the iron gate, when a monk dressed in an orange sarong came up to the entrance and asked in Chinese if they would like to come inside. Neither Kay nor Tommy knew much about Buddhism, nor had either of them ever visited a Buddhist monastery. Kay eagerly accepted the invitation, and the monk opened the gate and ushered them inside as he explained in perfect English that this particular monastery was over one thousand years old and home to over 400 monks.

The main path was lined with large stone figures with hideous faces and penetrating eyes made of green jade. It led into an inner courtyard and garden. The monk explained that these figures were intended to ward off evil spirits. Kay and Tommy braved the ferocious faces and followed the monk into the courtyard. The temple was built on top of a series of eight terraced courtyards, each somewhat smaller than the one immediately below. Waterfalls cascaded over successive stone retaining walls from the top terrace to the bottom inner courtyard. Kay could only wonder what feat of engineering ingenuity could bring water to the topmost terrace without the use of electric pumps.

As they climbed the stairs to each successive terrace, the monk explained that in Buddhist teaching, the eight terraces represented the eightfold steps to enlightenment. The terraces were named the right views, the right intentions, the right speech, the right actions, the right livelihood, the right effort, the right mindfulness, and the right concentration. By achieving all eight of these qualities one would eliminate desire and become free of earthly suffering.

Ornate and well cared-for gardens decorated each individual terrace. A series of marble staircases, each with thirteen stairs, led from one terrace to the next higher one. The stairs had much higher rises than standard stairs and required a bit of exertion to climb from one to the other. The sounds of bamboo wind chimes and waterfalls filled each terraced garden with gentle melodies. The monastery was indescribably peaceful, as if the outside world had ceased to exist within these walls. On the topmost terrace was a pagoda and pink sandstone temple. Two huge wooden doors carved with intricate symbols and figures guarded the entrance to the temple.

The monk removed his sandals, Kay and Tommy removed their shoes, and all three proceeded barefoot through the doors and into the temple. The temple air was heavy with the sickeningly sweet smell of incense. A huge bell hung from a wooden tripod in the center of the temple. In the nave, a twenty-foot high Buddha sat atop a three tier marble platform that the monk explained represented the "three characteristics of being." On the bottom tier, two huge copper dishes on either side burned with cedar wood-chip and whale-oil fires. Incense sticks released a pungent smoke on each step leading up to the Buddha and three orange-robed monks sat cross-legged on the bottom steps, spinning prayer wheels as they mumbled quietly in a monotone song. They paid the visitors no heed. The monk bowed deeply three times and Kay and Tommy did likewise. He then handed each an incense stick that he had lit from one of the large copper dishes and instructed them to place them on the bottom step, then bowed three times and backed down to the main floor.

After paying their respects to the Buddha, the monk led them through two of the many gardens that surrounded the temple complex. Small brooks coursed throughout the gardens and a winding path crossed over each on miniature stone bridges. Bonsai evergreen trees and flowering miniature fruit-trees graced the gardens. Ubiquitous displays of multicolored flowers bloomed throughout the garden. The monk led them into a small, open-wall house where another monk served them strong green tea and honey coated pastries. He asked Kay if he or his friends had any questions about

Buddhism, and Kay said that he would like to study this subject more, but right now, they did not have sufficient time. Kay asked him what he thought about Christ. The monk explained that Siddhartha Gautama (Buddha) and Christ were both great teachers, but Buddha did not teach about the existence of God as Jesus did, but the extinguishment of self. However, this was just one of many differences between these two great teachers. The monk finally led them back to the large iron gate, bowed and bade them farewell. Kay thanked the monk and he and Tommy climbed back down to the lower city.

The newer sections of the city on the western part of the promontory spread far along the banks of the two rivers, covering an area considerably larger than the Old City. During the early part of World War II, the offices of the Nationalist government had been relocated there from Nanking, and some of the older buildings were now the sites of government offices, museums and exhibition halls. Equally important were the suburban areas on the south shore of the Yangtze. Japanese bombs had destroyed the only two pre-war bridges that crossed the Yangtze, so a multitude of small boats continuously ferried people from one shore to the other. Spacious gardens and beautiful residences of the suburban areas contributed much to relieving the crowded conditions of the Old City.

Old Chungking, however, remained a city of narrow streets and crowded housing. The streets and lanes followed the contours of the hills. The houses were constructed of bamboo, wood, or thatch in the poorer residential areas, and brick in the wealthier areas. In all areas there was a high degree of congestion. The main transportation was by bicycle or coolie carts, although a few automobiles, buses, and trucks plied the narrow streets. A vigorous modernization program was introduced when the city became the seat of the Nationalist government. Part of the city wall was demolished to make way for new streets, and existing streets had been graded and widened. The tremendous demand for housing created by an influx of government workers and refugees had led to the rapid expansion of the sections west of the Old City.

The 1938-1943 bombing of Chungking caused massive destruction in the inner city. Parts of the old wall and most of the city's historic monuments and temples were either damaged or destroyed. Yet Chungking remained very cosmopolitan, and a city of striking contrasts. Trees and vegetable gardens surrounded large brick apartment buildings, generally four to six stories high. Houses of traditional design, blackened by weather, were still to be found on steep hills and along the highways to the suburbs. Bamboo houses lined the river bluffs, and a few large estates that obviously belonged to the very rich, occupied the Mount Chin-pi-Shan bluffs looking down on the city. Coolies lived in squalid shantytowns constructed alongside the river.

Kay and Tommy took a sampan ferry across the Yangtze and visited the Chiang-pie industrial area that supported countless light and heavy manufacturing companies. The harbor was a hubbub of activity, with a multitude of craft ranging from steamboats to barges, junks and sampans that plied the two rivers of the Yangtze and Chia-ling. Before the war, the two rivers had made Chungking the leading port of southwestern China, although the Japanese had made travel on the Yangtze below Ichang all but impossible. Small steamboats and barges sailed up to I-pin on the Yangtze and Nanchang on the Chia-ling. Junks and sampans navigated beyond these points.

The foundations of Chungking's industrial area were laid between 1938 and 1944, when factories transplanted upriver from the coastal provinces began production under the aegis of the Nationalist government. Because coal, iron, and other resources were in such close proximity, Chungking industry rapidly expanded. In 1944 Chungking was becoming one of the largest and fastest growing industrial centers in southwestern China.

Chungking had an enormous complex of integrated iron and steel plants located in Chiang-pei. A pall of black and yellowish smoke that poured from hundreds of tall smokestacks hung over the city and gave the air the unhealthy smell of sulfur. Other important heavy industries included war material manufacturing and truck manufacturing plants. There was also an alcohol plant making gasoline substitutes, and a rubber reconditioning plant. Chungking led the entire southwest of the nation in the number of light industries. Hundreds of small businesses lined the narrow streets of Chang-pei, most with from one to a dozen employees, and engaged in anything from metal working to light manufacturing and assembly. The Chinese called these businesses "Kitchen Industries."

After three days of sightseeing, Kay and Tommy hitched a ride back out to the Chungking Island airport and boarded their airplane back to Kunming.

When they returned to the AGAS office, Captain Mullen advised that he had scheduled them on a RAF flight to Calcutta the very next morning. Kay explained that they still did not have passports. Captain Mullen looked as frustrated as Kay, and finally said that he could not get them on another flight for almost three weeks. Despite the fact that they still did not have passports, he went ahead and issued them boarding passes, rationalizing that they would have better luck with the British Consulate in India to straighten out the passport issue. They met Sid that evening for a farewell dinner. Before they left, Sid slipped Kay $100 U.S., and apologized that it could not be more. More? Kay knew just how generous this gift was on a captain's salary of $40/month and profusely thanked him. Now they had money to pay the passport ransom, but their flight was leaving early the next morning and the consulate office, now closed, would not open until late morning.

"Oh, what the bloody hell, let the British Consulate in India deal with it!" Kay said.

CHAPTER FOURTEEN

India

⋇⇒◉⇐⋇

November 1, 1944, Calcutta

They took off from the Kunming airdrome on a C-54 early the next morning. The airplane was to fly over the hump of northern Burma, then refuel in Dinjan, Assam and go on to Calcutta. The C-54 was poorly heated and unpressurized. The only oxygen provided for passengers was by small tanks the size of a thermos bottle, and Kay and Tommy had to share one between them. Although they were warmly dressed and had zipped up their flight jackets, the cold penetrated to their very bones.

The C-54 climbed into the cerulean sky and passed over beautiful Lake Tali, a sizeable body of emerald green water that glistened in the early morning sun. Then they flew over the high, snow-capped and rugged mountains of the southern Himalayan Chain and across Burma (Myanmar) into the Assam state of northeast India. They had climbed to twenty one thousand feet to clear the mountains and despite his liberal use of the oxygen tank, by mid-flight Kay had developed a raging headache. When he had to use the toilet facilities located in the rear of the aircraft, the short walk at the high altitude caused him considerable discomfort. By the time he got back to his seat, he was gasping for air. Lightheaded and with his legs and arms feeling like lead, he gulped oxygen from the bottle for a full minute before he felt better.

By the time they landed at Dinjan Airport, the throbbing in Kay's head had become unbearable. Several other passengers complained of similar discomforts. Once the engines were shut down, Kay and Tommy stepped out into brilliant sunshine and hot humid weather. In fact, it was so hot that they dug their lightweight khaki shirt and pants from their duffel bags and quickly changed clothes. While waiting for the airplane to be refueled, the passengers sat in the shade provided by the airplane wing and ate C-rations.

A few minutes later, a jeep drove up to the airplane and a R.A.F. major climbed out. Kay recognized Major Lambert from Tientsin; a friend he had not seen since early 1941 when Kay's Shanghai field hockey team had beaten Lambert's Tientsin team. It was amazing that wherever Kay and his friends went, they would run into people they knew from Shanghai. At first, Lambert did not recognize Kay. He introduced himself to the passengers, and then announced that he was charge of field security at Dinjan airport and had come out to check passenger's immigration paperwork. He asked everyone to get their passports and exit permits ready and began to check them. When he got to Kay, he looked at him and almost dropped his clipboard.

"Pate, is that you Old Bean?" he said in utter amazement.

Kay teased, "Of course it's me, you Old Fart, have you forgotten your friends?"

Lambert laughed and warmly pumped Kay's hand. "No, I never forget old friends, especially quaint ones like you."

His smile then morphed into a back-to-business frown and he asked to see their passports and exit permits.

"Uh, that will be a bit of a problem," Kay admitted, "The damn British Embassy wouldn't issue passports to Tommy or me without its ten pounds of flesh. We escaped Lunghwa prison and walked all the way across China, only to be told 'no money, no passport!'"

"Damn British bureaucrats!" Lambert said. "Let's see your exit permits then."

Tommy and Kay handed him their exit permits and a letter of explanation from Captain Mullen. Lambert examined the papers and handed them back.

"Well, old friends, you have placed me in a bit of a sticky wicket," Lambert groaned. "This is a port of entry into India, and I am not supposed to let persons into the country who do not have a valid passport."

"Come on Lambert," Kay moaned, "You know who we are and that we are British citizens. Can't you vouch for us?"

Lambert looked perplexed, then his face softened. "You really shouldn't have left China without a valid passport, but given that you are now here and this Captain Mullen has vouched for your circumstances, I will overlook the fact that your papers are not in order. Be sure to visit the British Consulate in Calcutta as soon as you arrive, and get this passport thing straightened out; otherwise, you will find yourself in an Indian prison. The Indian government is quite sticky when it comes to proper paperwork. All those years of British influence I suspect."

"Well, thanks to my brother-in-law, we now have some money to pay the damnable fee," Kay explained.

Captain Lambert had some lukewarm Indian beer in the truck and they shared stories, laughed, and drank beer until the airplane was ready to continue the flight to Calcutta. Kay hoped the alcohol would soften his raging headache, but it only lessened when the airplane was again at cruising altitude.

The descent into the Calcutta airdrome was more gradual than that into Dinjan and by the time they landed at Calcutta International Airport, Kay's headache had diminished. A Crossly truck picked them up and drove them to the Customs Clearinghouse and British Administration building, where they waited a half-hour for a customs official to appear. When the Indian official finally arrived, the fact that neither Kay nor Tommy had passports became a huge issue. Kay tried to explain that the Consulate office in Kunming had screwed up their applications and the Embassy in Chungking refused to issue their passports for lack of the ten-pound fee.

The customs official, a British trained Indian bureaucrat, couldn't handle this discrepancy.

"You should not have left China without passports!" he insisted. "You are illegal aliens in my country!"

Those were fighting words to Tommy.

"Illegal aliens…illegal aliens?" Tommy shouted. "How dare you call us illegal aliens. We are British citizens who have escaped

China after months locked up in one of the Jap's stinking concentration camps. If we had a lousy ten-pounds sterling, we would have the damned passports by now. How can you stand there and accuse us of being illegal aliens?" How dare you!"

Tommy looked like he was about to deck the man, so Kay grabbed Tommy's arm and held him back.

"Tommy, this is not going to help our situation," Kay admonished.

The next thing they knew, a couple of Indian MP's appeared and placed handcuffs on them. The customs official then had a jeep take them under guard to the British Consulate office in downtown Calcutta. By now, it was 9 p.m. and the official on duty at the consulate was about to leave for the night when they arrived. He seemed extremely put off that he had to deal with Tommy and Kay at such a late hour. He called the embassy office in Chungking and they confirmed that their passports were ready but had not been issued pending payment of the ten-pound passport fee. He then asked to have the passports forwarded to his office. This would take a day or two, and in the meantime Kay and Tommy would be confined to the consulate grounds. In effect, they were jailed. Led to a holding cell, they fell into a restless sleep on lumpy cots.

November 2, 1944, Calcutta

At 9 a.m. a British Consulate officer came by to see them and apologized for the mix-up. He was a sensible chap, and sympathized with the unreasonableness of requiring ten pounds from refugees for passports, but "rules were rules". It would seem that everyone in the British Foreign office was indoctrinated with that stupid mantra. Their passports arrived at noon on the next Chungking-Calcutta airplane. There was one remaining problem. The photographs that they had taken in Chungking were not attached to the passports. They needn't worry, the Consulate officer said, because his brother-in-law owned a photography studio just down the street, and for $5 each, he would take their passport photos. He then walked them under guard to the studio and they had their pictures taken. Thanks to Sid and his generous gift of $100, they were able to pay the 10-pound (U.S.$40) fee for each and the

Consulate Office issued their passports. Of course, this left them with only $10 in their pockets.

Tommy and Kay were at last free to go, but needed directions to the British Intelligence H.Q. at No. 1 Ballygrung Park Road. No one, including a local police officer, was able to provide the directions to Ballygrung Park Road. Kay hired a local taxi driver who claimed to know the whereabouts of Ballygrung Park Road, but quickly became lost. The taxi was a three-wheel motor scooter with two rear seats. The ride through the crowded and narrow Calcutta streets was nerve-racking. He wandered in and out of narrow streets for the better part of an hour, but finally crossed over a narrow bridge, turned onto Ballygrung Park Road and deposited them at the front steps of the British Intelligence H.Q. building that also housed the BAAG folks.

The BAAG was the British equivalent of the American AGAS. It was the job of the BAAG to help refugees such as Kay and Tommy. Again as before they met with British bureaucrats who couldn't seem to handle their situation. The corporal in charge at the front desk told them that Lieutenant Elverston had been informed by the Kunming AGAS office that they would be arriving this morning, but Elverston had not yet arrived at work and they would have to wait until he showed up. Lieutenant Elverston finally arrived at 10:30. He seemed aloof and disinterested in their plight. Kay gave him the letter from Captain Mullen describing their situation and requesting the BAAG office to assist them to travel to the New Delhi British Intelligence Office for a debriefing. Elverston didn't seem to give a "rat's ass" about Kay and Tommy or their situation, but reluctantly said that he would arrange for train passage to New Delhi in two or three days. In the meantime, they should find themselves a hotel. Kay couldn't believe what he was hearing.

Stay in a hotel and buy meals for three days with less than $10 between them, ridiculous!

"We do not have enough money for such a stay," Kay pleaded.

"Well then, I suppose that is your problem isn't it." Elverston answered.

This devil-may-care attitude was too much for Tommy, and he exploded.

"You bloody numbskull!" he screamed. "You have orders in your hands that British Intelligence in New Delhi wants to debrief us as soon as possible. You damn well had better arrange for us to fly there, and not when you bloody please, but today! We are not going to wait three days in a bedbug-ridden hotel as you get around to arranging transportation for us at your leisure. In addition, no bloody way are we going to sit on a hot stuffy Indian train for 28 hours. No airplane today, no intelligence, end of story. You can bloody well explain THAT to your Commander and the folks in New Delhi!"

Lieutenant Elverston sat backed in his chair and looked like he had been hit in the face with a sledgehammer.

"You can't talk to ME like that!" Elverston stammered.

"I can and have done so!" Tommy almost spit at Elverston.

Then he turned to Kay and said, "Let's go talk to the Commander, we are bloody well wasting our time here!"

"Wait! That won't be necessary," Elverston mumbled as Kay and Tommy prepared to leave. He picked up his telephone and made a couple of calls.

Elverston hung up the telephone and glared at Tommy.

"Be at the RAF airport operations office at 9 a.m. tomorrow morning. There is an airplane headed for New Delhi before noon. Report to Brig. General Halpine of the RAF Air Priority Board office."

Kay and Tommy left Elverston's office without so much as a "by your leave."

"What a lazy, self-important asshole," Tommy exclaimed.

Unlike their boss, the four NCOs in the Ballygrung office were swell chaps, very helpful and friendly. Kay spoke with them as they waited for a taxi. It appeared that the NCOs overheard the conversation between Tommy and Elverston and didn't have much respect for the lieutenant either. They claimed that he came in late every day, left early and had a girlfriend on the side who he supported with money "borrowed" from the petty cash reserve fund. That probably explained why Elverston had been so reluctant to offer them a stipend. The NCOs went into their storeroom and came back with shirts, underwear and a pair of Indian "jop-lees" or sandals for Kay and Tommy.

The taxi ride to the hotel was as bone jarring and nerve shredding as the ride to the BAAG office had been. The driver had only two controls, the accelerator and the horn, and he made liberal use of each through the narrow, crowded streets. Kay was still angry about the way Lieutenant Elverston treated them; nevertheless, he complimented Tommy about the way he handled the situation. Tommy laughed as they bumped and jostled down the narrow streets. "One just needs to know how to talk to self-important bureaucratic fools like Elverston."

Later in New Delhi, Tommy reported Lieutenant Elverston's unmilitary behavior and indiscretions to the Commander there, and it is likely that his cushy job would soon end.

They were in desperate need of money, so Kay asked the taxi driver to stop off at the Calcutta Branch Office of the Steamship Company he had worked for in Shanghai. The branch manager, Jack McCarthy, almost fell over from shock when Kay walked through the door. After a warm greeting and explanations, McCarthy closed the office for the day and took them to an early dinner. Kay again told the story of their escape and trek across China. Jack gave them 250 rupees (U.S. $85) from petty cash for hotel and incidental expenses, then drove them to an upscale hotel on the outskirts of New Delhi. After converting their U.S. money to rupees and paying for taxis and other incidentals, Kay had only 25 rupees left, so the additional 250 rupees were very much appreciated.

November 3, 1944, New Delhi

At 6 a.m. they hailed a taxi and headed to the Air Priority Board office at the Calcutta airdrome. When they arrived, they met General Halpine, an elderly gentleman who couldn't do enough to accommodate them. The General's chest was covered in ribbons, all from the First World War. Now he "was doing his bit," as he put it, for the RAF in this latest war.

The attendant weighed their duffel bags. Passengers were limited to sixty-five pounds, but Kay's weighed in at seventy pounds. The General told the attendant to add the extra five pounds to Kay's weight, which was by now a slim one hundred and sixty pounds, down from his normal one eighty five. Then he picked up the telephone, called the BAAG office in New Delhi, and spoke with a Captain Lightbody to arrange for the refugees' arrival and hotel stay. He handed them boarding passes and a letter to present to the British Intelligence officer in New Delhi.

A dozen RAF officers and enlisted men and several civilians were also traveling to New Delhi on this airplane. Before noon, Kay and Tommy boarded the airplane, an Air India passenger DC-3, and after a considerable delay, took off for New Delhi. The late departure was due to mechanical problems with the DC-3. Air India mechanics took most of the afternoon to replace a defective hydraulic pump. The pilot told Kay that it was a good thing he detected the defect, for once in the air it would have been difficult to control the aircraft. Kay didn't gripe about the delay; better to lose a few hours than to make it this far and then end up in pieces spread across some Indian mountainside.

The first stopover was at the Allahabad Airdrome and RAF Airbase, where they went into the mess hall for dinner while the airplane was refueled. Forty-five minutes later they were at seven thousand feet and headed directly for New Delhi. An unusually bright, gibbous moon lit the countryside so that even at their altitude, rivers, lakes, and some of the larger partially lit villages were clearly visible. Toward the northwest, the snowcapped Himalayan Mountains dominated the horizon. At last, New Delhi came into view, a carpet of twinkling lights spread out from horizon to horizon.

After circling the airport for several minutes to get in line with other traffic, they landed and taxied up to the large brick terminal. Their orders from General Hapline directed them to the Swiss Hotel, where a British Intelligence officer, Captain Lightbody of the BAAG, was to meet them first thing in the morning. A RAF colonel whom they met on the airplane offered Kay and Tommy a ride to the hotel. This kindness was very much appreciated, for it was late at night and transportation into town was happenstance at best. The colonel dropped them off at the Swiss Hotel and they went directly to the front desk to check in.

The Swiss Hotel was an old colonial palace with a large second story verandah that extended across the entire street side of the building. The main lobby was ornate, decorated with plush red carpets, teak wall paneling, a sweeping staircase, and luxurious 19th century furniture throughout. A beautiful glass chandelier hung from the fifty-foot high lobby ceiling.

The clerk was dressed in a tuxedo and looked down his nose at the two scruffy refugees standing before him. He scanned his reservation book and said that he had no advance reservations for a Karoly Pate or Thomas Crosthwaite. Kay told them that Captain Lightbody would have made the bookings that very day, but the clerk insisted he had no record of such reservations. Kay showed him the letter from General Hapline, but the clerk was unimpressed. Finally, in desperation Kay asked the clerk if he had any rooms available at all.

"Oh, of course we do," the clerk said, "however that will be 54 rupees (about $18) EACH, in advance."

Kay looked at Tommy who shrugged his shoulders. He then turned back to the clerk and said, "All we have is 275 rupees between us, and that has to last for the duration of our stay in India. There is some mix-up because our rooms were to be pre-arranged and paid for. We cannot afford 108 rupees for a single night's stay. Captain Lightbody will be here in the morning and he will attend to our accounts."

"Well then," the clerk offered, "considering the fact that you are short of funds, I can let you have a single room tonight for 48 rupees; although, you will have to share a bed and pay in advance."

In light of the accommodations that Kay and Tommy had shared over the past few weeks, a single room and bed was no problem. They found their room, and without bothering to undress, collapsed on the feather mattress and fell soundly asleep in a matter of minutes.

November 4, 1944, New Delhi

They awoke at sunrise, dressed and went downstairs to breakfast. After a meal of curried eggs and English muffins, they sat in the hotel lobby waiting for Captain Lightbody to appear. They waited and waited, but the captain never showed. About four p.m., Tommy decided to call the BAAG office to see what the score was. He was told that Captain Lightbody had been too busy to meet with them, but would meet with them in the morning. It would certainly have been polite to let Kay and Tommy know of the change in plans rather than have them wait around the entire day for someone who had no intention of showing.

Kay was visibly upset. "I thought these folks were so bloody anxious to debrief us that they wanted us here today! Then the captain is 'too busy' to meet with us or even send a message excusing himself. Another day wasted by rude British bureaucrats!"

It really bothered Kay that they should be treated so well by the Chinese and Yanks, and so indifferently by their own countrymen. Throughout their stay in India, Kay and Tommy were forced to deal with bureaucratic and indifferent British officials. Tommy often said, it was easier to cut the wire in Lunghwa than to cut through the British red tape in this country.

They found an inexpensive restaurant where they had a decent curry dinner for less than three rupees apiece. Later that evening Kay managed to talk the hotel clerk into another night's stay in their room, without advance payment this time.

November 5-10, Delhi

Captain Lightbody met them in the lobby the following morning and signed a voucher to pay their hotel bill for a week. The snooty hotel clerk returned the 48 rupees that Kay had paid in advance, and assigned them room with two-beds. Lightbody then drove them over to the famous "Red Fort" that now served as the British Intelligence Office in Delhi. Many years ago, the Red Fort was once successfully defended by the Rajah's Native troops against a British brigade. It now served as a prison for Japanese captives, a place where the British could interrogate them at their leisure.

Most of the Japanese soldiers incarcerated at the Red Fort had been recently captured in Burma in the battle of Mykitkyina and several hundred of these captives and their officers were in this prison. As they walked past the various cells holding the Japanese officers, Kay thought how satisfying it was to see these war criminals on the other side of the bars. In prison garb and humbled by their incarceration, they now looked insignificant and pitiful. Gone was the look of arrogance and superiority of the Lunghwa officers. Gone was the haughtiness and inhumanity of the Japanese soldiers in Shanghai. All that now remained in these men was the desolation that comes from an inglorious defeat. They were mere shells of their former selves, hollowed by shame. Yes, they were to be pitied thought Kay.

Kay gave the interrogation officers carbon copies of the reams and reams of reports that he had already written. Three different officers interviewed Kay and Tommy, but there was not much to add other than what was already in Kay's report. On the first day of debriefing, the interrogating officers seemed very interested in the details of Lunghwa prison and the activities and strength of the Chinese guerrillas in Japanese held territories. The Allies were concerned as to what might happen to the Westerners held in Japanese prisons should the U.S. forces invade the Shanghai area. They had considered a pre-emptive raid to release Lunghwa and other camp prisoners, so details of the prison layout were crucial. He shared several detailed, hand-drawn maps, depicting the cities that the Japanese occupied and the guerilla held territory, Jap munitions dumps, airfields, camps, and the like. Later Kay heard that much of his information was used by the Allies to attack some of those Japanese emplacements. This made him feel that he had made a significant contribution to the Allied war effort.

Due to internal politics between the Nationalists under Chiang Kai-shek and the Communists in the north under Mao Zedong, the Chinese insurgency had made little progress since 1943. The British and Americans wondered if either the Nationalists or Communists could be counted on to defeat the Japanese Army in China. Both Chinese factions seemed more concerned about fighting each other than fighting the Japanese.

Yet from what Kay and Tommy had seen, the guerrillas were totally focused on defeating the Japanese Army throughout the provinces they visited. Kay shared his experiences with General Chang Bang-fee and his guerrilla led operations in Chekiang Province. The Japanese were in retreat throughout the Pacific Theatre, and were having an ever-increasing problem holding on to territories such as China, the Philippines, New Guinea, and Burma. There was little doubt in Kay's mind that the Chinese guerrillas could do the job. Yet, the Allies seemed to have precious little first-hand information of which cities the Japs held and which cities the guerrillas held. Again, Kay's information was invaluable, but after the initial debriefing, the officers seemed less and less interested in the details that Kay and Tommy wanted to share.

Kay and Tommy remained at the Swiss Hotel for several days while the debriefing at the Red Fort continued, and commuted to the fort by taxi. On the second day at the Red Fort, Kay discovered that Bill Henry had been at there the previous week and was staying somewhere in New Delhi. Captain Lightbody helped Kay contact Bill, who came over to see them at the Swiss Hotel. It was a joyful reunion; although, Bill was very frustrated that his commission in the British Army still had not come through. More British red tape! Captain Lightbody and his superior Major Mishull-Ford had been doing their best to work with the Americans to provide air transportation to the U.S. for Kay and Tommy and to obtain a military exit permit from the British for Kay, since he was still of military age. Tommy, who was 56 at the time, did not need a military exit permit.

When the week's prepaid stay at the Swiss Hotel ran out, Kay and Tommy could not afford to pay for such expensive lodging so they moved to an adequate Indian hotel in Old Delhi for 12 rupees per night. Most of the Government offices and shops were in New Delhi, about three miles away, and with limited funds, they could not afford taxi fares, so they rented two bicycles for ten rupees per month. Nearly everyone in Delhi traveled by bicycle, so Kay and Tommy fit right in with the local traffic. The narrow streets were clogged with thousands of bicycles, all making a racket with the handlebar bells. Kay and Tommy made many trips to the BAAG office to check on the status of their exit and air transportation permits, but the answer was always the same: "there is no news."

While in Kunming, Captain Mullen had suggested they contact Lieutenant Col. Jackman in the BAAG office. Captain Mullen knew him to be a "fine fellow" who would bend over backwards to help the refugees.

"Just mention my name to Jackman, and he will give you the shirt off his back," Mullen boasted.

Kay contacted Lieutenant Col. Jackman on the first day at the Red Fort and gave him Captain Mullen's name as a reference. The colonel said that he was late for a meeting, and would contact them later. If Jackman was the "fine fellow" Captain Mullen thought him to be it certainly never became apparent to Kay or Tommy. He didn't even have the decency to return their call or set up a time to see them, despite the fact that they were at the BAAG office every day and left their contact number. They attempted to schedule an appointment, but each time his adjutant rebuffed their request.

"Lieutenant Colonel Jackman is a very busy man," was the usual disinterested response. The name of Captain Mullen seemed to work no magic whatsoever in this office.

"Fine fellow" indeed! Colonel Jackman never contacted them. The Indian atmosphere of indifference seemed to permeate everyone who stayed in that country for any length of time. The more they saw of India, the more they appreciated China.

One afternoon they had a visit from Mr. Levy, one of the six other escapees from Lunghwa. He told them that four of the six fugitives were accounted for; Uhlich whom they had met in Shangjao, was staying on to help the guerrillas, Huxley was in Bangalore, Murray-Kidd in London and Condor in Bombay. It was great to know that these five had all made it out of Japanese held China. The only escapee of the six that was unaccounted for was Scott of the A.P.C. Levy thought he could be in Australia, but this was only a rumor.

As soon as Kay arrived in Delhi, he sent a wire to his wife, Lil, who was living in New York City. He told her that he was safe in India and staying at the Swiss Hotel in New Delhi while he attempted to arrange passage to America. He asked if she could contact her New York Congressman and persuade him to expedite the process. After 18 days in Delhi, Kay had yet to receive a response to his wire, although the Swiss Hotel had their forwarding address. Kay began to worry about his wife and son, but Tommy kept reminding him that a war was on, and personal telegrams were not a high priority.

One morning, Lightbody rang them up and asked them to come down to the BAAG office. When they arrived, he coldly informed them that the Military Intelligence office had completed their investigation and no longer needed their services. Therefore, he was instructed to turn them over to a Captain A.W.T. Webb, who was in charge of the Department of Commonwealth Relations for the Provisional Indian Government. No thank you, not a "by-your-leave," not any appreciation shown for their time and effort was offered. Kay asked how their transportation to the USA was coming along, and Lightbody said that nothing had yet come from the request they passed on to the Americans. Kay wondered just how hard Lightbody had actually tried to expedite their request, and suspected that he had done little along that line. Kay's military exit permit had not yet been issued either, and Lightbody did not really know when it would be. It was clear that Lightbody and the BAAG office intended to do nothing further on their behalf.

Kay felt like a wrung-out washrag that was thrown into the trash when it was of no further use. Just as well, Tommy rationalized. The BAAG had done virtually nothing to advance their cause, and it was unlikely they intended to do anything in the future. What a terrible way to be treated by the British Foreign Office! Best to forget those incompetent laggards and move on. Perhaps they would have better luck with the Indian Government office and Captain Webb.

Captain Archie Webb turned out to be a prince of good fellows. He did everything possible for them, and was the one man in all India that really brushed the red tape aside and got things done, and promptly! They spent the entire day in his office, where a sign hung over his desk that stated; "ACTION NOT WORDS". The first thing Archie did for them was to have his assistant, a Mrs. Elliadi, drive them to a haberdashery in New Delhi and outfit them with civilian clothes. The money for this shopping trip came from Archie's petty cash fund. Captain Webb arranged for a stipend of R500 per month for each of them as long as they were in India, and paid their hotel bills in advance.

Through Archie's persistence, Kay's exit permit from the British Foreign Office finally arrived the following week. Kay was certain that this was due to the dogged intercession of Captain Webb, and had they continued to depend on Captain Lightbody, hell would have frozen over before the necessary permit came about.

Webb put them in touch with General Dan Sultan of the U.S. Transportation Office to arrange passage to the USA. General Sultan was very candid and straightforward as he advised that air transportation to the States would be out of the question since U.S. military personnel had priority over British civilians. They could arrange passage with Pan American Airways, which operated a flying boat service across the Pacific that was available to civilians, but the fare was $850 each. Even if by some stroke of luck Kay and Tommy should come up with such a King's ransom, a very unlikely prospect, without a priority classification, they could be bumped off the Pan Am flying boat at any one of the many stopovers along the way. This could result in their being stuck on some remote, out-of-the-way island for days on end. Not a pleasant prospect. The General suggested that it would be much better for them to obtain passage on a troop ship out of Bombay.

Civilians usually waited for weeks or even months for passage on the few ships heading to the USA, but the General said he would pull a few strings and get them on the next available ship. Passage to the USA would take longer, but they would not be bumped and the cost was only $250. Two hundred and fifty dollars! It might as well have been a million. Not to worry, the General chided, he knew they had little money. Besides, Captain Webb was working on arrangements to pay the entire fare. What a swell bunch of chaps these Americans were. Now all they had to do was get to Bombay after the proper paperwork was processed.

Bill Henry had been in India for a month and a half, and not only had his commission with the British Army failed to come through, but no one at the British Military Office could give him any information as to when and if he would ever be commissioned in the army. He decided to go to Bombay with Kay and Tommy and try the British Navy. He was a marine engineer by profession, and perhaps the navy would be interested in his background. The three of them bought train tickets from the Thomas Cooke Travel Agency on the Frontier Mai leaving Old Delhi at 9 a.m. on Saturday. Second class tickets were six rupees each, but the clerk at the Agency strongly suggested first class passage since it was only 22 rupees each. This turned out to be very good advice.

November 18, 1944, On the Delhi to Bombay Express.

Although they had limited funds remaining, before leaving Delhi Kay wanted to purchase a watch to replace the one he lost in the Chinese rice paddies. Watches were very scarce in Delhi, especially a good one like Kay lost. He visited the street vendors and shops in Old and New Delhi, but had no luck. One of the sergeants at the Red Fort told Kay of a shop in New Delhi where he might get what he wanted, but there was a trick to successful shopping in Delhi.

"You go along Chandni Chowk Road opposite the Red Fort until you come to the old clock tower. About fifty yards past it on the left is a very tiny and dirty looking clock shop. Go inside and ask for wristwatches. I know the 'Babu' will tell you he has none, but you just tell him that begging his pardon, the sergeant at the Red Fort says he is a bloody liar. Then see what he does."

Kay found the watch shop and upon entering, asked the proprietor if he had any wristwatches.

"I am very sorry, Sahib, we not have watches for long time."

Kay then repeated the "bloody liar" bit as the sergeant had instructed him to say. At first, the Babu looked shocked, but feigning a slight smile he bowed and took a velvet tray of 20 or so watches out of a steel cabinet behind the display case and placed it on the counter. They were all excellent Swiss watches ranging from four to seventeen jewel movements. Kay picked out a gold-17 jewel Elgin watch with a luminous dial and flexible watchband for R.65 or about $22 U.S. This watch would serve as a reliable timepiece for many years. Before leaving Delhi, on the way to the train station the next morning they purchased canvas bags to carry all their possessions, clothes, and the like. These bags would be needed on the train and when they found passage on a ship.

The train station in Old Delhi was a smoke-blackened steel structure with a partial roof. It housed dozens of platforms and a maze of different tracks. Kay studied the train schedule posted inside the terminal and searched for the correct platform from which to board the Bombay Express. The problem was that there were several Bombay trains listed. The "Blue Train" the "Red Train" and the "Green Train" were scheduled to depart for Bombay within the hour, but which one was theirs? Their tickets said nothing about Red, Blue or Green trains, only that their train was the "Delhi-Bombay Express" and they had compartment J-12. Bill went over to the station master window, showed his ticket to the clerk, and asked from which platform it was to depart.

"Ah, Sahib, your train is the Bombay Express, the Red Train, and will depart from Platform 34 in five minutes," the clerk intoned in a singsong manner.

Five minutes! That was not much time to reach platform 34 on the opposite side of the station. Bill found Kay and Tommy and told them that they would have to hurry. The bridges that carried pedestrians from one platform to another were choked with arriving passengers rushing in the opposite direction from platform 34. Using their well packed canvas bags as battering rams, they pushed and shoved their way across several bridges, arriving at platform 34 just as the Red Train signaled its departure with a shrill double blast of its high-pitched steam whistle. They found compartment J-12, climbed onboard, and began to relax as the train pulled out of the station.

Indian train coaches have individual compartments for first class passengers that seat four to six persons in relative comfort. Second class passengers rode in cars with simple wood benches that looked very uncomfortable for such a long journey. Third class passengers were relegated to the cattle cars or had to find space on the roof of those cars. The steam engines, freshly painted with bright colors and fancifully decorated with colorful banners and flags, were the pride of each train engineer who took personal care of his locomotive, keeping it oiled and in excellent mechanical shape. The first class coaches were clean and neat, however the second class passenger cars were another matter. They were in disrepair, unpainted and dirty. The cattle cars were filthy beyond description.

First-class compartments were not interconnected with one another by inside passageways, so each came equipped with individual lavatories that emptied out onto the tracks. Small signs on the lavatory doors requested occupants not to use the facilities when in stations. If a passenger wanted to visit another compartment or the dining car at the front of the train, they had to wait for a train stop, then go out onto the platform to access the other cars.

Kay and Bill were hungry by noontime and waited for a

convenient stop to visit the dining car. Once on the platform, they found themselves struggling against a horde of locals all trying desperately to board the train. When the train whistle blew, the crowd made a mad dash for the second and third class cars inhibiting Kay and Bill's progress toward the dining car that was up front just behind the baggage car. In their mad dash to board the train, people shoved and pushed anyone in their way. Bill and Kay became ensnared in the melee, and before they could reach the dining car, the train whistle sounded again and the train began to pull out of the station. A huge crowd that had not found space on the train was still milling about on the platform as Bill and Kay tried to make their way back to their own compartment. No one would get out of their way, so they forced their way through the crowd as the train began picking up speed. Tommy watched his friends being jostled by the crowd, opened the compartment door, and grabbed Bill's hand and then Kay's as the train accelerated past their coach. They both spilled into the compartment and landed in a heap on the floor, much to the amusement of the other chap who shared their compartment. Had they missed the train, they would have had to wait until the following day for the next Red Train to Bombay. They later learned that the Yellow and Green trains were "locals" that stopped at every little station along the way and traveled by an entirely different route to Bombay than the Red Train did.

At each stop, the platforms were crowded with passengers, so for the balance of the 28-hour trip, they thought it best to remain in their compartment.

Indian trains did not provide berths, so most passengers brought along their own bedrolls. The beds could be made up by pulling out a board stored under the seats and placing it across the seats to create a platform. Thomas Cooke Inc. provided passengers with bedrolls for a nominal fee and would collect the pads upon arrival in Bombay. With four passengers to a compartment, it was quite an embarrassment to have to disturb everyone to visit the commode in the middle of the night. The railroad car rocked back and forth and lurched to such an extent that it was difficult to read or write or sleep while the train was in motion. Although none of them felt any discomfort, travel sickness was quite common among the other passengers.

Since he was unable to read, the next morning Kay sat by the window and watched the panorama of the vivid green landscape pass by. The train steamed through thick forests and traversed flat plains laced with creeks and streams, and clickity-clacked on cantilever bridges that crossed wide brown rivers. The train's high-pitched whistle woke residents as it chugged through dozens of small villages and towns. Since there were no gates protecting the infrequent road crossings, Kay surmised that the whistle was both a greeting and a warning. In each community, adults, and especially children rushed outside their shacks to wave at the passing train. Kay opened his window and waved back to the amusement of the Indian children who whooped, laughed, and returned excited greetings as the train passed by.

The train eventually entered an extensive dense jungle that seemed to enfold the little train in a green tunnel of vines and foliage. Adding to the oppressive humidity, a light rain began to fall and water dripped from the trees and foliage making a gentle pat-pat sound as it struck the broad leafed plants. The jungle intruded so close to the railway that Kay could have reached through the open window and grabbed a handful of undergrowth. In a half-overgrown clearing, the ruins of a Hindu temple, choked in vines, and long forgotten by time, housed a band of wild monkeys who, disturbed by the train, raced into the refuge of the buildings. The train eventually emerged from the jungle and steamed onto a wide brown plain inhabited by herds of grazing sheep, camels, and cattle. This was the dry season on the plains before the yearly monsoons, standing water was scarce, and many animals were stressed by the conditions. The various herds were in poor shape, many of the cattle exhibited protruding ribs beneath motley hides. The carcass of dead animals surrounded by squabbling vultures dotted the landscape.

Except for two parallel sets of railroad tracks at each station, there was only a single track for trains traveling in both directions. Kay noted the absence of semaphores or any other signaling devices that could prevent collisions on this single track. Occasionally they passed a train on a station siding waiting for its turn to proceed in the opposite direction. By carefully observing the railroad workers, Kay discovered the Indian railway method to prevent collisions. At each station, a station agent would pass to the engineer a one-foot wide hoop with ribbons that carried the unique color and markings for that section of track. At the next station, the engineer exchanged his hoop for a new one representing the next section of track. These hoops ensured the engineer that the track ahead was clear and that he could safely proceed to the next station. When our train arrived at a station where the station agent did not have a hoop to pass along, the engineer waited on a side- track until the next train from the opposite direction pulled through and exchanged his hoop for the next section. This simple low-tech method typified Indian ingenuity. It also prevented trains from following too closely to one another.

As the engineer held the train on a sidetrack to await his hoop, a vendor strolled up and down the line of railroad cars selling bowls of curried rice and chicken. A meal could be purchased from these vendors for a few coins called damns. The Indian damn was a small copper coin worth a fraction of the larger English pence. It was said that if one ignored a street beggar in India, and wouldn't even "give a damn," he was a penny-pinching rascal.

November 19, 1944, Bombay

The next morning a platform vendor at another siding strode up and down the platform selling rice balls and lentil soup, and Kay purchased a few bowls for their breakfast that day. The ceramic bowls were probably worth more than the few damns charged for the meal. At the next stop, another vendor collected the bowls to clean and sell to passengers traveling in the opposite direction. In this way bowls moved back and forth from one station to another in the same manner as the track hoops.

They pulled into the Bombay train station at 1 p.m. on Sunday, three months and 4,000 weary miles from the day they escaped Lunghwa prison. The train station was a huge iron truss building covered by a vaulted hemispherical roof. As in Delhi, the many platforms were crowded with thousands of people all shoving and pushing each other to board their respective trains. Again, access to the widely spaced platforms was by bridges that crossed high over the various tracks. As Kay crossed over one of these bridges to get to the main terminal, a train passed directly beneath him, spewing steam and burning embers all over him. He choked in the acrid steam as he beat the embers from his new clothes.

Archie Webb's friend, W.M. Martin, was to meet them in the main train terminal. They had never met Mr. Martin nor did they have a description of him, so they stacked the bags in a large pile, each prominently stenciled with their names in clear view. Soon, Mr. Martin came by and spotted the bags and their names. Introductions aside, they all piled into his Ford sedan and Mr. Martin drove each of them to separate destinations that Archie had arranged.

First Mr. Martin dropped Tommy off at a Mr. Blackwood's home, then on to Malabar Hill where Kay got out, and finally delivered Bill to a third residence. Kay was to stay as the guest of a Colonel and Mrs. Emerson, who had a lovely home overlooking the Malabar peninsula. The Emerson's were not at home at the time; however, a Mr. and Mrs. Case were house sitting for the Emersons and made Kay feel right at home. Mr. Case showed Kay to a room on the top floor with a private bath and a verandah that looked out onto the beach a few hundred yards away. The room was cooled by gentle sea breezes that drifted in from the bay, picking up the perfume from blooming flowers as it moved over the peninsula.

It felt grand to be in a private home again after so many months of being jailed and harassed by the Japs. After a wonderfully hot bath, Kay strolled about the grounds of the home. The Emerson's home was surrounded by tropical gardens, and the main feature in the backyard was a tennis court. Kay had not played tennis for years, but back in Shanghai, he was considered an excellent player. During his stay with the Emersons, Kay played several sets with Mr. Case, but didn't even come close to his former form. This was another example of how hard the previous months had been on his body.

The gardens were a gorgeous riot of color, well cared for and exquisitely manicured. Six-foot high Hydrangeas that were in full bloom made a natural fence across the back of the property. A large Mimosa tree grew in the center of the garden and two magnificently colored parrots were busily building a nest in its branches. It was comical to watch them, as neither of the birds seemed to agree on

nest engineering, so they squawked and quibbled over the place-
ment of each stick. The male would carefully put a stick in place
and the female would remove it and place it elsewhere. It was
amusing to watch and not unlike many human attempts at domestic
tranquility.

CHAPTER FIFTEEN

Homeward Bound

November 20, 1944, Bombay

Kay grabbed a taxi the next morning and met Tommy at the American Supplies Office in Bombay to see about their arrangements for shipboard passage to the good old U.S. of A. They met with Major Carroll who informed them that he had received orders from his head office to place Kay and Tommy in "Officer Class" on the first outgoing troop ship to the U.S. The fares and exit permits had all been arranged. What excellent first class treatment for a couple of British refugees! Neither Kay nor Tommy would ever forget the kindness extended to them by the Chinese and the Americans, and especially Archie Web. As for the British Foreign Office, well that was a different matter altogether. Perhaps these uncaring bureaucrats were affected by stress of wartime, but Kay had never before experienced such insolence and indifference from his fellow citizens as in Kunming, Chungking, and India.

The next stop was at the Bombay Police Station to register. By city ordinance, registration was required for all foreign visitors to Bombay. On the strength of their military exit permits and passports, they were issued temporary visitor passes. Then went to the U.S. Consulate to obtain entry visas, however, obtaining American visas turned out to be a bit more difficult than they expected. The American consular said that it would be necessary to have recent photos for their visa and to arrange for an American citizen to vouch for them.

Kay complained that they knew no Americans in Bombay who could vouch for them.

"Sorry gentlemen, but those are the regulations," the consular weakly apologized.

"Oh, by the way, you also need to visit a doctor and get a health certificate and all the necessary travel shots," he added.

A photographer could take their pictures and they would visit a doctor, but what American in Bombay could vouch for them? Neither Kay nor Tommy knew any Americans in Bombay, at least no one that Kay could think of.

It was mid-day Monday when on the way to find a restaurant for lunch, they passed by an Anglican Church. Kay decided to go inside and say a prayer of thanksgiving. Tommy was reluctant to join him, but Kay insisted, so they both went inside and sat in a pew. The church was filled with worshippers as the noontime service was in progress and the minister had just started his homily. The homily was about the need to be "saved." Being saved required one to profess his belief in Christ, change his life of sin, and receive baptism.

Kay listened carefully to the minister's words, which seemed as if they were directed at him. He even imagined that the minister was looking straight at him as he delivered his sermon. He now believed in God and Christ's saving grace, but he had never considered baptism. Tommy seemed quite uncomfortable, but quietly sat next to Kay. When the service was finished, Kay went over to a rack of small red candles, lit one, and put five rupees into the coin box. He then knelt down and said a prayer of thanksgiving. Tommy had joined the other parishioners as they left the church and went outside to stand on the steps and soak up the bright sunshine. Kay joined Tommy on the steps. As he was about to suggest that after lunch they find a doctor to administer the necessary shots and health certificates, someone tapped him on the shoulder.

"Kay, is that you?" a voice came from behind.

Kay spun around and faced Bill Robertson, an old rowing pal of his and a friend of Tommy's from Shanghai. All three exchanged handshakes and pats on the back.

"What in the world are you two doing in Bombay, I thought you were in Lunghwa?" Bill exclaimed, "and a church is the last place I expected to find either you."

"It's a very long story, Bill, and we were about to go to lunch. How about joining us?" Kay suggested.

Bill led them down the street to an Indian restaurant where they shared Taj Mahal beer and Chicken Ticki Masalla.

Kay poured out his story, which by now had assumed a rather standard format. Bill hung on every word, and when Kay finished, Bill shook his head solemnly.

"And what now?" Bill asked.

"We are going to the States on a troop transport," Tommy explained.

"That is if we can get someone to vouch for us at the American Consulate to obtain a visa," Kay added.

"Well, you know that I am an American Citizen," Bill said. "I can vouch for you."

"That would be wonderful!" Kay exclaimed. "Can you go with us to the consulate office this afternoon?"

"No problem," Bill said.

"Kay, I have just one final question to ask," he promised. "I never knew you to be a religious person, in fact quite the opposite. Last I saw you, you were a dyed-in-the-wool agnostic. I couldn't believe my eyes when I spied you on your knees in St. Stephen's Church, and then lighting a prayer candle to boot! What changed you?"

"It's a long story Bill, nonetheless it is sufficient to say that I have been, well, sort of converted by circumstances," Kay answered.

Bill had been a religious person all his life, yet had long ago given up trying to talk about religion with Kay.

"How and when did this conversion take place?" Bill asked.

"Well, it didn't just happen, like a sudden vision or something of that sort," Kay explained. "It was more like a process, a gradual awakening if you like. I just came to realize that God, like a good father, cared for me. There have been so many times over the past three months that He intervened to save us or provided succor when we needed it. I just came to believe in His presence in my life and that he cared about me and my friends."

"For example running into me when you needed an American to vouch for you?" Bill offered.

"Yes, exactly like that!" Kay affirmed. "Was it a coincidence that we decided to go into that church, and you just happened to be there at the same time? I don't think so. Three months ago I would have scoffed at the idea of a God who gave a damn about me, but now…"

Tommy sat quietly looking quite uncomfortable throughout the entire conversation. Finally, Bill turned to him and asked, "Tommy, how about you? Have you found religion as well?"

Tommy shook his head. "No, I have not. Kay may want to believe that all our good fortune was because God took an interest in helping us, but I think it was just good luck."

"And I suppose that you think it was just good luck that you were in the church at noon today, and I saw the two of you. If not for Kay's insistence on saying a prayer, we would never have met," Bill reminded him.

Tommy did not answer, but looked over at Kay who was sporting a wide grin.

Bill took Kay and Tommy to his doctor who gave them a thorough examination and a series of shots. Although the drugs Tommy was taking for the past weeks had prevented a serious recurrence of his malaria, the fact that he had such a disease was a health risk. The Indian doctor was reluctant to issue the required health certificate. Malaria was a disease that could not be cured, only controlled with drugs. Should Tommy stop taking these drugs and then have a mosquito bite him in the States, the disease could be passed on to some unsuspecting American. Bill talked privately with the doctor, who then reluctantly filled out a provisional certificate and signed it. He gave Tommy three different drugs, admonished him that these medications must be taken daily, and that he must see a doctor in the USA as soon as he arrived. Then they were off to a photographer who took their pictures and quickly developed prints while they waited. Finally they arrived back at the consulate and Kay and Tommy were issued the required visas. All they needed to do now was wait for their assignment to a troop ship.

As they walked together down the street, Kay asked Bill if he could do him another favor.

"And what might that be, Old Chap?" Bill asked.

"I would like to be baptized, but I will need a sponsor," Kay said matter-of-factly.

Tommy stopped dead in his tracks. He couldn't believe his ears. Kay wanted to be baptized? Baptized? What in the world was wrong with him? With his mouth agape, Tommy stared at Kay but no words would come.

"Of course," Bill said, a bit taken aback with Kay's request. "When would you like to do this?"

"Well, the church is just down the street," Kay pointed out, "how about now?"

"Right now? Bill asked.

"Sure, right now!" Kay responded.

They walked back to St. Stephen's Church and found the minister. Bill told him that his friend wanted to be baptized.

"Today... right now?" the minister asked.

"Yes, right now if it is possible," Kay affirmed.

The minister asked Kay a few questions, then satisfied about Kay's intentions, took him over to the baptismal font at the front of the church, and baptized him. Kay held tightly to Lil's Bible that he always carried with him as the minister poured water over his forehead and said the words of baptism. Bill Robertson was his sponsor. Kay felt like a weight had been lifted from his shoulders, a long journey from the agnostic who cut the fence in Lunghwa to a baptized Christian in Bombay. How fortunate for some folks who are born Christian while others, like Kay and St. Paul have to "be knocked off their horse" so to speak, before seeing the light. He considered his escape and rebirth all part of God's overall plan for him.

Kay had yet to receive a response to the initial wire he sent to his wife from Delhi, but since transpacific communications from the States were on a strict priority basis, civilian return wires were of lowest priority. Besides, it would have been difficult to track Kay since he left the Swiss hotel in New Delhi. While visiting the U.S. Consulate in Bombay, Kay was again allowed to send a wire to his wife in New York City. He told her only that he would soon be on a ship bound for the USA and gave her his Malabar address. This was all that he was allowed to transmit. He also wired a box of candy to his son, Darryl, who was by now almost six years old. He had not seen him since over a year ago. Kay thought Darryl would hardly recognize his father, and was certain that by now his son would have added an inch or tow to his height. Before he left Malabar Hill, Kay finally received a reply from Lil to his cable. Outside of the one letter from Goa that Lil sent to him while he was still incarcerated in Lunghwa, this was the first communication that had caught up with him. He later learned that Lil had sent dozens of letters since Sid had told her of Kay's safe arrival in Kunming, however all had been returned to her as "undeliverable." She had even cabled him at the Swiss Hotel in New Delhi, but that cable never reached him.

While in Bombay, Kay and Tommy contacted and met with many of their old British friends and acquaintances from Shanghai. While they waited for their sailing orders, they were invited to attend polo and cricket matches, movies, concerts, and several dinners that were hosted in interesting restaurants. Most Indian movies were produced in India and were in English. However, even when in English, the Indian movies were so steeped in Indian culture, especially the romances, that Kay found them hard to watch. In these movies, handholding was the extent of physical intimacy, and violence was restricted to mahouts beating their elephants. Celluloid kissing and physical violence toward humans was strictly forbidden, but elephant beatings did not seem raise an eyebrow.

While in Bombay, Bill Henry had made the rounds with the local British Navy office and complained to them that his army application was not getting anywhere. Given his marine engineering background, he felt certain that the Royal Navy would jump at the chance to give him a commission. Despite his qualifications, the navy gave him no indication that their red tape would be any less involved that that of the army.

He was extremely frustrated when a friend told him of a job with the local gas company. After interviewing with them, they offered him a job based on his engineering background and previous experience with the Shanghai Gas Company. He accepted without hesitation. Two months after accepting this job the navy finally offered him a commission; but since he was already employed, he refused it. Despite the fact that on paper he was already a part of the

British army and had never been formally discharged, he never again heard from them. He worked many years for the Bombay Gas Company, and eventually retired and took up residence in Kent, England. His paperwork was not the first or last to become mired in the bureaucracy of wartime England.

November 22, 1944, Bombay

Finally, Kay and Tommy received their sailing orders. The ship, the USS General Butner, was due to sail at two p.m. the very next day. Kay and Tommy said goodbye at dockside to their friends, hosts, Bill Robertson and to Bill Henry. They were only allowed one small bag weighing not more than forty pounds in their shared cabin, and access to their other baggage in the hold would not be possible during the voyage. At dockside, an USN Ensign meticulously checked their papers, which included their military exit permits, letters of introduction from Archie, visas, passports, medical certificates, and the Thomas Cooke, Inc tickets.

The officer was especially concerned with Tommy's *provisional* health certificate, and extensively queried him about his malaria. At one point in the interrogation process, he said that Tommy would not be allowed into the USA with a provisional health certificate. Tommy was devastated by such news. He wondered that if this were the case and given that malaria was incurable, how he would ever be allowed to immigrate to the USA. After checking with the Ship's doctor, and hearing Tommy repeat his pledge to take his medication, the officer finally gave Tommy a boarding pass. The commander made them unpack their small bags to ensure that they carried no contraband, and then to do the same with the rest of their luggage. They repacked everything under the careful eye of the officer, then marched up the gangplank to the ship's deck.

The USS General Butner was a relatively new twenty thousand-ton Navy transport outfitted as a light cruiser with four five-inch guns, six batteries of one inch, quad-r gun emplacements, and ten twenty mm anti-aircraft Oerlikon guns. The ship was reputed to be able to cruise at twenty knots. This was welcome news, as such a swift ship would get them home all the faster and be able to outrun Jap submarines that still patrolled the South Pacific. They were told nothing about the itinerary except the fact that the voyage could take several weeks and travel on a zigzag course to the west coast of the United States via Australia.

The USS General Butner had a maximum capacity of sixty four hundred troops and crew, and before they eventually reached San Pedro Harbor over six thousand persons were aboard. Even for a big ship designed as a troop transport, there was very limited living space on board, and there was almost no room on deck. Every inch of deck space was used for lifeboats, rafts, gun platforms, ammo, hoists, and the like. Everyone on board wanted to get out of the cramped, humid conditions below deck and visit the main deck to breathe fresh air. In order to accommodate everyone, each passenger and crewmember was issued a "deck pass" good for an assigned time slot. Everyone was allowed on the upper deck for three hours each day. Passengers could either position themselves along the deck railing and look out to sea, or take a walk around the ship's deck. Kay opted for the daily walk. Despite overall good weather, the crossing to Australia across the Indian Ocean was exceptionally rough, and often the ship heaved back and forth with such force that the walk around the ship's deck tested one's balance. Many of the passengers and even some of the crew were seasick for the first week at sea, although neither Kay nor Tommy felt any discomfort.

Tommy and Kay shared a stateroom with ten other passengers, twelve bunks in tiers of three on each side of the cabin. It was midsummer in the Indian Ocean and the South Pacific was oppressively hot this time of year. Their windowless cabin was uncomfortably small, actually smaller than the Lunghwa cells. The ship had not been outfitted for the Pacific run, and the forced air ventilation system could not cope with the equatorial heat. The odor of twelve men, some of whom were constantly seasick, plus being confined to a small, poorly ventilated cabin, was enough in itself to jostle even the strongest stomach. The Head was located down a narrow passageway from their room, and considering the constant heaving motion of the ship, Kay and his roommates would stagger down the hallway using the bulkheads to steady themselves. The temperature, humidity, and stench were obnoxious, but it didn't matter to the escapees. With all that Kay and

Tommy had endured in prison and on the road, they could put up with anything, for they were on their way home.

A half-hour before sunset each day, the bo'sun pipe reminded passengers to "lay below" as the decks were being swabbed. Then decks were flushed down and all portholes closed for the nightly blackout. Tommy and Kay went to the Officer's Lounge to play cards or watch movies, but it was a sweatbox and usually over-crowded with four hundred other shipmates, each trying to get a little relaxation. The chow was excellent; three squares each day. Kay and Tommy had lost a lot of weight since they were interred in Lunghwa. Back in Shanghai, Kay was five-foot ten inches and a robust one hundred and eighty-five pounds, yet now he was all skin and bones and the doctor weighed him at one hundred and forty-five pounds. Tommy had experienced a similar weight loss. However, by the time Kay and Tommy arrived back in the States, they each had regained much of their lost weight.

Meal sittings were designated by deck, and their deck was assigned the first meal shift, or six a.m., eleven a.m. and four p.m. The officer's dining room was on the upper deck near the bow, and portholes were left open to the sea breezes except for blackout hours. Outside of the deck itself, it was the only place they could get a bit of relief from the oppressive heat. Every day Kay looked forward to his meal and deck times.

Kay and Tommy made several new friends while onboard. Kay became friends and bridge partners with a couple of chaps, Major McLaughlin of the 14th Air Corps and Captain Michaelson of the U.S. Infantry. Captain Michaelson had received two Purple Hearts and a Silver Star in the Pacific Islands campaigns and was returning to the States to be outfitted with prosthesis for his missing lower leg. The jostling ship deck was especially difficult for Captain Michaelson to negotiate even with the help of crutches, yet every day he walked on the deck for all three hours assigned to him. Also homeward bound was the same Captain Mullen who had helped Kay and Tommy in Kunming. The chief steward, Mr. Segurra, was a retired navy man and a fine chap at that. When he and Kay compared notes, they discovered that they had previously met on the USS Augusta in Tsingtao harbor while Kay was doing salvage work for the U.S. Navy. The USS Augusta later served as the historic meeting place for President Roosevelt and Churchill. Indeed, it was a small world. Later on the voyage, Kay became a lifelong friend of another civilian, Norman Schwartz of the Red Cross. Norman was returning to the USA after a two-year assignment in Sydney working with the USO.

Tommy and Kay were among the few passengers invited to the Captain's table for dinner. The Skipper, a Captain Isrig of the USN, had been a submariner for most of his career. A pleasant and charming middle-aged old salt, the captain was recently reassigned from submarine service to the General Butner. They exchanged war experiences and Captain Isrig seemed very impressed with their tale of escape from China, as he himself had cheated death on several occasions. His last assignment was as captain of the USS Santorina, a sub that was presently being repaired in Bombay. He told of participating in the battle of Leyte Gulf in October of that year and placing three "fish" (torpedoes) into the side of a Jap heavy cruiser which "sent it and its scurvy crew to Davie Jones' locker." After the cruiser sank the crew was forced to sit on the bottom of the ocean for several hours rigged for silent running as the Japanese fleet dropped depth charges all around them. After that encounter, the Santorina leaked like a sieve, so they put into Bombay for much needed repairs. The depth-charge attack had permanently damaged Captain Isrig's hearing, which led to his reassignment to the USS General Butner. Somewhat embittered by his latest appointment, he claimed that the US Navy had no need of a partially deaf submarine captain. He said that he planned to retire from the navy when this voyage was over.

December 18, 1944, Australia

At noontime they steamed into Sydney bay, passed under the famous Sydney Harbor bridge and tied up to a berth in the inner harbor. Originally, they had planned to dock in Melbourne, but much later they were told that the U.S. and British fleets were assembling a task force in Melbourne for an all out attack on the Japanese fleet, thus the USS General Butner had been detoured to Sydney. This was a fortunate change of plans for Kay because it provided him an opportunity to look up his uncle and cousin who lived in Sydney, neither of whom he had seen for many years.

Kay searched the telephone directory and found his cousin listed under K.M. Pate, his own initials, except the "K" stood for "Kitty" rather than "Karoly." Kitty was amazed to hear her cousin's voice. Both Kitty and her father thought Kay was still in Lunghwa. They immediately drove down to the dock and Kay had a wonderful visit with them that lasted two full days while the USS General Butner was being outfitted for the long voyage across the Pacific.

December 20, 1944, Brisbane

That afternoon, the USS General Butner sailed out of Sydney Harbor and headed north along the coast. They were not told that there would be another stopover in Australia; and two days out of Sydney they took on a pilot, sailed into Brisbane Harbor, and navigated into the mouth of the Brisbane River. The ship proceeded up river and tied up at a small dock some distance away from the main harbor. Everyone was very curious as to the purpose of this unannounced visit to Brisbane and both crew and passengers crowded on deck as they docked.

The low hills above Brisbane were covered with trees arrayed in bright red Poinsettia flowers, and the area looked more like a small town than the city it was purported to be. Most all of the buildings were single story, and if there was a "downtown" of high-rises, it wasn't visible from their vantagepoint. It wasn't long before the passengers and crew's curiosity was satisfied. Two buses pulled up to the dock and forty Aussie women, several of whom carried babies in their arms, climbed off the buses and clambered up the gangplank to a cascade of appreciative hoots, hollers and whistles.

"They aren't coming on board as our shipmates, are they? Tommy asked. "Where the hell are we going to put them?"

As soon as soon as the women were on board they weighed anchor, headed out of Brisbane Bay and set course eastward across the Pacific.

The passengers and crew soon learned that these Australian women were war brides immigrating to the USA to join their American husbands waiting for them in the States. Imagine five thousand men in close quarters with forty young women (some of whom were certainly easy to look at) for a voyage that would take several weeks. The troop ship was not configured with separate men's' and women's' quarters, nor were there separate heads, so some considerable shuffling of quarters and lavatories was necessary. Three of the heads, two below deck and one on the main deck, were converted to women's lavatories with hastily painted signs.

Kay and Tommy's quarters were given to a dozen of the childless women passengers, and Kay and Tommy along with their twelve former bunkmates were assigned bunk space with other officers. The reassignment worked out to Kay's advantage, as the cabin he was assigned to was on the upper deck, next to the radio room and not very far from the Captain's quarters. This was considered the upscale part of the ship. Kay shared a small stateroom with five other passengers, so it was just as crowded as his previous quarters had been; however, at least this stateroom was on the outside so that they could open a porthole during daylight hours and let in some fresh air. Tommy was less fortunate, as his new quarters were located next to the ship's infirmary in the heart of the ship and next to the noisy engine room. If he thought their old quarters were hot and humid, they were cool compared to these quarters deep within the ship. He complained that the thump-thump-thump of the engines kept him awake.

December 24, 1944, New Caledonia

The USS Butner sailed into the harbor of Noumea, French New Caledonia on a beautiful, warm tropical afternoon. As they cruised between the two islands that protected the harbor, Kay's attention was drawn to an attractive church built on a hill overlooking the town. The ship tied up to the main wharf, and the Captain announced that since today was Christmas Eve, everyone was invited to attend Midnight Mass at St. Catherine's Church overlooking the harbor. The church on the hill certainly did not look large enough to accommodate many visitors; nonetheless, Kay enthusiastically accepted the invitation. Tommy decided to stay onboard to attend the ship Christmas party as did most of the other passengers and crew.

St. Catherine's occupied the summit of the highest hill behind the town, about a twenty-minute walk from the harbor. Kay, along with several dozen other passengers and crew including most of the women passengers, disembarked about 11 p.m. and hiked through the town and up the hill to the church. Both the church and adjoining convent, constructed from blocks of pink coral, shone an iridescent pale salmon color in the bright moonlight. As they mounted the hill, they could hear the sweet voices of women singing Christmas carols accompanied by a pipe organ. Multicolored rays of light streamed through the stained glass windows of the brightly-lit church, then splashed across the adjoining grounds in an array of colors.

The shipmates climbed the dozen limestone steps leading into the church and entered through ornately carved double doors into the vestibule. Kay was amazed at the size of the nave and its richly decorated walls. High overhead, rough wood beams thrust majestically toward heaven. White and black polished marble covered the floor of the church and the sanctuary. The altar and ambo were carved from logs of driftwood teak, blackened by years at sea. On both sides of the sanctuary, life-size wood statues stood on pedestals in niches along the walls. Each statue was adorned with real clothing and painted with facial features so realistically done that they obscured the fact that the statues were wood and not real flesh and blood. A huge crucifix hung over the sanctuary, again created so realistically that visitors could almost feel the pain of the nails in Christ's hands. The church and especially the sanctuary were bathed in bright electric lights that illuminated the frescoes and paintings lining the walls.

The passengers and crew tiptoed into the church, feeling a bit conspicuous due to their late arrival. The church was already crowded, but the parishioners squeezed into the center of the pews to make room for their guests. Ushers passed out candles to each member of the congregation and precisely at midnight, the large bell in the tower began to peal as the church lights were dimmed. Several boys dressed in white garments over black robes came up the aisle and lit the candle of the first person in each pew and they in turn lit the candle of the person next to them. Within a few minutes, the entire church glowed from the yellow light of hundreds of candles. A robed priest processed up the main aisle as the nun's choir broke into "Silent Night, Holy Night." Never had Kay heard more sweetly sung music or witnessed a more moving Christmas service. Although he had only a vague understanding of the ceremony in which he was participating, now that he was baptized he felt one with the congregation. The priest gave a homily about the impoverished circumstances of Mary and Joseph, who were such poor and simple people that they didn't even have circumstances to assure a place to stay in their home town of Bethlehem. He painted a picture of a young woman about to give birth traveling one hundred miles down a dusty road on the back of a donkey led by her husband. Kay could relate to this picture. Yet, it was a strange way for the Christ Child, who was the long anticipated Messiah, to enter our world with nothing better than a manger and animals to greet him. Kay thought that God could have done better, much better.

The question that Kay had been asking himself for the past three months, "why me?" again took center stage in his mind. Why had God taken an interest in helping him, a person who barely admitted to God's existence and hadn't entertained a spiritual thought in his entire life? Kay continued to ponder this mystery until the priest as part of his homily quoted something from the Old Testament that made it all clear. God had said to Isaiah, "For My thoughts are not your thoughts, neither are your ways My ways." That explained it! Kay realized that God's ways were not the ways of humans. Here on an island in the middle of the Pacific Ocean and in a church on Christmas Eve, Kay's question was finally answered. The question itself was a foolish one. Kay was part of God's creation, and how could the Creator not care about His children, even one who had ignored Him. God's ways were profoundly not the ways of humans.

After the service, Kay and his fellow passengers wound their way back down the hill to the ship in silence. It seemed as though everyone had been touched in a very deep way by this experience, and talk would only interrupt his or her thoughts. Kay would remember this Christmas experience forever.

Before the ship sailed from Noumea, the Captain distributed 5,000 gift packages from the Red Cross, one for each passenger and crew.

December 31, 1944, On the USS Butner

It was New Year's Eve in the middle of the Pacific Ocean and the mess hall of the USS Butner was decorated for the occasion. Captain Isrig was dressed as Father Time with a 1944 sign draped over his neck, and led off the celebration with great news. The Japanese fleet had been sunk in the Battle of Leyte Gulf and the end of the war in the Pacific was in sight. Several of the more talented persons on board formed a great band to entertain their shipmates. They called themselves the *Butner Dirty Dozen Minus Two*, since there were ten of them. Although there were only forty women on board, each danced the night away, taking turns with as many partners as possible. Oh how their feet must have ached the following morning! That night they crossed over the International Date Line, and the following day it was again New Years Eve! Although few had yet recovered from the first party, Captain Isrig declared a second party to celebrate the occasion, and named the festivities "It Was a Good Year", although the "year" had only been 24 hours long. Two parties to celebrate 1944. Not many folks can brag that they had welcomed the same New Year twice.

CHAPTER SIXTEEN

Across America

January 6, 1945, California

The USS General Butner was met by fireboats sounding their horns and spraying water high into the morning sky as they proudly steamed into the Los Angeles port of San Pedro and tied up to the dock. Army and Navy personnel were the first passengers to disembark. Thousands of friends and family crowded the dockside to greet them, along with the Marine Band from Camp Pendleton. Due to an Immigration and Naturalization Department foul-up, the civilians on board were forced to wait until the next day to disembark. This delay was especially hard on the Australian War Brides. A few of the women's husbands impatiently waiting on the dock, whistled, and waved to their spouses, and the brides waved back and cried. Kay leaned against the deck railing and longed to place his feet on U.S. soil. That last day seemed to Kay to be the longest day and night of his life. It was inhuman to keep these folks on board another day, but that was what happened.

January 7, 1944, Los Angeles

The next day the women, some with babies in arms, were the first to run down the gangplank into the anxious arms of their husbands. When it was finally Kay's turn to disembark, he took the last step off the gangplank, knelt down and kissed the ground as he had seen many servicemen do the previous day. No one was on the dock to greet Kay or Tommy but it didn't matter to them. All that mattered at this moment was that they were safe in the good old U.S. of A. It was a wonderful and indescribable feeling of total relief and joy. To be in Lil's arms and have Darryl in his were the only things that could make Kay happier or more satisfied, and that event was just a few more days away. Tommy was more fortunate, because his wife and daughter were somewhere in the Los Angeles area, and his reunion only waited locating them in the phone book.

Once they disembarked, the passengers were ushered into a large dockside warehouse where they stood in line to go through the makeshift Customs and Immigration process. By four p.m., their papers in order and luggage inspected and tagged, Kay and Tommy stepped outside onto the street as completely free men for the first time in years. No need to carry papers, or be wary of hostile military patrols and aggressive police, or to hide from Japanese ready to shoot them for the sport of it. Best of all, they no longer need to fear hunger, cold, filth, and death. They were safe and free to do whatever they wanted to do and go wherever they desired. The concept seemed alien and dreamlike. What a country!

It is impossible to describe the feeling of freedom and safety that we are so accustomed. Most of us take it for granted, unless, of course, a person has been deprived of it for some length of time. Kay and Tommy stood curbside and took in deep breaths of their newfound liberty along with forty or so other repatriated civilians. They were free, but what next? Each person was wondering just where he or she would spend the night when a delegation from the USO (United Service Organization) came to the rescue. A dozen station wagons drove up to the passenger-loading zone and all the orphaned civilians, the few who were not met by friends or family at the dock, were ushered into waiting cars. They were then driven to various hotels around Los Angeles where the USO and the American Red Cross had arranged accommodations and meal tickets for all. Tommy and Kay were taken to the Ambassador Hotel along with Norman Schwartz. Because Norman was a staff member of the Red Cross, he received executive treatment, and since Tommy and Kay were in his company, they were extended the same courtesy.

They could not believe their eyes when their car pulled up to the Ambassador, one of the most luxurious hotels in Los Angeles. The porter took their bags and led Kay and Tommy to their room. The double room was spacious and well decorated, and after thirty-nine days on board a troop ship where they shared a much smaller room with eleven other bunkmates, these accommodations seemed almost decadent. Kay lay down on the double bed. It was so soft and comfortable that he almost immediately fell asleep. Norman was lodged in an adjoining single room.

As soon as they were settled, Kay placed a telephone call to Lil in New York City, "person to person." Kay was thrilled to hear Lil's voice on the other end of the line. Neither one of them realize as the red bus disappeared down the dusty road outside Lunghwa prison, that it would be eighteen months before they again spoke to one another. Kay and Lil talked and talked, until Tommy asked if he, Kay, was a millionaire. Kay at first did not understand the question, but then it dawned on him that he was talking coast-to-coast, and person-to-person to boot! When they checked out, the telephone bill for that call was $36, but Kay thought it was worth every penny.

That evening Norman invited them to a Red Cross/USO event for repatriated prisoners and returning service men and women. It was held at the Coconut Grove. The dinner was wonderful, the best chow Kay had eaten for years. After dinner, as guests of the USO, they took a taxi to a performance at the Hollywood Bowl given by Bob Hope. Kay and Tommy had never laughed so hard in years. All the trials and tribulations of the past five years seemed to melt away, and the future was all that mattered. Bob Hope had this effect on everyone in the audience. He was a wonderful entertainer, although many of his jokes were beyond the understanding of two British blokes like Kay and Tommy. Dorothy Lamour was also in the show. Bob Hope offered her ten dollars if she could guess which of his pockets the ten spot was in. She guessed his right pants pocket.

"Reach in and see if you are right," Bob offered.

Dorothy reached into his pocket and said, "I feel so silly."

Bob responded with a twinkle in his eye, "reach much further and you'll feel nuts!"

The audience howled as Dorothy turned a deep shade of pink.

After the performance, Kay and Tommy returned to the Ambassador Hotel and retired for the night. About 2 a.m. there was an incessant knocking on their door. Kay answered the door in his pajamas, and as soon as he opened the door and without an invitation, in swept a young girl closely followed by Norman. Norman explained that she had shared a taxi with him from the show to a bar. He bought her a drink and she gave him some sob story about not having a place to stay for the night. Norman told her that she could stay in their room.

Of all the dimwit ideas, Kay thought. It was obvious that she was "two sheets to the wind" so to speak. How rude it was of Norman to dump this sot on their doorstep. Kay told Norman that she was his charge, and none of their responsibility. As Kay and Norman argued, the girl collapsed in a heap on the couch, and since no one was willing to move her, she stayed there until morning. When she awoke, she had no idea of where she was or how she ended up in a hotel room with two strange men. Kay woke Norman and told him to get rid of her. By the time Tommy and Kay showered, shaved, and dressed, she was gone. Norman never explained how he managed to get rid of her, and neither Tommy nor Kay asked.

January 8, 1945, Los Angeles

After breakfast Kay, Tommy and Norman caught a cab from the hotel to the Red Cross headquarters in L.A. where Kay expected they could arrange transcontinental travel for him and help Tommy locate his wife's whereabouts in Los Angeles. Tommy had not been able to contact his wife and 22-year-old daughter since they were repatriated from Lunghwa, and he only knew from Captain Mullen's investigation that they were living somewhere in the Los Angeles area. However, they were not listed in the Los Angeles phone directory. To the Red Cross folks who tried to help, it seemed strange that Tommy did not have an address for his wife, but this was part of the circumstances of war. If not for Kay's chance meeting with his brother-in-law in Kunming, he wouldn't have known the whereabouts of his own wife and child. They finally located his wife in Indio and she gave them the number of his daughter, who was now married and lived in Inglewood.

As Tommy attempted to contact his daughter, Kay left him at the Red Cross office and went across town to the Canadian Consulate to ask for their assistance in arranging his transportation to New York City. When he arrived, he was ushered into the office of Vice-consul Mac McMasters. After Kay told him his story and showed his British passport and U.S. visa, Mac made a phone call and said that transportation to New York City via Santa Fe Railway could be arranged, and that Kay should go to their Santa Fe office and ask for Mr. Lunge. Kay did so and met with Mr. Lunge, who immediately issued a ticket on the *California Limited* leaving for Chicago at 6:30 p.m. that very evening. Kay was impressed at the level of service he received from this Canadian Consul office as opposed the British Consulates in Kunming, Chungking, and India. It was only later that he discovered that Mr. Lunge was the brother-in-law of Vice-consul McMasters. No wonder tickets on the train were so readily available.

Kay had only enough time to go back to the hotel, pack his belongings and say goodbye to Tommy and Norman. When he arrived at his room, he found Tommy visiting with his daughter, Doris. As soon as she heard from her mother that Tommy was in town, she rushed over to the Ambassador Hotel to see her father and help him pack his things for the drive to Indio, California where his wife now lived. Norman was also packing to catch the overnight flight to his home in Buffalo in upstate New York. Kay said good-bye to Norman and Tommy and made plans to meet them in New York City that summer. Kay and Tommy's parting was difficult. Along with Bill, the three friends had been through so much together these past few months. Wherever they were on earth, they vowed to contact each other and Bill on August 19 every year and if possible to meet together on that date to celebrate the escape and trek out of China. The three friends would keep this vow throughout their lifetimes.

The *California Limited* pulled out of the Spanish style Los Angeles train station at 7:15 p.m., forty-five minutes "late as sched-uled" the conductor said with a sarcastic chuckle. Kay sat in the observation car and watched the California landscape glide past until it was too dark to see anything. The train climbed out of the Los Angeles basin and into the high desert of Southern California.

The first major stop was Barstow, where engines and crew were changed, then on to Las Vegas.

Vegas didn't favorably impress Kay. It was a rather small town with a few high-rise hotels and casinos along the "strip" and in the downtown area. The train was scheduled to stop for a half-hour, and Kay figured there was time enough to get off the train and wander around the station. Slot machines lined the corridors and the main waiting room of the depot. Kay had never played one of these one-armed-bandits, so he reached into his pocket and found six quarters. A quarter slot machine on the aisle sported a large sign that advertised a $250 jackpot and Kay decided to try his luck. He dropped a quarter into the slot and pulled the handle. The machine went clunk-clunk-clunk and a bunch of cherries, a pear, and a plum appeared in the window. Kay tried another quarter, then a third with similar results. He popped in a fourth quarter and three cherries appeared in the window. Twenty quarters, one at a time clunked into the pan below the machine.

"Wow!" Kay thought, "that was certainly easy." "Twenty quarters for three!"

He placed another quarter into the machine, clunk, clunk, clunk and no matches appeared. By now the machine had him, he was addicted. He tried again, and again, and again, but each time the machine paid nothing. One time he got two bars (three was a jackpot worth $250) and the third bar appeared in the last window and momentarily hesitated, only to finally slide backwards leaving a plum showing. No pay out! Kay soon realized that these machines were called "one-arm-bandits" for a very good reason. He looked into the tray at his pile of dwindling quarters and thought,

"Oh what the heck, I only had six quarters to start out with anyway."

He was down to his last three U.S.A. quarters, when all three bars stopped in the window and a bell began to ring as a light flashed over the machine. He had hit the $250 jackpot!

"What do I do now?" he asked the fellow working the machine next to him. The young man was madly pulling his machine handle as fast as he could feed quarters into the slot, and did not interrupt his work as he answered.

"You have to wait for the fellow with the maroon apron to come over and pay you off," he explained.

"Don't leave the machine," he admonished as the bell continued to ring.

Kay looked around, but there was no fellow with a maroon apron in sight. He waited patiently for some time until over the clamor of the bell, he heard his train whistle, then a minute later watched as his train began to pull out of the station. The machine continued to flash and ring, but no one appeared to give him his payoff. The train picked up speed. He looked at the fellow next to him and said,

"It's yours, my train is leaving," and dashed out the door.

By now the train had accelerated to a considerable speed, and all the doors were closed, save for the doorway to the observation car, the last car on the train. Kay ran as fast as he could toward that door, but by now car after car had passed him by. A porter was standing on the platform steps of the observation car with his hand outstretched.

"Come on, you can make it!" he shouted.

Kay ran to catch up with the train, grabbed the porter's strong hand as he jerked him onto the train.

"It happens every time we stop here," the porter said, slowly shaking his head. That's why I always leave this last door open. Did you win anything?"

"Yeah, but the pay out clerk never showed up!" Kay lamented.

The porter chuckled and said, "Oh, they never do. You see, that's their little game. If a passenger wins a jackpot as the train is leaving, the payout clerk hides until the winner runs to catch his train. Then they clear the machine and pocket the jackpot. They must make a good living off suckers like you."

Kay hoped that the young man playing the machine next to him was able to claim the $250, and not the dishonest payout clerk.

The train continued across mile after empty mile of desert stopping only once in a one-horse town called Milford according to the name over the station, then on to Salt Lake City, and Ogden, Utah. Night fell as the train pulled out of Ogden and puffed eastward up the canyons and into the Rocky Mountains. Kay had an upper berth ticket on a sleeper car, and after talking to a man in the observation car until almost midnight, he finally crawled into his berth and fell asleep dreaming of his reunion with Lil and Darryl.

January 9, 1945, On the Great Plains.

Kay awoke the following morning to a porter ringing a triangle and announcing Laramie, Wyoming as the next stop. Disappointed that the train had passed over the scenic Rocky Mountains in the dark, Kay rose and went to the dining car for breakfast. As the train crossed over the Nebraska plains, there was nothing to see but empty fields blanketed by a layer of snow. By late afternoon they stopped in Omaha, then headed across Iowa. Kay didn't feel well and skipped lunch. He developed a fever, took two aspirin, and sat alone in the day-car. Eventually a young Marine Gunny Sergeant sauntered down the aisle and took the seat next to him.

"You don't look so good," the soldier commented. "Your eyes…are you all right?"

"What's wrong with my eyes?" Kay replied.

"They're bloodshot!" the Gunny said.

"Well, you ought to see them from my side," Kay grumbled.

"Would you like some sulfonamide tablets?" the Gunny offered. "The doc gave them to me to cure the Clap, but I have extras."

"More than I wanted to know," Kay thought. Nevertheless, he accepted two tablets and downed them with a glass of water.

"Thank you, but what rotten luck!" Kay complained. "After all that I have been through, eighteen months in a Jap hell-hole of a prison and three months walking across China without a single health problem, I get sick two day's journey from home."

The Gunny wanted to hear his story, so Kay related the short version. When he finished, the soldier looked at him thoughtfully and said, "That indeed was a terrible experience, but God must have been watching over you, otherwise you would not be here—would you?"

"No, I wouldn't. God must have been looking after me the whole way, although I really don't think I deserved such care. I am grateful nevertheless," Kay answered.

"One can never rationalize God's choices," the Gunny said, "but He was watching over me just as He was watching over you. I was in the invasion of Guam in July and August of last year and survived six weeks of Hell on earth. Four of my buddies were killed, and everyone in our patrol, except for one of my buddies and myself, were either killed or wounded. I cannot begin to put into words the horror of those six weeks, so filled with death and suffering, but I prayed and prayed. God was with me every step of the way, and here I am almost home."

"You must be a good Christian then," Kay surmised.

"A Lutheran yes, but not such good one," the Marine confessed. "I almost never attended church until a Marine Chaplain at Pendleton convinced me otherwise. Now I have changed my whole attitude, and have accepted Christ as my Savior."

"So have I," Kay admitted, "and I was just baptized."

"Which faith?" the Marine asked.

The question initially had no meaning for Kay. "Which faith?" Well Christian of course! A bit miffed he thought for a few seconds, and then answered,

"Well, the minister in Bombay was Anglican, so I guess this makes me an Anglican."

"No matter," the Gunny said thoughtfully. He stood up and excused himself to go get something to eat. He shook hands with Kay and walked out of the observation car.

After listening to this young soldier, Kay felt that in comparison his own experience had been a walk in the park. Yes, his life was threatened, and yes, he was often cold, hungry, and footsore, but he didn't see his buddies bleed to death in a muddy foxhole as this soldier had. While his experience was horrific, others surely had even worse times. He told himself it would do well to keep his experience in perspective. After the soldier excused himself to go to the dining car for breakfast, Kay's fever seemed to abate somewhat, but he still felt terrible.

As the train sped across the barren Iowa plains Kay gazed out the window hypnotized by the monotonous landscape. He couldn't get his conversation with the young Marine out of his head, and began to ponder the events of the past several months. He thought back to September of 1943 and the day Lil and Darryl disappeared down that dusty road leading out of Lunghwa Prison and his subsequent decision to escape. Although he was certain that the Japanese would be defeated and his eventual repatriation was assured, he was also aware that the war could take years. To be away from his family for years was unacceptable. Regardless of the dangers, he had planned his escape and waited for the right opportunity. He knew the Shanghai countryside quite well, but he had almost no knowledge of the vast and diverse landscape of the Chinese interior, nor did he have the slightest idea how he could walk across fourteen hundred miles of perilous territory. If captured by the Japanese or Wang Ching-wei soldiers it would have meant certain death, or even worse, detention in a Chinese Prison. Yet, he was willing to risk his life for the distant prospect of freedom, and even now, with all that pain and suffering behind him, he knew that he would not hesitate to do it all over again.

Only an optimist would have taken on such a journey, and Kay was a consummate optimist. His many cellmates back in Lunghwa could only focus on the dangers and unlikely prospect of a successful escape, and so they remained mired in their pessimism and unable to act. He, on the other hand, was a traditionalist who spent his life convinced that tomorrow held a better promise than today. His love for his family had driven him to escape, yet as his escape and trek across China unfolded, he became convinced that a greater power was helping him get back to his family.

There were so many examples of God's benevolence in his adventure that it was impossible to remain skeptical. One example was the thunder and lightning storm that erupted just as they cut the wire in Lunghwa. It distracted the guards and covered their escape into the woods. Then there was the time Japanese soldiers on patrol were distracted by some children and walked right past Kay and friends as they hid in the reeds. Was it a coincidence that the Japanese soldier who stopped them near the golf course was friendly, and after discovering that they were British, let them go? When the Chinese puppet troops confronted and interrogated them, Kay had found just the right words to fool the captain into thinking they were French police on a holiday and let them go on their way. One of the most enigmatic encounters was that with the elderly Chinese villager, who took Kay into his church and instructed him how to pray, then disappeared when Kay attempted to introduce him to Bill and Tommy. The fact that they stumbled into the Guerrilla camp near Kashing had to be a miracle, not happenstance. Their fortunes had soared when they discovered the secret U.S. Army base in the Checking Mountains and received much needed medical attention. In addition, God was certainly watching over them when they were almost shot down on their flight from Kanchow.

Repeatedly, when they faced danger and ultimate failure or needed a moral boost or sustenance, someone or something would reach out and provide for them. He had slowly realized that this provider could only be God, a God who actually cared about Kay Pate and his friends. This realization completely altered his lifelong commitment to Agnostic thinking. God wasn't this nondescript being who sat in his heaven unconcerned with the goings on of insignificant humans, but he was a loving, devoted Father who only wanted the best for his children. God had his hand in Kay's entire escape and trek across China. Kay would remain convinced of this for the rest of his life. Kay may have escaped Lunghwa an Agnostic, but he escaped *Out of China* transformed and became a Christian. The thought that all this had been God's plan for his conversion was disturbing. Kay mused how strange that some folks found their way to heaven from birth, while others have to be "knocked from their horse" so to speak. Then he had to admit to himself that he was a pretty tough nut to crack and was reminded of the Christmas Eve sermon in New Caledonia, "For My thoughts are not your thoughts, neither are your ways My ways."

The snow began to fall with increasing intensity and wind gusts rocked the train coach back and forth as it chugged across the featureless prairie. The otherwise monotonous landscape was interrupted by a farmhouse here and there, indistinctly identified by a stand of leafless trees or a lone windmill defiantly surviving in the middle of an otherwise empty field. The snow blanketed everything with the exception of an occasional tree or a few fence posts that defiantly poked above the snowdrifts forming along fence lines. By late afternoon, the storm had developed into a full-fledged blizzard. The wind driven snow now stuck to the coach windows, and visibility in the blizzard whiteout was reduced to a few feet. By the time the train pulled into Omaha, the tracks were covered by two to three feet of snow and a rotary snow plow engine was hooked to the front of the train. When they arrived at Des Moines, the train was running four hours late, and it was likely Kay would miss his connection from Chicago to New York City. In Des Moines he sent a cable to Lil explaining the delay and suggested that she should not try to meet him at Penn Station. He intended to hire a cab when he arrived in the Big Apple.

He was still not feeling very well and hadn't slept much the previous night. He no longer felt like talking to folks in the observation car, so he climbed into his berth about 7 p.m. and fell into a fitful sleep.

January 10, 1945, Chicago

On the third day out of L.A., they pulled into the Chicago station twelve hours behind schedule. Kay's train from Chicago to New York City had long since departed, so he went to the ticket counter to find out when the next train for New York was due to leave.

"In ten minutes on track nine," the ticket agent said. "You had better hurry."

"How about my baggage?" Kay asked.

"Well, you can either wait for your baggage and miss your connection, or go without it and pick it up tomorrow in New York City. It's your choice."

Kay carried one duffel bag with him, but his other luggage wouldn't make the transfer in time. He thought to himself, "the heck with my luggage," and ran for track nine. He arrived just as the porters picked up the platform steps and began to close the coach doors. He threw his duffel bag through the doorway grabbed the handhold and swung himself into the intra-car passageway. After one hundred and forty-five days and twenty three thousand miles, he was not going to wait another day to see Lil and Darryl.

The longest part of the entire trip was the last ten minutes as the train lumbered into New York City and Penn Station. Those ten minutes seemed like hours as the train lurched into the station at five miles per hour. Finally the train screeched to a stop and the doors opened. Kay grabbed his duffel bag, jumped off the train and

ran through the station to the street where he hailed a cab.

"Go to 58 West 8th Street," Kay ordered the cabby. Eighth Street was only a five minute cab drive from Penn Station, and when they arrived, Kay paid the cabby, slung his duffel bag over his shoulder and climbed the steps into the apartment house two at a time. He looked over the mailboxes in the entryway until he found "PATE" over the one marked #301. He rang the bell, and a little boy's voice answered.

"Daddy…is that you?" Darryl asked.

"Sure is!" Kay answered.

"Daddy's here, Daddy IS HERE," Kay could hear Darryl yell in the background.

With his heavy duffel bag slung over one shoulder Kay ran up the steps to the third floor. As he opened the fire door and stepped into the third floor hallway, he could see that the door to #301 was open and Lil was standing in the hall. Darryl ran past his mother and into Kay's arms yelling, "Daddy…Daddy!"

With Darryl sandwiched between their legs, Kay grabbed Lil and gave her the biggest kiss she ever had.

It was a gorgeous, wonderful, hectic, and unbelievable home-coming.

When the excitement had died down and Kay had given Darryl the presents he brought from India, he took Lil's Bible out of his duffel bag and handed it to her.

Lil took her Bible and gently opened it.

"My Bible from Shanghai! You carried this 23,000 miles with you?" she asked incredulously, tears in her eyes.

"Well…yes…I did…and it got me through some pretty tough times," Kay said.

"You read it?" Lil asked.

"Sure did. It was all I had to remind me of you. And I have another surprise for you," Kay teased, "I've been…well, converted."

Lil was speechless.

"I saw a church just down the street. Let's go there and say a prayer of thanksgiving," Kay suggested.

Lil could not believe her ears. Church…pray? Kay was suggesting going to a church to pray! Moreover, this was coming from the mouth of a man who once said his god was a kumquat and made Jesus jokes. Unbelievable!

"I think that church is St. Agnes, a Catholic Church," Lil advised. "You want to go to a Catholic Church?"

"I guess—I was baptized an Anglican, but it doesn't matter," Kay said.

"Baptized—converted—baptized?" Lil repeated in utter amazement.

Kay nodded, put his arm around Lil, and took Darryl's little hand in his and they walked together the two blocks to St. Agnes Church. It was at the same time the longest and shortest walk he had experienced in the past two years. They climbed the marble steps leading into the church, found a pew and Lil and Darryl sat down. Kay went over to a rack of red candles that stood beneath a stature of the Virgin Mary, slipped a quarter into the box, and lit one.

"Thank you Lord for bringing me safely back to my family," Kay said in a loud, clear tone as he smiled at Lil. His prayer echoed throughout the empty church and tears began to cover Lil's cheeks.

His long journey was over. Kay was home at last!

Printed in the United States
42056LVS00006B/235-282